Frontiers in
PHYSIOLOGICAL PSYCHOLOGY

Contributors to this Volume

THEODORE HOLMES BULLOCK

RUSSELL L. DE VALOIS

RAÚL HERNÁNDEZ-PEÓN

E. ROY JOHN

MORTIMER MISHKIN

SIDNEY OCHS

ROGER W. RUSSELL

Frontiers in
PHYSIOLOGICAL PSYCHOLOGY

EDITED BY

ROGER W. RUSSELL

DEAN OF ADVANCED STUDIES
INDIANA UNIVERSITY
BLOOMINGTON, INDIANA

1966

ACADEMIC PRESS   New York and London

ACADEMIC PRESS INC.
111 Fifth Avenue, New York, New York 10003

United Kingdom Edition published by
ACADEMIC PRESS INC. (LONDON) LTD.
Berkeley Square House, London W.1

LIBRARY OF CONGRESS CATALOG CARD NUMBER: 66-28313

PRINTED IN THE UNITED STATES OF AMERICA

This volume is dedicated to
ROLAND C. DAVIS

*For many years a leader among
American psychologists in research
on bioelectric phenomena.*

Contributors

THEODORE HOLMES BULLOCK, Department of Neurosciences, University of California San Diego School of Medicine, La Jolla, California

RUSSELL L. DE VALOIS, Department of Psychology, Indiana University, Bloomington, Indiana

RAÚL HERNÁNDEZ-PEÓN, Instituto de Investigaciones Cerebrales, A.C., Moras 445, Mexico City, Mexico

E. ROY JOHN, Brain Research Laboratories, Department of Psychiatry, New York Medical College, New York, New York

MORTIMER MISHKIN, Section on Neuropsychology, National Institutes of Health, Bethesda, Maryland

SIDNEY OCHS, Department of Physiology, Indiana University School of Medicine, Indianapolis, Indiana

ROGER W. RUSSELL, Dean of Advanced Studies, Indiana University, Bloomington, Indiana

Preface

During recent years the integration of concepts from several of the traditional disciplines has led to some of the most significant advances in the history of the biological sciences. The development of modern microbiology—focusing upon an understanding of the chemical nature of genetic coding and its control over the anatomical, biochemical, and electrophysiological properties of organisms—is a prime example. Among the effects of these advances has been the rise of new views about interactions between the molar behavior of living organisms and the multitude of events which characterize them at more molecular levels. These views have very considerably extended the frontiers of research in the general area of problems traditionally encompassed by the term "physiological psychology." An important result has been the enlistment of the interests and efforts of other biological scientists—particularly biochemists, biophysicists, neuroanatomists and neurophysiologists—in the search for answers to questions which, until recently, had been considered the major realm of the psychologist.

With the new developments has come the task of making knowledge at these new frontiers readily available to students and to colleagues who are interested but not actively working in them. It is to these persons that the present volume is primarily directed, regardless of the specific discipline to which they may be formally attached. We hope that those who are already engaged in research in the areas we have chosen to consider may also find something new in the as yet unpublished information we have included in our discussions and in the ways in which we have presented our views about the current state of knowledge in these "Frontiers in Physiological Psychology."

Several approaches to our task seemed possible. No one person involved in the planning felt sufficiently bold nor adequately qualified to undertake the sole responsibility. The preparation of an extensive "handbook" seemed premature because the very rapid developments which are now in progress demand frequent restructurings of the knowledge they are producing—even within the limited time during which the volume was prepared some chapters underwent as many as four substantial revisions. The optimal approach appeared to be the preparation of a series of scientific essays on selected topics in areas where the nature of the problems under attack and the methodology employed could be clearly and critically discussed. Therefore, the volume is deliberately selective, rather than encyclopedic in its coverage.

As preparation for his assignment each of the authors held an initial series of meetings with groups of advanced undergraduates, graduate students, and staff members representing those readers to whom the essays are addressed. Feedback from these meetings contributed greatly to the methods of presentation which characterize each of the chapters to follow. We wish to acknowledge our indebtedness to those who assisted us in this way.

The seven chapters have been prepared by persons actively engaged in research on the particular topics for which they were responsible. The volume begins with two chapters which consider advances in our knowledge of the properties of neural tissue from the level of its simplest anatomical units to the complex mechanisms involved in the functioning of its most highly evolved structures. It is the "language of nerves" upon which behavior from reflex to creative activity depends; current research is taking great strides toward the fuller understanding of this language. Similarly, recent investigations are clarifying the ways in which the properties of neural tissue and associated sense organs are involved in the encoding and transmission of information from an organism's constantly changing environment and in the integration of such information into behavior. The third and fourth chapters are focused upon these issues as they are evidenced in information received through visual receptor channels. The discussion turns next to the topic of "attention," which, from the start of modern experimental psychology, has been a matter of central importance to any systematic attempt at understanding the complexities of behavior. How from among the thousands of "bits" of information to which an organism is constantly exposed by changes in its environment are certain bits effective in influencing behavior and others not? The fifth chapter considers new advances toward answering this question in terms of physiological mechanisms within the nervous system. Chapter six confronts the very complex issues of how changes in behavior encompassed by the psychologist's use of the term, "learning," are reflected in neural processes.

This is an area of problems which, because of its central importance in understanding how organisms adjust to their environments, has received perhaps more attention than any other in the history of psychological research. New techniques are turning up new knowledge which calls for the imaginative construction of new theoretical models as well as the revision of many older conceptualizations. The volume ends with consideration of the evidence that behavior has its biochemical substrates. The final chapter argues that the biochemical property of living organisms has a kind of priority based upon both the phylogenetic and ontogenetic histories of each individual. The development of biochemistry has now made it possible to search for specific interactions between biochemical events and behavior patterns. The search has already turned up a body of facts upon which new ideas and new research results are being produced at an accelerating pace; it has also given rise to studies and speculations which, to many, appear to verge upon science fiction.

Fact and fiction are sometimes difficult to distinguish at the frontiers of a rapidly developing science. As every Ph.D. candidate knows, "much research is still needed." But each effort advances the series of approximations by which a particular discipline develops. If our success in preparing this volume even approaches our level of aspiration, the reader will become familiar with the kinds of questions that now typify "Frontiers in Physiological Psychology" and with the directions in which advances are being made in the effort to find suitable answers to them. Psychology now has the opportunity to fill the once empty O of its traditional S-O-R formulation with meaningful interrelations between the molar R and other properties of the organism.

September, 1966   ROGER W. RUSSELL

Contents

CHAPTER 7

Biochemical Substrates of Behavior

ROGER W. RUSSELL

Introduction

ROGER W. RUSSELL

Dean of Advanced Studies,
Indiana University,
Bloomington, Indiana

It has been suggested that science typically moves ahead by quantal steps. Physiological psychology certainly appears to be currently in the midst of such an advance. The advance is taking place in a climate characterized by exciting new developments of knowledge and technique in biochemistry, microbiology, pharmacology, neuroanatomy, and neurophysiology. Psychologists have been joined by their colleagues from these other sciences in the search for relations between behavior and other properties of living biological systems at such levels as the "chemical coding of behavior" and the "macromolecular storage of memory." This direction of attention toward behavior should not be a surprise, for as Harlow (1958) has pointed out: "It is a safe generalization, I believe, to state that the universal common interest of the biological scientists is behavior, the single characteristic which best defines and differentiates the living animal." What is particularly interesting is the fact that developments in so many quite different contexts are converging to stimulate new hypotheses about the natures of some of psychology's basic variables and constructs. The developments have already led to very significant increases in our understanding of the three properties which, together with behavior, are involved in the description of living biological systems: anatomical or structural, biochemical, and electrophysiological. And it is in terms of relations between these properties and behavior that the new hypotheses are being stated.

The climate in which advances in physiological psychology are now occurring has another important characteristic which has arisen from a change in the attitudes of psychologists toward the

1

relevance to their science of hypotheses of this kind. The contro-
versies between molar and molecular views about behavioral
theory, which earlier had generated more heat than light, have
given way to the generally accepted position that psychology has
a place for both. Leaders in the development of psychological
theories, whose perspectives were as divergent as those of Tolman
and Hull, distinguish between the characteristics of molar behavior
and those of other properties of living organisms while agreeing
that the former ". . . are presumably strictly correlated with, and,
if you will, dependent upon, physiological motions. But descrip-
tively and per se they are other than those motions." (Tolman,
1932.) Hull (1943) argued that ". . . any theory of behavior is at
present, and must be for some time to come, a molar theory. This
is because neuroanatomy and physiology have not yet developed
to a point such that they yield principles which may be employed
as postulates in a system of behavior theory. . . ." The situation
is now different and is continuing to change so rapidly that the psychologist is hard pressed to keep abreast of even those major developments in other biological sciences which are most relevant to
his primary interest in behavior.

With his attention directed entirely toward the molar level the
student of behavior may appear to have forgotten the existence of
the anatomical, biochemical, and electrophysiological properties
of his subject, but they are there, contributing inevitably to his
observations—constituting substrates of the behavioral variables
which he is measuring. He is concerned with the behavior of *living*
organisms; he selects some sensory modality through which to
stimulate the subject; and he measures some response pattern
evidenced as muscular or glandular activity. He varies the stimulus
and notes any concomitant variations in the response, frequently
observing that the latter are not exclusively related to the former.
He may discover that the stimulus-response relations are affected
by the organism's past experience, which must in some way have
been "stored" to have carried over from the past to the present.
He sees what appear to be "innate" individual differences among
his subjects in the stimulus conditions to which they respond and
in the nature of the responses they make. The nature of such phenomena may be clarified and thinking about them sharpened by
searching for relations they may have to the anatomical features—
cells, tissues, organs, and organ systems—and the thousands of

dynamic electrophysiological and biochemical events which constitute the somatic substrates of behavior.

In searching for relations between behavior and other properties of organisms the physiological psychologist is not engaging in reductive thinking which might endanger the existence of psychology as an independent discipline. "Even a physiologically based or 'neuropsychological' theory of behavior remains a *psychological* theory. Its main features must be determined by certain constructs, theoretical conceptions, whose *raison d'etre* is behavioral instead of physiological." (Hebb, 1958.) This view places a heavy responsibility upon the objective development of self-consistent behavioral theories at the molar level. Once such theories are established relations can be systematically sought between the variables and constructs of which they are fabricated and phenomena at other levels of description, i.e., anatomical, biochemical, and electrophysiological. Physiological psychology need not, of course, wait for the "ultimate" behavioral theory to be developed. There is sufficient agreement about the essentiality of a number of variables and constructs, regardless of the nature of specific theoretical models which may attempt to tie them together, that physiological psychologists have no scarcity of questions to answer.

These basic variables and constructs provide a continuity to the chapters which follow. Since the objective is to explore *frontiers* in physiological psychology, no attempt has been made to give detailed maps of areas that have already become familiar territories. Indeed, there are points where, during the process of its writing, the discussion awaited the completion of ongoing research before it could be brought to its present conclusion. The frontiers of a scientific discipline may be defined in several ways: by the construction of new theoretical models, by the discovery of new areas of problems to be solved, by the report of new empirical observations which enable a stalled attack upon important familiar problems to move forward once again, by the development of new investigative techniques, and by the convergence of knowledge which hitherto had not been integrated. All these criteria are involved in the discussions to follow. As Lashley (1950) foresaw in his dramatic midcentury summary of the state of affairs in the "search for the engram" of learning, dynamic events within the organism, biochemical and electrophysiological, are now much more in prominence than they have been at any other time in the history of physiological psychology. Earlier efforts had, by mid-century, strongly suggested that there was something in the continual changes in behavioral variables as an organism adjusted to its continually altering environment which might better be understood in terms of the dynamics of somatic events than in terms of the more static features of its structural property. Recent developments in techniques have made it possible to understand much more about relations between behavior and electrophysiological events within areas of the central and peripheral nervous systems and even within different sites in single nerve cells. Other technical advances now enable researchers to measure and to alter experimentally biochemical events at the level of neurohumoral systems involved in nerve conduction and even at the level of changes in the synthesis and in the configuration of macromolecular components of individual neurons. Knowledge from the use of such techniques has led to the development of theoretical models which, although at times seeming to approach science fiction, are stimulating new directions in research. Since dynamic events occur within structural features of the organism, the search for sites of actions continues to be as important as it has been conceived to be in the past; indeed, the recent discovery of neurochemical substances which control the differentiation and growth of divisions of the central nervous system (CNS) make the structural property appear more "dynamic" than ever before. Clearly apparent throughout all the frontiers to be discussed is the integration of knowledge from several disciplines, an indispensable integration in the advance toward the description of living biological systems in terms of interactions among *all* their basic properties.

REFERENCES

Harlow, H. F. Behavioral contributions to interdisciplinary research. In H. F. Harlow & C. N. Woolsey (Eds.), *Biological and biochemical bases of behavior.* Madison, Wisc.: Univer. Wisconsin Press, 1958. P. 4.

Hebb, D. O. Alice in Wonderland, or psychology among the biological sciences. In H. F. Harlow & C. N. Woolsey (Eds.), *Biological and biochemical bases of behavior.* Madison: Univer. Wisconsin Press, 1958. Pp. 459–460.

Hull, C. L. The problem of intervening variables in molar behavior theory. *Psychol. Rev.*, 1943, **50**, 273–291.

Lashley, K. S. In search of the engram. *Sympos. Soc. exp. Biol.*, 1950, **4**, 454–482.

Tolman, E. C. *Purposive behavior in animals and man.* New York: Appleton-Century-Crofts, 1932.

CHAPTER 1

Integrative Properties of Neural Tissue

THEODORE HOLMES BULLOCK

Department of Neurosciences,
San Diego: School of Medicine, University of California,
La Jolla, California

I. INTRODUCTION

It is helpful to distinguish between two groups of functions of the nervous system in living organisms: the regulatory role and the initiating role. The older and simplified view of the function of neural tissue was that it is primarily *regulatory*. Any environmental event which impinges upon the organism and falls within a certain class of events that tends to throw the organism off the norm produces an adaptive, compensatory reaction to restore the norm. This role is represented by many reflexes and on a longer time scale by many higher level responses as well.

We now appreciate that there is another role, in addition to this one, namely, the functions in which the nervous system *initiates* departures from the status quo, thus manifesting spontaneity, even in the absence of any relevant environmental change. It is not just a question of time scale of regulation. The internal states that permit such spontaneity are only indirectly correlated under the usual habitat conditions with the biological need.

At another level of formulation, the following may help in deciding on the functions of neural tissue, thought of in terms of mechanisms. On the one hand, the system has to recognize and evaluate input, comparing it with predetermined criteria, inborn or learned. On the other, it has to formulate output, as commands to the effectors, adaptive to the environmental situation. These may be either because the input has reached a criterion that the system recognizes or because of its own spontaneity. In this chapter the unit basis for these integrative properties and the mechanisms involved at the level of the neural tissue and its cellular components are examined.

The way these two major roles of the nervous system have been formulated emphasizes the integrative properties of the system as a whole, and it is these properties that the author wants to account for at their lowest level. The word *integration* is here used in a very broad sense for the processes that underlie any relation between input and output which is determined but other than one to one. Whenever the output is controlled by the input, i.e., is some function of the input but is not identical to it, we say that integration has occurred. Obviously it is a term that includes processes taking place at junctions between units and at the level of single units themselves as well as processes involving the whole system. This embracing usage is the one most compatible with the dictionary definition and with the mathematical meaning of the term, both of which place emphasis upon the putting together of parts to make a whole.

II. Units and Processes

Since we will be looking at the functions of neural tissue at the unit level, we should first ask what those units are. There is probably no part of the animal body where the cell doctrine is better entrenched or has a more sweeping significance than in the nervous system. The nervous system is composed of cells called *neurons*. Neurons, therefore, have a reality as a unit of the system, as do cells in all other systems. But here the significance is greater because the units can work independently, i.e., discharge individually, nonsynchronously, or in ordered sequences, whereas in other tissues they tend to work in great masses or groups, more or less synchronously. The discovery of the neuronal basis of the nervous system was a particularly influential moment in the understanding of this system and continues to be as we learn more about the activities and role of these units.

Let us now ask what separate *processes* and how many separate interacting processes there are at the unit level which can contribute to integration. While answering these questions it is important to keep in mind four of the classical dicta about the nervous system. The first is that the neuron acts as a whole; we will see that this has to be changed considerably in the light of present knowledge; it acts as a unit and individual in much the same way a human being does—sometimes as a whole, sometimes not. The second is that the synapse is the seat of all lability. If neurons act as a whole, then it can only be between neurons that valve action, or fatigue, or changes in transfer function, learning, or other labile functions can take place. We will see ways in which this view must be modified by adding intraneuronal sites of lability. Third, dendrites were believed simply to conduct impulses toward the cell; now the dendrites are known to have quite a different significance even if they sometimes do conduct impulses in proximal regions. Fourth, the nerve impulse was long thought to be the only form of nerve cell activity in a signal transmitting sense; now we know other forms.

The best approach at this point in the development of this theme is to list the forms of nerve cell activity as we can now identify them. We will see that the nerve impulse is only one of several. In examining the forms of nerve cell potentials—or *electro-genesis*—it is important to note that this is only one mode of examining the activity of cells. In basing our descriptions upon it we may be missing important events that do not show up as changes in the electrical potential across the membrane of the nerve cell. There are changes, for example, in excitability, not reflected in the potential and there certainly are other forms of neuronal activity such as neurosecretions. We confine ourselves to the electrical signals

TABLE I

NERVE CELL MEMBRANE POTENTIALS

A. Electrotonic potentials (passively displaced by imposed current; no active
response)
B. Resting potentials (normal is not necessarily the maximum level)
C. Potentials of activity (may be graded and decremental or all-or-none and propagated)
   1. Transducer potentials (exogenic; from external events)
      a. Generator or receptor potentials
         i. Polarizing
        ii. Depolarizing
      b. Synaptic potentials
         i. Polarizing
        ii. Depolarizing
   2. Autogenic potentials (intrinsic spontaneity)
      a. Sawtooth
      b. Sinusoidal
      c. Quantal miniature random events
   3. Internal response potentials (endogenic; from antecedent activity within
the cell)
      a. Local potentials
      b. Spike potentials
      c. Afterpotentials

---

because this is the only technique that is available so far by which
we can observe the activity of neurons in the short time span during
which most of the signals are handled.

In referring to Table I it is useful to recognize that there are
three main classes of potentials: passively changing, resting, and
actively changing. The first of these is very simple but very important. We use the term, *electrotonic potentials,* for these changes
in electrical voltage across the membrane or from one part of a
neuron to another which are the passive result of any imposed
voltage. If force is exerted upon a pencil when writing, it moves
and the movement is equivalent to an electrotonic potential: It
is perfectly passive, but it is the result of the applied force and of
the inertial properties of the pencil. The standing potential, commonly called the *resting potential,* is the unchanging or very slowly
changing voltage that exists in the absence of arriving or spontaneous nervous signals. It may require that the nerve cell be alive
and metabolizing, but in neurological usage it is not the sign of
activity but of "rest." In our context activity means the occurrence
of nervous *events.* The *potentials of activity* are the ones most

relevant to our present considerations because only with changing potentials can we send signals.

III. POTENTIALS OF ACTIVITY

A. *Transducer Potentials*

It is helpful to divide these potentials of activity into three sub-classes. Those which are the result of external activity, of impinging events, will be called *transducer potentials;* Professor Fessard at Paris persuaded the author to use a neologism, exogenic potentials. These potentials arise as a result of transducing adequate events impinging upon the cell. A microphone is a transducer; it takes one form of energy which impinges upon it and it delivers output in a different form. Thus in a sense organ we would expect, and indeed we can observe, transducer potentials when light or sound or a suitable stimulus impinges upon the organ; these receptor potentials are sometimes called *generator potentials.* For other neurons that are not receptors, including central neurons, the main class of impinging events will be the activity of antecedent neurons. Such events cause potentials we call *synaptic potentials* because they occur at the place of contact between neurons and are peculiar to those places. We have at least two varieties: *inhibitory synaptic potentials* and *excitatory synaptic potentials.* The inhibitory synaptic potential is not just the absence of activity; it is an active process in the opposite direction from an excitatory one. It may cause an increase in polarization, but it also may simply cause a decrease in membrane resistance. We see from this formulation that synaptic potentials and receptor potentials are much alike and are essentially equivalent forms of response to arriving events. Therefore, the author predicts on grounds of symmetry that we will find both depolarizing and hyperpolarizing receptor potentials. So far we have direct evidence of the former occurring as excitatory receptor potentials. But there are sense organs which normally function by receiving an adequate stimulus and being thereby inhibited, which means that they must have some ongoing background activity to be inhibited.

B. *Autogenic Potentials*

The second subclass among the potentials of activity we can call *spontaneous* or *autogenic potentials.* These are the active potentials which are not responses to any events arriving from the outside, but are as spontaneous as the tick of a clock. They are, of course, not independent of the environment but require that certain conditions must be met: The temperature must be right, there must exist a proper milieu, perhaps it must be daytime and the belly full. But given the right conditions, the watch being wound in other words, the cell will show intermittent activity which is timed internally, hence is truly spontaneous. Autogenic potentials appear in two forms: as *sinusoidal* and as *sawtooth activity*. The latter is fundamentally different from the former in that a slowly changing process eventually reaches a critical point and triggers some new event that restores the system to the starting state, analogous to the phenomenon of relaxation oscillation. A third form of spontaneous activity is manifested by miniature postsynaptic potentials that occur in the absence of arriving nerve impulses and with the characteristics of (*a*) quantal size and (*b*) temporal distribution suggestive of random, independent origin. The average rate of occurrence is subject to change with various conditions including certain impulse barrages in fibers making presynaptic synapses. Miniature quantal random events at nerve endings may be an important and widespread integrative mechanism in junctional interaction.

C. *Internal Response Potentials*

The third subclass includes the internal response potentials which are active responses to antecedent events. Since the antecedent events were potentials occurring earlier within the same cell, they must have belonged to either the autogenic or transducer subclasses. If a receptor or a synaptic potential, a sinusoidal or a slowly rising spontaneous potential rises to a sufficiently high level, then it will trigger an internal response, which can be a *local potential* and graded or can be all-or-none and propagated. In the latter case we call it a *spike potential;* this is the classical all-or-none nerve impulse, which is thus only one form of neural activity among the several. One final form of internal response potential is the significant *afterpotentials:* those that follow an impulse or a train of impulses. Afterpotentials are labile and graded, not all-or-none, and probably of distinct varieties.

These are the several forms of nerve cell activity that are presently known. It is quite possible that as a result of future research some of these will be subdivided further or new types discovered.

We can see that, among them, the nerve impulse or spike potential is, in fact, a specialized form of neural activity, one of a rather long list. It probably developed because of its special capability of propagating information over long distances with fidelity. This role is distinct from those functions of neural tissue which are decision-making, integrating, labile, and graded processes that must precede the determination to fire the all-or-none event characterizing the spike potential.

IV. RESEARCH PREPARATIONS

In order not to leave these principles in a vacuum, let us examine some of the kinds of material on which such conclusions are based. The first are examples to show how we record these events experimentally. In some animals the conditions are especially favorable for recording at the unit level. One is the stellate ganglion of the squid, where a giant presynaptic neuron makes synaptic contact with a giant postsynaptic neuron. Innumerable minute contacts occur over a considerable part of a millimeter. With modern techniques it is possible to introduce microelectrodes internally into the presynaptic and into the postsynaptic fibers close to the synapse, making it possible to record exactly what is taking place electrically as the impulse arrives in the former and what effect this has in the latter fiber. One example of the finding obtained by the use of this technique is that an impulse arriving in the presynaptic membrane causes no visible electrical change in the postsynaptic membrane at the time when the presynaptic potential change is occurring. Such a change would be expected if the transmission were electrical. In other words, the possibility of electrical transmission in this junction can be directly excluded. This is an observation we cannot make in most other preparations. By itself the observation provides no positive evidence for chemical transmission, but we are forced to infer it by exclusion. After the presynaptic event is all over and there has been some delay, then the postsynaptic electrical event begins. The quantitative function relating the amplitude of the input and the amplitude of the output can be measured and proves to be very nonlinear. If the presynaptic spike falls below 80% of normal height, then there occurs no postsynaptic event whatsoever. Between 80 and 100% of the normal presynaptic spike height, the full range from zero to a fully normal postsynaptic event can be recorded.

Another preparation which has particular anatomical advantages is that of the Mauthner cells in the medulla of fish and aquatic amphibians, giant cells with large axons descending in the spinal cord. Here recent experiments by Furshpan and Furukawa have shown that the curious synaptic junction between spiraling pre-synaptic fiber endings and the axon hillock of the Mauthner cell is inhibitory and electrically transmitting. In contrast to the squid junction, here there is an electrical sign inside the postsynaptic unit at the time the presynaptic impulse arrives and proportionate to it.

Still another preparation with special advantage is that of the lobster cardiac ganglion. The lobster's heart is neurogenic: The beat is determined by nerve cells in a little ganglion located in the heart, quite unlike vertebrate hearts which have intrinsic auto-maticity in the muscle. This ganglion has exactly nine nerve cells, always in about the same places and with distinct functions. This has been a favorite object of investigation by the author and his collaborators for some years. Certain of the cells are pacemakers and others are followers, but not slavishly in a one-to-one rela-tionship. They integrate and deliver some output which is different from their input. Besides this spontaneity and integration, there is extrinsic inhibition and acceleration. The former arrives in a single axon coming from the central nervous system, whereas there are two accelerator axons on each side. The system is analogous to a miniature brain. The cardiac ganglion formulates patterned bursts that repeat with every heartbeat and therefore permit analysis of small modulations, to reveal integration at a simple level. We can record from the cells individually and penetrate known cells. Not with ease, to be sure; its something like trying to spear a jellyfish, barely visible in murky water, from the deck of the Queen Mary.

A fourth preparation which has become prominent in recent years and will contribute a great deal in the future is the central nervous system of mollusks, especially the abdominal ganglion of *Aplysia*. *Aplysia* is a tectibranch, opisthobranch gastropod, a sea slug. In the ganglia of this and many other gastropods, there are large cells, up to 800 μ in diameter, along with hundreds of small cells. The large cells permit easy penetration even by two elec-trodes and, consequently, the recording of the graded prepoten-tials which occur before an impulse arises. It is also possible to recognize the same cell in different specimens and to examine each of several distinct types, while controlling the steady membrane potential and introducing presynaptic input.

Recordings from the cells in these preparations teach us that all the processes discussed earlier are basically the same in all animals and in all neurons. All the events listed in Table I are common to all the neurons examined. At the neuronal level, even at the synaptic and integrative levels, the mechanisms appear to be basically the same, although they vary quantitatively in important ways from cell type to cell type within the same animal.

V. Sites of Membrane Potentials

So much for a brief touch of realism; now let us return to speculation. The information in Table I leads to the locus concept. The evidence from research preparations suggests that the various forms of inactivity do not occur everywhere in the neuron, but that each occurs in a special part of the neuron. There are, on a given neuron, not only localized synpatic sites, but often several different kinds of synapses each of limited extent and associated with distinct sizes, forms, and temporally dependent synaptic potentials. Synaptic events are certainly local, each synaptic potential occurring in a certain part of the cell which is capable of producing its own particular form of activity. Spike potentials occur in only a limited part of the neuron. In certain favorable cases it is possible to localize with considerable accuracy the region where spikes arise; it is sometimes far from the cell body. The impulse is conducted both toward and from the cell, but in some cases it does not propagate into the cell body or the dendrites. This is not true of all neurons; in some the spike does propagate back up into the cell body to varying extents, but probably not far out into the dendrites. In some neurons there is more than one locus of spike initiation or the locus may shift. There is some point in every neuron, we believe, beyond which the spike cannot spread. The membrane beyond this point has either too high a threshold or, more generally, is simply incapable of the explosive type of response which requires a regenerative chain reaction. The type of membrane capable of supporting a nerve impulse is specialized and limited broadly to what we call an axon. The role of such an impulse is long distance, high fidelity propagation of neural signals; the integrative events have all taken place before it starts.

There is some compelling evidence that in the axon terminals, the spike gives way to graded, local processes and therefore the all-or-none event itself does not go to the very ends of the axons. At least in some cases we can have lability there. Whatever signal does enter the terminals causes the release of a transmitter, probably involving chemical reactions. This transfer function is labile; that is, there can be more or less transmitter released per impulse depending upon the neuron's recent history and other parallel events occurring in the same neighborhood.

The neuron, we now think, must be conceived of as a constellation of loci, a mosaic of different kinds of membrane within electrotonic shouting distance of each other, interacting especially in these regions where the activity is not all-or-none. The interaction mainly involves electrotonic spread, not active propagation, and that is why the passive properties of the nerve cell are so important. The activity at a given synapse can influence the origin of an impulse some distance away in the axon only as it can spread electrotonically, that is, with decrement highly dependent upon the geometry of the loci.

VI. The Dendrites as Integrative Structures

This kind of concept gives a new role to the dendrites. It seems difficult to think of dendrites in a cell like the Purkinje neuron of the cerebellum as carrying impulses. What would be the reason for the tremendous ramification of branches? Now we think that on the whole dendrites do not support impulses, either toward or away from the cell body, with the exception in some cases near the base of the dendrite for a limited distance. Rather, the vastly ramified dendrite is like an analog computer where graded events are occurring locally here and there, influencing each other as the branches converge. The more remote of these dendrites probably exerts a very indirect effect upon the initiation of impulses in the axon. So we think of dendrites as being the prime integrative structures, most highly developed in the animal species with most complex behavior.

A. Kinds of Excitabilities

This view distinguishes several kinds of excitabilities. Classical excitability is simply measured by the threshold, i.e., the critical level at which a spike takes off. Certainly this is very important because the moment of origin of an impulse, the number of impulses per second, and the total number of impulses in a message will be determined by this threshold. But this is only one form of excitability and this form is only important at one place in the whole neuron, the place where the spike potential arises. Further out in the axon, where we usually record, the spike threshold is really quite unimportant physiologically because each part of the axon is always more than adequately stimulated by activity upstream from it; that is, there is a large safety factor.

Each of the other forms of neural activity also has an excitability, even though it does not have a sharp threshold. If we plot the output, i.e., the response voltage, as a function of the input, i.e., the amplitude of the preceding event that caused it, we generally get very nonlinear curves. These outputs are labile and are independent for each of the transfer functions: between stimulus and receptor potential between presynaptic event and postsynaptic event, separately for each form of synapse, between preceding events and local potential, and between preceding events and afterpotentials. There is then a constellation of excitabilities sequentially related but independently variable; this provides great opportunities for integration.

B. Kinds of Inhibition

Similarly, there are several kinds of inhibition. The abrupt, discrete increase in membrane conductance to specific ions, generally leading to a hyperpolarizing potential transient [inhibitory postsynaptic potential (IPSP)] is one. Sometimes the inhibition is due only to the short circuiting effect of the conductance change. Slowly accumulating hyperpolarization without IPSPs may be a different form. Refractoriness sometimes accompanies subthreshold excitatory postsynaptic potentials (EPSPs), therefore representing a true inhibition whereas refractoriness after a spike response is not. However, excess depolarization from accumulated excitatory input is different and has been considered a form of inhibition. A relatively new discovery currently catching attention is the so-called presynaptic inhibition. It is now known that at least in certain cases specific fibers cause an inhibition of the presynaptic event just before it reaches the synapse. It looks as though there are junctions between the ending of one axon and the ending of another axon. Some reports of the anatomy of this region by electron microscopy support the probability that this is actually the case. Similar arrangements account for presynaptic facilitation in certain places. This principle enormously expands the range and flexibility of integrative possibilities at the unit level.

C. Interactions between Neurons

Finally, there are several types of interaction known to occur between neurons. Interactions at the synapse, which we have just been considering, are only one type. There are some firm cases of hormonal effects, where certain parts of the nervous system control the liberation of hormones which, in turn, influence other parts of the nervous system.

A more surprising kind of interaction has emerged recently in a number of species though we do not yet know whether it is a bizarre phenomenon found in special cases or whether it will turn out to be a common mechanism. We call this *specific electrotonic interaction.* If an electrode is inserted into one cell, in certain places, and connected to a battery so that a current can be passed into the cell, then, amazingly enough, a recording from an electrode in another cell a millimeter or so away shows the presence of a potential proportional to the imposed current in the first cell. It is, of course, true that when a current is introduced anywhere into a conducting solution, some fraction of that current can be detected at other points in the solution; this is called the electrical field. It is easy to control for this possibility: If either electrode is withdrawn just a few microns outside its cell, the interaction phenomenon disappears. This demonstrates that the field potential is much smaller than the potential resulting from some connection between the interiors of the cells. Current is somehow specifically piped from cell to cell. It is not synaptic in the usual sense; it is not necessary to initiate an impulse in the first cell. In fact, if a nerve impulse is initiated in the first cell, using the lobster cardiac ganglion preparation, nothing is recorded in the second cell. The connection that carries the current is of such small diameter or has such a high capacity and low safety factor that it cannot even carry a brief event like a nerve impulse. We see something in the second cell only if we impose a fairly long (e.g., 50 msec) pulse of current. Under such circumstances the pulse may be in either polarity. Even in cells separated by more than 7 mm, by which distance electrotonic spread has suffered a decrement to a few per cent of original amplitude, we can see a normal influence of this kind. Though the potential itself is too small to record reliably, it nevertheless modulates the frequency of a pacemaker in the second cell in the expected direction, according to the polarity, provided the imposed current lasts 50 msec or longer.

Finally, we have the possibility of interactive *field effects*, effects of the currents observed with large extracellular electrodes in masses of tissue, such as the EEG and ERG. This subject is also still in an early state of development: We do not yet know how to evaluate the importance of field effects in normal physiology. There are many preparations where we can demonstrate a generalized diffuse effect in a whole region as a result of imposed currents in the tissue. Some authors feel that these are laboratory curiosities; others believe that they are signs of what happens normally. For example, the questions are often asked: Is there any causal significance to brain waves? Are brain waves a mechanism by which cells influence each other or simply an inevitable result of their activity like the noise of an engine? All cells in a mass of tissue are subject to this influence because the brain waves are conducted through the entire mass. There is at least some evidence that cells do interact by these weak field effects without necessarily involving nerve impulse transmission.

VII. Time Functions

To be more accurate, the picture must be complicated a little more, for there exist degrees of freedom among the interactions and transfer functions we have cataloged, which are due to functions of time. It is not sufficient merely to say that a presynaptic impulse arrives and causes a postsynaptic potential, or even that this postsynaptic potential is in the direction of excitation or the direction of inhibition. We know now that it is sometimes crucial that the transmission has the property facilitation in some cases, whereas in others there can be anti-facilitation. What we mean by this is that a matter of timing is involved. If a presynaptic impulse arrives at a junction, it can cause an excitatory postsynaptic event. If we repeat this input within a certain length of time and get a larger second response, we infer a process called *facilitation*. In other instances we repeat the input and get less response; this is called *anti-facilitation*. A third case is where there is no difference; we get exactly the same response the second time. Messages usually arrive as barrages of impulses; they will have an influence depending on the inherent properties of facilitation or anti-facilitation in the junctions involved and the number and spacing of the impulses. There are often long-term and short-term facilitations.

Another type of time function which is important in certain cases is involved in what we call aftereffects. Aftereffects may be related to afterpotentials, but we are not sure that they are simply determined by the afterpotentials. Aftereffects are evidenced as post-excitatory activity or post-excitatory inhibition, or post-inhibitory excitation or post-inhibitory inhibition. If we deliver excitatory stimulation for some period of time, the response may continue for a while after the stimulation has ceased; this can be called a *positive aftereffect*. In other cases, the response will immediately overshoot in the opposite direction; this would be called a *negative aftereffect*. The response itself can be inhibitory, and the aftereffect can be after-inhibition or rebound excitement. These phases are very labile in duration, amplitude, and sequence and certainly reflect or influence integration of any input to determine output.

There is still another way in which degrees of freedom are provided as a function of time. In some cases we believe that integration is accomplished by *shifting of loci* of graded activity and spike initiation as a function of previous activity, milieu, or other input. Spontaneous activity arises in the neuron at certain places which we can speak of as the pacemaker loci of the neuron; these places may shift and there can be more than one. We have records of two independent rhythms in the same cell, interacting to a certain degree.

One consequence of the properties of neurons is that much of the control of neurons by each other is probably best described as a *modulation of ongoing activity,* rather than simply an input-output function of silent cells waiting for impinging events. Modulation of ongoing activity can be much more sensitive than response to an input in a previously silent cell. If there are field effects, as suggested earlier, they probably work in this way; that is, small changes in the general level of current flowing through the tissue may modulate the ongoing activity by slightly increasing or decreasing its frequency. This may be accomplished with great sensitivity compared to the threshold necessary to fire a silent cell.

All this adds up to a discouraging degree of complexity at the single neuron level and becomes even more perplexing when we consider a constellation of them organized in special ways. The position is quite different from that of a few years ago when we wondered whether it would be possible to explain behavior, with all its nuances and variety, simply in terms of configurations of neurons that can fire or not fire. The neurophysiologists were very brave who at that time said "Yes, we think so," although the extrapolation involved is tremendous, and we certainly cannot prove that behavior as complex as that of human beings can be obtained by a finite number of units which fire on an all-or-none basis. Now we have an embarrassing richness of ways in which the individual units can integrate and can be labile. The pendulum has swung to the other extreme when we ask: How on earth does the organism have any constants? How does it maintain body temperature as it does? How does normal man adapt so adequately to his physical and social environments day after day, in cold weather or in warm, in morning and in evening? Not everybody has absolute pitch, but we all have physiologically an amazing degree and number of relative constants which, in the face of all the lability possible in the neuron, we are hard put to explain at the present time. The consistency of our behavior is more impressive in this light than its variability; think of a piano player or of our recognition of letters, words, voices, and the like.

VIII. PATTERNING

The last point is of special interest to psychologists. It is that most messages carried in the nervous system are in groups of impulses of a certain number and spacing which, therefore, can be spoken of as having one degree or another of *temporal pattern*. Some appear to be highly patterned and others much less so. At any rate, we can ask the question: Does the nervous system utilize the microstructure of the impulse trains to carry information? A nerve cell may repeat a certain sequence and spacing of impulses like a little tune or phoneme. It may be "pop—pop,pop,pop—pop" or "pop,pop—pop—pop,pop." We find this happening in some of our records, for example, from the lobster cardiac ganglion cells. We have no classical physiology that adequately attacks the related question: How does the neuron formulate its patterned output? There are two basic possibilities: The pattern may be formulated by neural circuitry, by some kind of feedback upon the unit that starts it; or the pattern may be independent of feedback, the unit that starts it being capable, by itself, of delivering a patterned output. The evidence is still fragmentary but seems to indicate that each of these possibilities occurs in different systems.

The other side of the coin is the questions: What effect does pattern, especially the microstructure of a train, have apart from its average frequency, its duration, and number of impulses? How much does the neuron care about the detailed spacing? Experiments are even fewer on this topic. The information now available appears to support the view that in some cases neurons care a great deal, but in others not at all. The normal occurrence of significant differences in microstructure is still being cataloged. There are characteristic differences in statistical distribution of interspike intervals about any mean; some show a degree of serial correlation providing therefore a strongly patterned sequence. Clearly this is a parameter available to the system, but how much it increases the information capacity per channel we do not yet know.

Two major functions of neural tissue were emphasized: integration of incoming signals to determine output, a complex of steps occurring chiefly in dendrites, and propagation of signals faithfully over long distances, chiefly occurring in axons. Several important problems have not been treated. One is the spatial summation that permits complex change in the meaning of messages as in shape recognizing visual cells. Another is the transduction processes in neural receptors. The elaboration and fate of substances in certain so-called neurosecretory cells is more than a special problem in peculiar places. The functions served by the class of accessory cells called neurolgia cells are still moot though under active discussion today. Although there is still much to be learned about the functions of neural tissue, it is safe to say that recent developments in our knowledge of its integrative properties have taken us significantly closer to understanding how the degree of lability required for the behavior of living organisms, which is the particular concern of psychologists, may be achieved.

CHAPTER 2

Neuronal Mechanisms of the Cerebral Cortex[✿]

SIDNEY OCHS

Department of Physiology, Indiana University School of Medicine,
Indianapolis, Indiana

I. INTRODUCTION

Because it is the most recent phylogenetic acquisition, the cerebral cortex has long been supposed to have an important role in higher functions. Recent studies of the electrical activity of the cortex have shown that electroencephalographic (EEG) and evoked response changes can be correlated with conditioning in ways which are described elsewhere in this book. The nature of the cellular mechanisms underlying the electrical activity of the cerebral cortex and behavior is the subject of this chapter. In the first part the direct cortical responses (DCRs) elicited by means of elec-

✿ The studies described in this chapter were supported by U. S. Public Health Service Grants NB-1993 and MH-4815.

trical pulses through electrodes applied directly to the exposed cerebral cortex, a response first studied by Adrian (1936), will be discussed. The electrical responses excited in this way have relatively simple wave forms which helps in the analysis of these grouped discharges.

Recently, a new approach to problems of cerebral cortex function has been developed making use of the phenomena of spreading depression (SD) discovered by Leão (1944). Cortical function is temporarily depressed by SD and the "reversible decortication" brought about by this means offers a powerful new way to study the relation of the cortex to conditioned behavior without the traumatic and plastic changes incident to the usual surgical ablations. In the second part of this chapter the basic nature of SD is briefly outlined and then some uses made of it in behavioral studies related to cortical function are discussed.

II. DIRECT CORTICAL RESPONSE

A. General Considerations and Types of Direct Cortical Response

The direct cortical response (DCR) is an operational term. It simply means that the cortex is excited via stimulating electrodes placed directly on its exposed surface. Other terms for this response are: dendritic potential, superficial response, local response, etc. The DCR is also categorized as an evoked response, as are the sensorily evoked responses obtained by exciting an afferent fiber input to the cortex. In evoked responses a group of neurons are forced to respond together, often in greater than usual numbers. The response, therefore, is a measure of the response capabilities of neuronally connected regions rather than of their normal discharge characteristics. Unlike the sensorily evoked response, the population of cells which may be stimulated to give rise to the DCR is not limited to a sensory input area. Therefore, the properties of the motor areas and associational cortex areas, as well as sensory receiving areas can be studied by this means.

The DCRs obtained at different strengths of stimulation of a sensory area show characteristic differences in form. With a weak stimulus, the response recorded within approximately 5 mm from the stimulating electrodes has a simple smooth rise and a fall, the response lasting 10 to 20 msec. A positive-negative sequence of these longer duration waves is found with stronger stimulation in sensory areas. The sequence is similar to that of the sensorily evoked responses which are obtained when stimulating afferent fibers entering a primary sensory area. In both cases, one or several small spikelike fast waves are seen at the onset, the first one signifying discharge of afferent fibers carrying volleys into the responding region (Ochs, 1959a).

In recent studies made with Suzuki, microelectrodes were used to stimulate responses from various depths within the cortex (Ochs, 1962a; Ochs & Suzuki, 1965; Suzuki & Ochs, 1962; Suzuki & Ochs, 1964). With this technique of laminar stimulation, a localized excitation of elements is accomplished, and it was possible to selec-

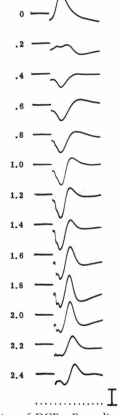

FIG. 1. Laminar stimulation of DCRs. Recording electrodes on surface 1 mm distant from the stimulating microelectrode penetrating the cortex to the different depths indicated at left of each trace. Calibration: 2 msec, amplitude 2 mv. (From Suzuki & Ochs, 1964.)

tively excite several types of DCRs depending upon the depth of
the stimulating electrode within the cortex. Stimulation within
the upper cortical layers of a sensory area (Fig. 1) gave rise to a
simple negative wave (N wave) DCR; stimulation in middle layers,
a positive-negative sequence of potentials; and stimulation of the
deeper cortical layers, again a simple negative wave similar to
that obtained by stimulation of the surface, but preceded by one
or more small amplitude fast waves. These results indicated that
the DCR excited by using a pair of widely spaced bipolar leads
is compounded of several types of response patterns. This is particularly the case when strong surface stimulation is used and
stimulating currents can reach further down to lower cortical
levels. The positive-negative type of DCR excited from the middle
layers was obtained from specific sensory areas and not so readily
from other regions. Therefore, this response sequence is apparently evoked from the same neurons excited by a specific sensory
input volley, as is also indicated by the loss of this complex response when recording from chronically isolated islands of cortex
(Suzuki & Ochs, 1964).

B. Negative Wave Direct Cortical Response

The simple N wave DCR was excited from the surface of all
areas of cortex investigated (sensory, motor, and associational).
Such an ubiquitous distribution suggests that the system excited
by surface stimulation is of general significance for cortical function. Its simple form also indicates a relatively simple mechanism
underlying the response. Most of our attention has been, therefore, directed to this response. Upon exciting an N wave DCR by
surface stimulation and a short distance away using a microelectrode inserted to successively deeper levels of the cortex for
laminar recordings, the N wave DCR was found to be localized
to the upper layers of the cortex. On the basis of elementary electrical considerations, a fairly large number of cells should by synchronously active. Also, the population of active cells must be
present in a restricted part of the cortex or depolarization must be
present in parts of regularly oriented neurons to give rise to the
relatively large potentials recorded. The pyramidal cells are sufficiently numerous and have the requisite orientation to be the responding element. Their cell bodies are found in all layers in the
cortex, and a large number of them send their branching apical

dendrites upward to ramify profusely in the uppermost molecular cortical layers (Sholl, 1956). Laminar microelectrode recordings of the N wave DCR showing its distribution in the upper layers (Suzuki & Ochs, 1964) conform with the concept that the apical dendrite of the pyramidal cells becomes depolarized to give rise to this surface negative response.

Chang (1951) considered the dendritic potential (N wave DCR) to be similar in nature to an action potential excited in one part of apical dendrites spreading laterally outward, or downward and then outward in the apical dendrite branches. Another hypothesis, introduced by Eccles (1951), was that the responses, because of their simple form and long duration, are excitatory postsynaptic potentials (EPSPs). He considered that some surface elements found in the molecular layer, possibly the Cajal cells, are electrically stimulated, and these elements conduct for some distance laterally in the molecular layer before synapsing on apical dendrites in the molecular layer to give rise in them to the EPSP. Although in spinal cord motoneurons the EPSP recorded from inside the soma will excite a propagated action potential upon reaching a critical level (Eccles, 1964), no comparable spike is found associated with cortical responses in the neocortex. The EPSP is less sensitive to pentobarbital than the spike mechanism. In correspondence with this, the DCR was found to be insensitive to relatively high levels of pentobarbital (Ochs, 1956). Further, Purpura and Grundfest (1956) reported that when injected in high dose levels, d-tubocurarine appeared to have a depressing action on the response, presumably by blocking at the synapse between the transmitting element and the apical dendrites. Such evidence was used to support the EPSP hypothesis. However, large doses of d-tubocurarine injected systemically most likely do not readily pass through the blood-brain barrier (Curtis, 1961). d-Tubocurarine probably produces its effects on the DCR indirectly through a blood pressure dropping effect (Brinley, Kandel, & Marshall, 1958; Ochs, 1959b). Ammassian and Weiner (1966) have recently confirmed the reduction of DCR amplitudes as due to a hypotensive effect of d-tubocurarine. Of interest in this respect are those earlier experiments which appeared to show a failure of conditioning in curarized animals, which had suggested a central blocking action (Girden, 1940; Girden and Culler, 1937). However, later studies showed that fully curarized animals were capable of being conditioned (Black, 1958; D. W. Lauer, personal communication, 1962). And in man, a level of curarization two and one-half times that adequate for paralysis obtained with *d*-tubocurarine given gradually and with artificial respiration produced no loss of consciousness, impairment of memory, or disturbance of sensation, nor were alterations found in the EEG (Smith, Brown, Toman, & Goodman, 1947).

Evidence casting doubt on the EPSP nature of the directly evoked cortical response was obtained from studies designed to show summation or lack of it. If the N wave DCR acts like the EPSP obtained in spinal cord motoneurons, it should show summation similar to that demonstrated for EPSPs in the motoneuron (Curtis & Eccles, 1960). Trains of repetitive shocks were used to excite N wave DCRs in the cerebral cortex (Ochs & Booker, 1961) and, in the majority of cases, little evidence of their summation was found. Instead, what could be described as refractoriness was found. The first response appears to make the neurons giving

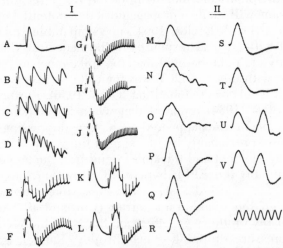

FIG. 2. Repetitive stimulation and N wave DCRs. (1) *A*, single stimulus and N wave DCR. *B* through *J*, repetitive stimulation at 50, 75, 100, 200, 300, 400, 400, and 500 pulses/sec, respectively. *K* and *L*, single stimulus and responses followed by a stimulus train at 200 and 300 pulses/sec, respectively. (II) From another brain region; *M*, single stimulus and response. *N* through *T*, repetitive stimulation at 75, 100, 300, 400, 500, 500, and 600 pulses/sec, respectively. *U* and *V*, single stimuli and responses followed by a train of stimuli at 300 and 400 pulses/sec, respectively. Calibration 100 cps, amplitude 0.47 mv. (From Ochs & Booker, 1961.)

rise to the N wave DCR refractory to the next stimulus and successive stimulations keep the membranes in a refractory state
(Fig. 2). A similar result was obtained by Merlis (1965) in a study
of excitability cycle though differently interpreted.

It might be argued that with such trains of impulses a lag in
mobilization or a rapid depletion of synaptic transmitter substance
(Eccles, 1964) from the presynaptic elements terminating on apical
dendrites could account for the apparently refractory-like behavior. That this is not the case was shown by stimulating N wave
DCRs from two separate sites on the surface and recording their
interaction at a point midway between them. (See insert of Fig.
7 for electrode positions.) If the response is excited from apical
dendrites on which transmitting elements from each stimulated
source terminate, and if they are EPSPs, summation of responses
should be seen. We found (Ochs & Booker, 1961; Ochs & Suzuki,
1965) with such spatiotemporal interactions carried out in many
different places on the cortex that the results were typically those
of an apparent refractoriness (Fig. 3). At the various time separa-

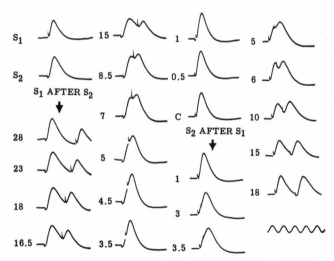

FIG. 3. Occlusive-like interaction of N wave DCRs. S_1 and S_2, stimulations to
two points on the surface with a common site of recording between them. (Compare
figure shown as insert in Fig. 7 for electrode arrangement.) Stimulus to S_1 and then
to S_2 with time in milliseconds between then given by the numbers to left of each
trace. C, coincidence of the two stimuli. Later, stimulus to S_2 after S_1. Calibration
100 cps, amplitude 0.37 mv. (From Ochs & Booker, 1961.)

tions between shock stimuli presented to each of the sites as shown in this figure, the response to the later stimulus was decreased in amplitude, gradually returning toward normal amplitude in approximately 30 msec. In other words, the response does not summate as expected on comparison with the behavior of EPSPs in the motoneuron.

We should not be surprised in dealing with as complex a tissue as cerebral cortex that other patterns of neuronal behavior may appear in such studies of temporal and spatiotemporal interactions. With weaker stimulation there is less refractoriness. To put it another way, there appears to be a smaller phase of summation lasting from coincidence to approximately 5 msec. This is to be expected if the N wave DCRs are being excited by synaptic potentials too small to be detected with these external electrodes. Therefore, the responding pool, will, with weaker stimuli, show more capabilities for a subliminal excitability increase. With stronger stimulation more cells of the pool are responding and will therefore show occlusion to interacting stimulation sources. While this suggests that the N wave DCR is like an all-or-none action potential (of longer duration), the response does not have all of the properties of an action potential as will be discussed later in the chapter.

The period of apparent refractoriness may be much longer than 30 msec, in some cases the second response returning to normal amplitude only after several hundred milliseconds or longer. Such long periods of depressed excitability most likely represent another mechanism of inhibitory action which at present is not understood (cf. Krnjević, Randic, & Straughan, 1964). Later appearing excitatory increases, lasting several hundred milliseconds, are also seen; possibly these are related to the second negative wave described by Chang (1951) which appears after the N wave DCR.

In a few cases, repetitive stimulation gave the appearance of a summation of cortical responses with a plateaulike hump (Fig. 4). This type of response, which in our work was seen in a smaller proportion of the animals studied, we consider to be a shift of the steady potential level of cortex in the negative direction upon repetitive stimulation (Ochs & Booker, 1961). Shifts in the steady potential level, first studied by Libet and Gerard (1941; 1962), appear to reflect the state of polarization of the apical dendrites and to be related to the excitability of the cortex in some important manner (Morrell, 1961; O'Leary & Goldring, 1959). This subject

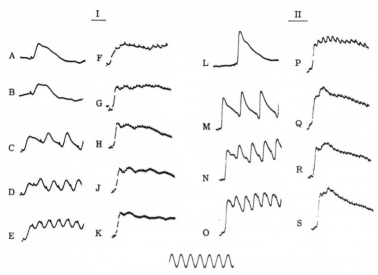

FIG. 4. Repetitive stimulation and apparent summation or potential shift. (I) Weaker stimulation: A and B, single stimuli and responses. C through K, different rates of repetitive stimulations at 50, 75, 100, 200, 300, 400, 500, and 600 pulses/sec. (II) Stronger stimulation: L, single response. Repetitive stimulation, M through S at 50, 75, 100, 200, 250, 300, and 400 pulses/sec. Calibration 100 cps, amplitude 0.37 mv. (From Ochs & Booker, 1961.)

has recently been comprehensively reviewed by O'Leary and Goldring (1964).

Studies of the mechanism of transmission of cortical responses laterally in the cortex have, for some years, been of interest with regard to the electrogenesis of the response. Burns and Grafstein (1952) found that shallow cuts through the uppermost layer blocked transmission of the surface negative response, therefore indicating a transmission link superficially placed in the molecular layer. Previous work with cortical cuts between stimulated and responding sites supported a cortico-cortical link under the cortex as well as a short-spreading intracortical transmission path (Ochs, 1956; Ochs & Booker, 1961). Using the more localized stimulations afforded by the microelectrode stimulating technique, the problem was reinvestigated. When cuts were made between stimulating and recording electrodes below the molecular layer down through and including the underlying white matter, transmission of the N wave DCR was little effected (Ochs, 1962a; Ochs & Suzuki, 1965). This type of experiment, which is the converse of Burns and Grafstein's (1952), showed that most, if not all, the N wave DCR is transmitted by elements in the molecular layer. The transmission of potentials to lateral distances of 10 mm and more (Brooks & Enger, 1959) when using stronger stimulating intensities, and where a greater population of neurons is excited in the stimulated site, appears to be due to a cortico-cortical link; i.e., axons in the white matter just under the gray matter of the cortex. Transmission of DCRs, therefore, is at least dual: a shorter intracortical spread via a transmitting element in the molecular layer synapsing on apical dendrites to give rise to the N wave DCR and cortico-cortical axons transmitting impulses in the underlying white matter to give rise to complex DCRs at the greater distances (cf. Ochs, 1958). Long distance cortico-cortical transmission of DCRs has also been reported using cortical cuts by Javrishvili (1965).

The question arises as to the nature of the transmitting link in the molecular layer exciting the N wave DCR. We had already mentioned one theory where the apical dendrites are supposed to be excited and also serve to propagate the response laterally. Such a mechanism would require the apical branches to extend at least 4 mm laterally and more, considering the spread of the recorded responses. However, present anatomical evidence indicates that the apical dendrites have a lateral extension of only a few tenths of a millimeter at most (Sholl, 1956). While Burns and Grafstein (1952) believe the response to be generated in the same axonal element transmitting the response laterally in the molecular layer, a difference between the transmitting element in the molecular layer and the element giving rise to the response was indicated by the occlusive interaction of the responses (*vide supra*) and also by the action of γ-aminobutyric acid. When this agent is placed on the cortex at the responding site, it very quickly abolishes surface negative responses (Iwama & Jasper, 1957; Purpura, Girado, & Grundfest, 1957). On the other hand, Iwama and Jasper (1957) found, and we have confirmed (Ochs & Suzuki, 1965), that γ-aminobutyric acid is ineffective in blocking the N wave DCR when placed either on the stimulated site or on the cortex between stimulating and responding sites. γ-Aminobutyric acid is relatively inert on axons (Curtis, 1961); therefore, it would be ineffective if the transmitting link in the molecular layer is axonal. By varying the distance between the stimulated and responding sites a conduction velocity of approximately 0.5–1 meter/sec was indicated for the axonal transmitting element (Suzuki & Ochs, 1964), a velocity of the order earlier reported by Chang (1951; 1952) and one which would fit with conduction in small myelinated or in nonmyelinated fibers.

Recent additional support for an axonal element in the molecular layer transmitting laterally has been obtained with the use of tetrodotoxin (Ochs & Ng, 1966). This substance is effective in remarkably low concentrations to block propagated potentials in nerve fiber and muscle, acting on the mechanism controlling the selective increased permeability to Na^+ on excitation (Furukawa et al., 1959; Nakamura et al., 1965). In our studies of the action of tetrodotoxin on the cortex, a concentration as low as 10^{-6}–10^{-5} wt./vol. caused a block of excitation when placed on the stimulated site without interfering with the responses recorded a few millimeters away to stimulation at another site (cf. electrode disposition shown in insert Fig. 7).

The possibility that these superficial transmitting axons are nonspecific afferent fibers known to extend up to the molecular layer was eliminated by an investigation of DCRs obtained from within chronically isolated islands of cortex (Suzuki & Ochs, 1964). The N wave DCRs were found remaining in islands 40–55 days after neuronal isolation during which time all afferents would be degenerated. Nearly all of the positive-negative sequence and all responses from the lower layers were eliminated. The underlying cortico-cortical axons were apparently all degenerated. The molecular layer transmitting element is, therefore, derived from the local cell population. The two likeliest candidates supplying such a transmitting element are the stellate cells, which are known to send axons up to the molecular layer, these then extending laterally (Sholl, 1956), and the collaterals of pyramidal cells, which also may reach the molecular layer to pass laterally for the required distance (Fig. 5).

Is there anatomical evidence that the transmitting axons synapse on the upper reaches of the apical dendrites to excite the N wave DCR? Previous anatomical study suggested that synapses on apical dendrites were sparse or not present at all sharing a similar opinion previously expressed with regard to the farther reaches of the motoneuron dendrites (Eccles, 1957). Gemmules, spinelike extensions, have been seen in the classical Golgi preparations arising from along the shaft of the apical dendrites (Chang, 1952) and have been

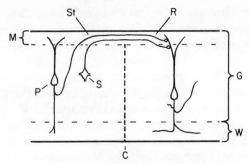

FIG. 5. Schematization of neurons possibly involved in transmission and generation of the N wave DCR. To left of molecular cut C, stellate cells S and pyramidal
cells P are shown with axons passing up and laterally in molecular layer M. Axonal
elements stimulated by electrode St. One or both of these axons terminate on apical
dendrites of pyramidal cells in which the N wave DCR is generated and recorded
by surface electrode R. Gray matter indicated by G, white matter by W. (From
Ochs & Suzuki, 1965.)

considered to be synaptic sites, i.e., of the axodendritic synapses;
those on the soma (the axosomatic synapses) are similar to synaptic
endings found on other cells. In electron micrographs, Gray (1959)
has shown after identification of dendrites near the soma that the
dendritic spines have the appearance expected of a synaptic site.
Pappas and Purpura (1961) have also identified synaptic endings
present on the upper apical dendrites in electron micrographs.
Synapses on apical dendrites in the outer reaches of the molecular
layers are harder to analyze because of the uncertainty of identification of fine branches of apical dendrites as such. However, it
seems likely from the electron microscopic studies that synapses
are present all along the apical dendrites.

C. Electrogenesis of the Negative Wave Direct
Cortical Response

On the basis of our studies of interaction we consider that the
N wave DCR is not an EPSP. Excitatory postsynaptic potentials
are presumed to be present but too small in amplitude to be recorded with external electrodes. The identification of the N wave
DCR as an EPSP also appears to conflict with the current conception of how action potentials are excited by synaptic activity. The
EPSP is considered to excite the cell by electrotonically depolarizing the initial segment of the axon, the nonmyelinated portion near

the cell body (Eccles, 1964) where threshold for the firing of an action potential is lower than in the membrane of the soma. However, there is a rather rapid attenuation of the electrotonic potentials with increasing distances from their site of activation at synapses, electrotonic potentials estimated to fall to $1/e$ of their original amplitude within 300 μ (Eccles, 1957; Eccles, 1960). In the case of the pyramidal cell, the reduction of effective depolarizing action from synapses on the dendrites is exaggerated by the relatively greater lengths and the branching of the apical dendrites. Therefore, by passive spread of electrotonus, the activation of EPSPs at the far reaches of apical dendrites in the upper cortex should have little effect on those cells in the lower layers as pointed out by Eccles (1957; 1960).

On the above consideration, the N wave DCR may represent an active response excited by synaptic activity which propagates in some active fashion down to the soma, to fire or at least modify the excitability of cells in the lower cortical layers. Is there evidence for such an active response being excited in dendrites? Grundfest (1957) has argued that dendrites are electrically inexcitable and, hence, not able to give rise to active responses. However, Eccles, Libet, and Young (1958) found abortive action potentials excited in the dendrites of chromatolytic spinal cord motoneurons during regeneration. Conduction in the dendrites of normal nonchromatolytic motoneurons was obtained by Terzuolo and Araki (1961). In their single cell study of the hippocampal neuron, Spencer and Kandel (1961) considered that the prepotential spikes they recorded were excited at the main branches of the apical dendrites of hippocampal neurons, and Anderson and Jansen (1962) have evidence for antidromic propagation in hippocampal dendrites. Hild and Tasaki (1962) were able to visualize the dendrites, soma, and axons of neurons grown in tissue culture. By stimulating and recording from dendrites and soma they found a propagation of responses in dendrites along lengths 100 μ from the soma. These results tend to support the proposition that the apical dendrite may be electrically excitable and can support an active propagation.

Action potentials in the finer apical branches may have long durations 10–20 msec because of different membrane properties. However, there are good arguments against the simple identification of the N wave DCR with an action potential propagating all the way down to the soma and out along the axon. Eliciting N wave

DCRs (superficial responses) in the motor area of the cortex controlling the arm, Adrian (1936) found that these responses were present without evidence of discharge in the pyramidal tract. However, pyramidal tract discharges were obtained if, with a stronger cortical stimulation, a "deep" cortical response was excited. This and similar kinds of evidence (Chang, 1952) have tended to make the EPSP hypothesis attractive: It would represent a response subliminal for axonic discharge.

Perhaps the neuron should not be considered from a too rigid point of view and a special type of response of the apical dendrite should be considered. Bullock (1959) has described a number of different kinds of discharge mechanisms present in invertebrate neurons. To account for the N wave DCR the hypothesis was made (Ochs, 1962a; Ochs & Booker, 1961) that it is a graded or decrementing type of response which propagates down the apical dendrites to the soma, but fails before exciting an action potential in the axon, an hypothesis similar to Bishop's (1956) except that in our hypothesis the response is considered to be nonsummating. The failure to fire the axon could be significant for cell operation. The depolarizing current could, by adding to EPSPs excited by axosomatic synaptic activity, help bring the initial segment of the pyramidal cell to a critical firing level. The conjoint activity of electrotonic dendritic and EPSP somatic activity is envisioned as a type of "coincidence counter" action. Excitatory and inhibitory synaptic activity present all along the apical dendrites could control the degree of decrement and thereby the success or failure in the firing of the pyramidal cell's axon.

To analyze and test this hypothesis the cortical surface was directly stimulated to give rise to an N wave DCR while recording extracellularly from Betz cells deeper in the cortex. The Betz cells were identified by the short latency of their response to an antidromic pes peduncular stimulation. A facilitating effect of cortical stimulation on the Betz cells was found which lasted for approximately the duration of the resulting N wave DCR (Matsunaga, 1963; Matsunaga, Suzuki, & Ochs, 1962). The facilitation, therefore, could be brought about by the presence of the N wave DCR in the apical dendrites with spread of depolarizing current to the initial segment or by excitatory increases in the apical dendrites. However, other evidence obtained from intracellular recordings made from Betz cells appears to show that this is not necessarily the case because facilitation was found without obvious signs of a wave of depolarization expected from a decrementing conduction.

An alternative hypothesis has been suggested (Ochs, 1965a) based on experiments with frog sartorius fibers. It was found that electrotonic spread from a region of maintained depolarization had a much longer "length constant" than was found present with single brief pulses of current to determine λ in the usual way. The possibility therefore exists that a far spread of depolarization into the initial segment may occur as the result of sustained depolarization caused by repeated synaptic activation of the apical dendrites.

D. Relation of Negative Wave Direct Cortical Response to Cortical Function

While the mechanism of the cell underlying the response is not yet elucidated, the characterization of the N wave DCR as a decrementing or graded nonsummating response can help resolve some problems relating to other surface potentials and to behavior. During arousal, either excited by external sensory stimulation or through reticular formation tetanic stimulation, decreases of various surface negative cortical responses have been reported. For example, the negative waves of a spindle discharge are blocked (Whitlock, Arduini, & Moruzzi, 1953) and the directly excited cortical responses reduced in amplitude (Purpura, 1956). This has been interpreted as an inhibitory synaptic effect in the cortex, an inhibitory postsynaptic potential (IPSP) brought about by activity in the ascending fibers of the reticular formation. A study of unit response activity in the cortex shows that reticular formation stimulation may give rise to both excitatory and inhibitory synaptic effects (Jasper, 1958). On the basis of the behavioral changes in the direction of arousal produced by stimulation of the reticular formation, it might be expected that its over-all influence on the cortex would be excitatory (Magoun, 1958). It appears likely that the difficulty of interpretation comes about because the cortical responses have generally been considered to be summating, i.e., synaptic potentials or EPSPs. Considering that the N wave DCRs are occlusive, inputs from the reticular formation terminating on apical dendrites in the cortex could, by exciting responses, make those membranes refractory to other inputs. Therefore, the amplitude of the N wave DCR would be reduced during concurrent reticular formation activation. In line with this interpretation is the

observation that the N wave DCRs excited in curarized animals
become larger in amplitude and more regular in size when an anes-
thetizing amount of pentobarbital is administered. The barbiturate,
by suppressing reticular formation activity (French, Verzeano, &
Magoun, 1953), thereby removes background responses of the
apical dendrites of the cortex with resulting increased amplitude
of response to direct cortical stimulation.

The occlusive nature of the N wave DCR also militates against
a simple acceptance of these 10 to 20 msec waves as the "units"
of discharge which become summed to give rise to the longer lasting EEG wave (Bremer, 1958). There are other types of evoked responses which may be more closely related to the EEG; possibly
the longer lasting second negative wave of Chang (1951). Certainly
additional mechanisms resulting in synchronous and repeated
discharges are operating in EEG activity (Ochs, 1965b). This is
indicated, for example, by the much greater sensitivity to asphyxia
of the EEG compared to the DCR. The EEG wave disappears as
quickly as 15 to 20 seconds after asphyxiation, while the DCR
may be recorded with gradually diminishing amplitudes for as
long as 2 to 4 minutes afterwards (Ochs, 1959a). The DCR completely disappears at the onset of the rapid and large increase in
cortical resistivity following asphyxiation which has been ascribed
to the loss of semipermeability of the apical dendrites with an
entry of extracellular Na^+, Cl^-, and water into the cells (Collewijn
and Schadé, 1964; van Harreveld, 1962; van Harreveld and Ochs,
1956).

III. Spreading Depression in the Cortex

A. *Properties of Spreading Depression*

Some of the characteristics of spreading depression (SD) of particular relevance for its use in psychological investigations will be
outlined. A more comprehensive treatment will be found in recent
reviews (Marshall, 1959; Ochs, 1962b). Although SD is regularly
obtained in the rabbit and rat, in the higher species it is a somewhat capricious phenomenon, possibly because of the presence of
subsidiary mechanisms in the cortices of higher species acting
to inhibit its appearance. However, even in man some observations
indicate that it may occur, at least in pathological states.

When the cortex is excited either by a mechanical stimulus,

application of KCl, electrical stimulation with cathodal currents, or a train of strong electrical pulses, then, as shown by the depression of the EEG, SD spreads at the rate of 2 to 5 mm/min, recovery taking place within 10 to 20 minutes. It is an intracortical process which preferentially takes place in the upper layers of the cortex, although not entirely confined to the several uppermost layers (Monakhov, Fifková, & Bureš, 1962; Ochs & Hunt, 1960). Its spread is not altered as it passes through various neocortical regions (motor, sensory, or associational). There is a difference, however, upon meeting with a different type of cortex. In the region medial to the parasagittal sulcus and identified as cingulate cortex, neocortical SDs usually fail to invade unless facilitated by cooling, prolonged exposure, or other means (van Harreveld & Bogen, 1956). Also, SD excited in the neocortex will not invade archipallial cortex (hippocampus) and vice versa (Weiss & Fifková, 1960).

The slow rate of propagation in the cortex is of interest because it signifies an unusual mechanism of spread. Cuts made through the upper half of the cortex block transmission of SD (Ochs & Hunt, 1960). Such studies confirmed the work of Grafstein (1956b) and van Harreveld, Terres, and Dernburg (1956) on the blocking effect on SD of cuts placed in the path of spread and rules out the possibility that transmission is brought about by electrical fields spreading from active to inactive neurons which could bridge such cuts (Sloan & Jasper, 1950). Spreading depression is readily excited by local application to the cortex of KCl and other substances including, at relatively low concentrations, glutamic acid (Bureš, Burešová, & Krivanek, 1960; van Harreveld, 1959). Potassium (Grafstein, 1956a; Grafstein, 1963) or glutamic acid (van Harreveld, 1959) could be released from the cells involved in SD to in turn act as the agent exciting SD in contiguous cells. An important link in the chain of evidence indicating that chemical substances released from cells could be the agents transmitting SD is the quite large outflux of K^+ from cells of the cortex found during an SD by isotopic measurements (Brinley, Kandel, & Marshall, 1960).

Besides the depression of the EEG, other indices of loss of neuronal function in a depressioned region are found. The depression of the N wave DCRs (Ochs, 1958) and the negative shift in the steady potential found during SD suggest that apical dendrites are greatly affected. An increase of the electrical resistivity found during SD amounts to approximately 10–15% above the resting level of resistance (van Harreveld & Ochs, 1957). At the frequency used (1000 cps) the measuring electrical currents pass between cells in the extracellular compartment and not through cell membranes (Cole, 1940). Therefore, the electrical resistivity measured is related to the size of the extracellular compartment and the increase in resistivity found during SD was considered to be due to loss of conducting elements; i.e., Na^+ and Cl^- from the extracellular space. These ions enter neurons and possibly glia as a result of their alteration in membrane permeability during SD (van Harreveld & Ochs, 1957). This hypothesis was supported by direct measures showing that a swelling of apical dendrites had occurred during SD (van Harreveld, 1958) and by histochemical evidence of an entry of chloride into apical dendrites during SD (Schadé, 1964; van Harreveld, 1966; van Harreveld & Schadé, 1959; van Harreveld & Schadé, 1960). It appears probable, therefore, that during

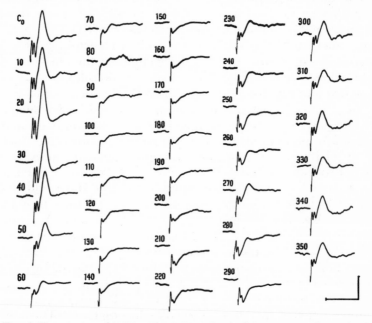

FIG. 6. Depression of DCRs. The DCRs obtained from unanesthetized rabbits with chronically implanted electrode assembly. Strong single shocks in visual area gives rise to fast waves which precede the slow negative phase. Control C_0 response and then SD excited. Time in seconds after SD elicitation indicated by the numbers to left of each trace. Calibration 20 msec, amplitude 1 mv. (From Ochs *et al.*, 1961.)

SD apical dendrites have an increased permeability and the extra-cellular ions (Na^+ and Cl^-) enter the neurons on the basis of their electrochemical gradients, while intracellular constitutents (K^+ and/or glutamate) are released into the extracellular spaces to excite the process in contiguous neurons.

Figure 6 is of interest with regard to the hypothesis of a chemical substance released during SD involved in the mechanism of spread. The DCRs were excited by single strong shocks to the cortex by means of a chronically implanted electrode assembly (Ochs, Hunt, & Booker, 1961). These DCRs show several fairly large spikelike fast waves followed by the usual slow negative wave. Upon initiating SD the slow negative wave was depressed as expected, but also found was a briefer period of depression of the fast spikes; in particular, the first spike taken to represent activity in sensory afferent terminations (Ochs, 1959a). The inter-

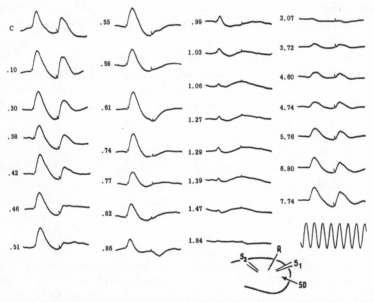

FIG. 7. Spreading depression on N wave DCR. Two N wave DCRs elicited from two stimulating sites S_1, S_2 at 30-msec intervals and recorded from an electrode R between them, as shown in lower insert. Stimulation of S_2 and then S_1 in control C. Then SD excited near S_1 and time in minutes thereafter shown by numbers to left of each trace; S_1 amplitude depressed before S_2 is depressed with later recovery of both responses. Calibration 100 cps, amplitude 0.37 mv. (From Ochs, 1962b.)

pretation of this result (Ochs, 1962b) is that some substance released in their near vicinity causes the depression of the activity
present in those fibers because no intervening synapse is present
for this wave. This is also illustrated by the experiment shown in
Fig. 7. Here a block of the excitation of a DCR occurred at one of
the stimulating sites while the responding site had not been in-
vaded, as shown by the responses remaining to the stimulation of
the other site. As discussed in the first part of this chapter, an axonic
element transmitting the N wave DCR is directly excited by the
stimulating pulse. Therefore, it is likely that the substance released
during SD is acting directly on this axonic element.

B. Behavioral Studies Using Spreading Depression

In order to keep the cortex continuously depressed for an hour
or so (a period of time convenient for a behavioral conditioning
session), electrical stimulation with a chronic implanted assembly
was found to be unsuitable because of the variable refractoriness
found to successive SDs (Ochs & Hunt, 1960). The procedure generally used at present is patterned after the KCl technique introduced by Bureš and Burešová (1960; 1960b). Small pieces of filter
paper were dipped into a 25% KCl solution and placed on the exposed dura over the hemispheres of rats through holes trephined
in the skull causing a series of waves of SD to pass out from this
point and in effect to depress cortical activity for hours.

In Bureš and Burešová's studies (Bureš, 1959), SD was initiated unilaterally to block one hemisphere and the animal was conditioned on the "open" side. Then with the other side depressed
an interhemispheric transfer to the other side was shown. These
studies enlarged the sphere of possibilities first opened up by the
introduction of the "split-brain" preparation in the analysis of
brain function (Myers, 1955; Myers, 1956; Sperry, 1961; Sperry,
1964).

A study of unilateral engrams and their interhemispheric transfer and of the problem of cortical-subcortical relations was initiated
in this laboratory using a technique whereby SDs might be elicited
repeatedly over a period of days and weeks. Plastic wells were implanted over small holes drilled in the skull, one over each hemisphere so that KCl could be introduced to elicit SD in the cortical
hemisphere on either side as desired (Russell & Ochs, 1961; Russell
& Ochs, 1963). Rats so prepared were trained to a bar-pressing habit
on a fixed-ratio schedule (FR-1) where every bar-press resulted in

the delivery of a small pellet of food into a hopper in the experimental box (Ferster & Skinner, 1957). While one hemisphere was depressed, the animal was first conditioned to eat from the food hopper and then it had to learn the FR-1 conditioned response. Usually several days were required for learning to take place, as indicated by the increased rate of responding. When learning had occurred, the other hemisphere was depressed and the low scores found indicated a lateralization of the engram to the cortex which had been "open" during FR-1 training and responding.

Transfer of the engram from the trained to the untrained hemisphere was also shown. After lateralization of the engram to one side, the animals were allowed to make only a few bar-press responses, or even one response while both sides were undepressed one hour before depressing the trained side. The higher response rate then found with the trained side depressed indicated that a shift of the engram from the trained to the untrained side had taken place. Various other schedules of reinforcement were used and with increased FR schedules an increased rate of responding was required for transfer (Russell & Ochs, 1963).

After repeated elicitations of SDs, it was not clear whether on the later days SD was no longer effective in producing SDs. In order to eliminate some of the defects previously found with the use of repeated KCl applications, a new well was developed in experiments with R. Strohaver and R. Miller (unpublished results, 1963). It had a larger size so that small cotton pledgets soaked in Ringer solutions (in some cases) could be kept in the wells overnight to keep the dural surface moist. In some cases antibiotics which were not epileptogenic were used to wash out the well in order to prevent bacterial growth. In an example shown with its use (Fig. 8), the animal was first trained to a bar-pressing performance and the wells later implanted in their skulls. Performance rate did not recover fully for the next few days. Upon application of KCl to both wells on the tenth day, the response rate fell to a low level, apparently to chance striking of the bar. This was also the case with bilateral SDs induce on days 13 and 16. One-sided depressions were then elicited with KCl on days 19 and 20, and an apparent difference between the two sides was indicated by the lower score with the left side depressed. However, with KCl on both sides on day 22 the animal's response rate remained high. There was evidence of cortical damage under the well but again it was not clear if damage per se was the reason during later days

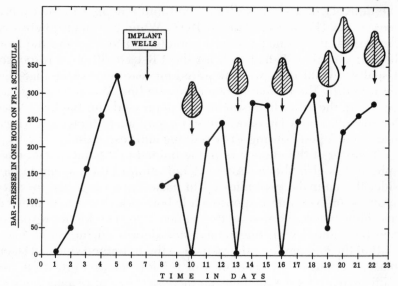

FIG. 8. Effect of SD on instrumentally conditioned rats. Animal learned to bar-press on an FR-1 schedule during days 1–6. Ordinate shows rate of bar-pressing during each one hour session. Wells implanted on day 7. Thereafter response rates with and without SD bilaterally initiated by KCl placed in both wells to elicit SD on days 10, 13, and 16; KCl placed on left side on day 19, on right side on day 20, and bilaterally again on day 22.

for failure of KCl to depress performance or if there was a change in the cortex due to repeated elicitations of SD.

Some of the later difficulties found with the larger well was the accumulation of a material which was apparently fibrous tissue. This was removed by suction every several days as required, and using the new type of well EEG and SP changes during SD were studied in rats with chronically implanted electrodes for a period up to three weeks and more (Gollender & Ochs, 1963). These studies showed no apparent accumulated deterioration on the EEG of the repeated SD elicitations although convulsions did occur in some animals. An observation of interest in the study was that with SD unilaterally present as indicated by repeated waves of SP change in the hemisphere, a single SD shown by one wave of a steady potential change might sometimes be seen in the opposite hemisphere. Such a crossed effect could represent a release or an excitatory effect produced by cortical neurons undergoing SD on the opposite side. However, this phenomenon is not seen in the acute preparation and further study is required.

In the original studies of the effect of SD on bar-pressing be-havior, it should be emphasized that lateralization of the learned responses was achieved by not reinforcing the animal when the opposite hemisphere was depressed (Russell & Ochs, 1963). Trans-fer of the lateralized engram to the untrained hemisphere was then indicated by the high rate of bar-pressing without reinforcement present. As shown in later experiments in this laboratory, when reinforcement was present with the opposite side depressed, learn-ing was as quick or quicker than on the original side. However, what is learned with the opposite hemisphere depressed and with reinforcement present may not be the same behavior as that learned on the first side. This is indicated in the example shown in Fig. 9

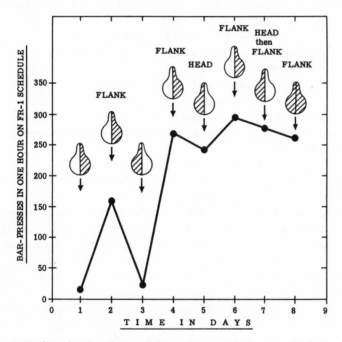

FIG. 9. Unilateral SD with two different response behaviors. Shaded side indi-cates KCl applied to that hemisphere to induce SD. Response rate on ordinate. Animal on FR-1 schedule; KCl on right on days 1 and 2. Animal learned to bar-press on day 2 as shown by higher rate, striking bar with its flank. With KCl on left side on day 3, animal struck bar with head to give only a low number of responses. Day 4 with KCl on right, flank responses; with KCl on left on day 5, head respond-ing. Again on day 6 with KCl on right, flank response. Change appeared on day 7, with KCl on left side. First 9 responses were made with head, then remaining re-sponses made with flank. Bilateral KCl on day 8 and no block of flank responses.

where with KCl on the right side the animal learned an FR-1 schedule on the second day. The animal was observed to hit the bar with its right hind flank. With KCl placed on the left side on day 3, the animal made only a few responses, in this case by hitting the bar with its head. With KCl again placed on the right side on day 4, the animal again hit the bar with its flank at a high rate. On day 5 with KCl on the left side it had learned as shown by the high rate of responding, doing so by hitting the bar with its head. Once again with KCl on the right side on day 6, the animal hit the bar with the flank as before. Later, a change occurred. On day 7, with KCl on the left side, the first 9 bar-presses were made with the head as expected. Then, the animal moved back from the bar and after some apparent hesitancy it finished the session with flank-striking responses. Bilateral application of KCl on day 8 did not block the performance thereby indicating that KCl was not getting through to elicit SD. Therefore, the animal apparently had learned to make two entirely different responses depending upon which hemisphere was depressed: With SD on the right side the response to the bar was "flank striking"; with SD on the left, the response was "head striking." The results up to day 7 were very much like those found in the split-brain preparation where two entirely different and even antagonistic engrams could be laid down on each of the two sides (Sperry, 1961; Sperry, 1964).

This experiment is in accord with the original conception that engrams are laid down in one hemisphere (cortex) and after interhemispheric transfer the engram is present in the other hemisphere (Russell & Ochs, 1963). However, there are simpler types of learned behavior—escape and avoidance where decortication and SD have been shown to have little effect (Bureš & Burešová, 1960a; Olds, 1962), although in one type lateralization using SD has been obtained (Ross & Russell, 1964). For several years we have been studying the effects of SD on an avoidance behavior, which for these purposes has the advantage of being learned in only one trial (W. Essman, personal communication, 1962). The apparatus consists of a small platform facing a hole in a box. A naive rat placed on the platform will rapidly enter the box where it can be shocked through a floor grid. In Essman's (1964) study, a 30-second trial period was used and learning occurred in one trial after a shock, as shown when tested on the following trial day. In our experiments (Ochs and Smith, 1966) the trial period used was 5 minutes and although many one-trial animals were found, more often two trials, but rarely more, were required. Also, most likely as a result of this increased time period, extinction took longer, weeks or even months. The time of extinction was variable from animal to animal and could show periodic variations in entry time during extinction and it generally took longer with the two-trial animals.

Animals which had learned this avoidance behavior showed little change with bilateral SD present. They generally remained out on the platform for the full 5-minute trial period. In a few cases the animals entered the box near the end of the session. This result is in line with reports indicating a rather minimal effect of SD on learned avoidance behavior. However, in another group of experiments, when SD was introduced before the learning sessions, the number of trials required to reach criterion increased to 3–5. Besides the increase in the number of learning trials required, the animals afterwards showed a remarkably short extinction period. They began to enter the box within a few days after meeting criterion and extinction was complete within a week. This result suggests that the cortex is required to lay down an enduring engram while a shorter lasting memory, one which survives from day to day in order for the animal to reach criterion, is not blocked by SD. The cortex may therefore be involved in the laying down of an enduring subcortical engram.

Once learning has occurred, the cortex may be depressed with little effect. A subcortical sight for closure of classical conditioning and an engram has been discussed, among others, by Gastaut (1958) and John (1961). If we consider that a subcortical engram is present for all learned behavior, the block of responses found with bilateral SD in operant conditioned animals would suggest that the cortex is required to make the proper discriminations in order to utilize the subcortical engram. On this hypothesis, transfer of a lateralized behavior from the trained to the opposite "naive" hemisphere would then amount to utilization in some degree of this subcortical engram by the cortex of the other side. That the specific engram as a whole may not be so utilized was shown by the above example of different behaviors controlled from each side. However, that some such effect occurs, at least in part, is suggested by the faster learning found when reinforcement is present on the opposite hemisphere after the first side is trained. Further studies will be required to decide between these two alternatives.

REFERENCES

Adrian, E. D. The spread of activity in the cerebral cortex. *J. Physiol. (London)*, 1936, **88**, 127–161.

Ammassian, V. E., & Weiner, H. The effect of (+)-tubocurarine chloride and of acute hypotension on electrocortical activity of the cat. *J. Physiol. (London)*, 1966, **184**, 1–15.

Anderson, P., Jansen, J., Jr. The local cortical response in the hippocampus of rabbit. *Arch. ital. Biol.*, 1962, **99**, 349–368.

Bishop, G. H. Natural history of the nerve impulse. *Physiol. Rev.*, 1956, **36**, 376–399.

Black, A. H. The extinction of avoidance responses under curare. *J. comp. physiol. Psychol.*, 1958, **51**, 519–524.

Bremer, F. Cerebral and cerebellar potentials. *Physiol. Rev.*, 1958, **38**, 357–388.

Brinley, F. J., Jr., Kandel, E. R., & Marshall, W. H. The effect of intravenous *d*-tubocurarine on the electrical activity of the cat cerebral cortex. *Trans. Amer. Neurol. Ass., 83rd Ann. Meeting*, 1958, pp. 53–58.

Brinley, F. J., Jr., Kandel, E. R., & Marshall, W. H. Potassium outflux from rabbit cortex during spreading depression. *J. Neurophysiol.*, 1960, **23**, 246–256.

Brooks, V. B., & Enger, P. S. Spread of directly evoked responses in the cat's cerebral cortex. *J. gen. Physiol.*, 1959, **42**, 761–777.

Bullock, T. H. Neuron doctrine and electrophysiology. *Science*, 1959, **129**, 997–1002.

Bureš, J. (1959). Reversible decortication and behavior. In M. A. B. Brazier (Ed.) *The central nervous system and behavior*. Second Macy Conference New York: Josiah Macy, Jr. Foundation, 1959. Pp. 207–248.

Bureš, J., & Burešová, O. (1960a). The use of Leão's spreading cortical depression in research on conditioned reflexes. In H. H. Jasper and G. D. Smirnov (Eds.), *The Moscow colloquium on electroencephalography of higher nervous activity.* 1960. Pp. 359–376. *Electroenceph. clin. Neurophysiol.*, 1960, Suppl. 13.(a)

Bureš, J., & Burešová, O. The use of Leão's spreading depression in the study of interhemispheric transfer of memory traces. *J. comp. physiol. Psychol.*, 1960, **53**, 558–563.(b)

Bureš, J., Burešová, O., & Křivánek, J. Some metabolic aspects of Leão's cortical depression. In D. B. Tower, and J. P. Schadé (Eds.), *Structure and function of the cerebral cortex*. Amsterdam: Elsevier, 1960. Pp. 257–265.

Bureš, J., Burešová, O., & Fifková, E. The effect of cortical and hippocampal spreading depression activity on bulbopontine reticular units in the rat. *Arch. ital. Biol.*, 1961, **99**, 23–32.

Burns, B. D., & Grafstein, B. The function and structure of some neurones in the cat's cerebral cortex. *J. Physiol. (London)*, 1952, **118**, 412–433.

Chang, H.-T. Dendritic potential of cortical neurons produced by direct electrical stimulation of the cerebral cortex. *J. Neurophysiol.*, 1951, **14**, 1–21.

Chang, H.-T. Cortical neurons with particular reference to the apical dendrites. *Cold Spr. Harb. Sympos. quant. Biol.*, 1952, **27**, 189–202.

Cole, K. S. Permeability and impermeability of cell membranes for ions. *Cold Spr. Harb. Sympos. quant. Biol.*, 1940, **8**, 110–122.

Collewijn, H., & Schadé, J. P. Chloride, potassium and water content of apical dendrites and their changes after circulatory arrest, at body temperatures from 37°C. to 20°C. *Arch. int. Physiol.*, 1964, **72**, 194–210.

Curtis, D. R. The effects of drugs and amino acids upon neurons. In S. S. Kety and J. E. Elkes (Eds.), *Regional neurochemistry*. New York: Macmillan (Pergamon), 1961. Pp. 403–422.

Curtis, D. R. & Eccles, J. C. Synaptic action during and after repetitive stimulation. *J. Physiol. (London), 1960,* **150,** 374–398.

Eccles, J. C. Interpretation of action potentials evoked in the cerebral cortex. *Electroenceph. clin. Neurophysiol.,* 1951, **3,** 449–464.

Eccles, J. C. *The physiology of nerve cells.* Baltimore: Johns Hopkins Press, 1957.

Eccles, J. C. The properties of the dendrites. In D. B. Tower & J. P. Schadé (Eds.), *Structure and function of the cerebral cortex.* Amsterdam: Elsevier, 1960. Pp. 192–203.

Eccles, J. C. *The physiology of synapses.* New York: Academic Press, 1964.

Eccles, J. C., Libet, B., & Young, R. R. The behaviour of chromatolysed moto- neurones studied by intracellular recording. *J. Physiol. (London),* 1958, **143,** 11–40.

Essman, W. Single-trial avoidance conditioning in rats. *Psychol. Rep.,* 1964, **15,** 775–783.

Ferster, C. B., & Skinner, B. F. *Schedules of reinforcement.* New York: Appleton- Century-Crofts, 1957.

French, J. D., Verzeano, M., & Magoun, H. W. A neural basis of the anesthetic state. *Arch. Neurol. Psychiat.,* 1953, **69,** 519–529.

Furukawa, T., Sasaoka, T., & Hosoya, Y. Effects of tetrodotoxin on the neuro- muscular junction. *Japan J. Physiol.,* 1959, **9,** 143–152.

Gastaut, H. (1958). Some aspects of the neurophysiological basis of conditioned reflexes and behavior. In *Ciba foundation symposium on neurological basis of behavior.* Boston: Little, Brown, 1958.

Girden, E. Cerebral mechanisms in conditioning under curare. *Amer. J. Psychol.,* 1940, **53,** 397–406.

Girden, E., & Cullen, E. Conditioned responses in curarized striate muscle in dogs. *J. comp. Psychol.,* 1937, **23,** 261–274.

Gollender, M., & Ochs, S. Evaluation of EEG depression as an index of spreading depression in chronic preparations. *Amer. Psychologist,* 1963, **17,** 431.

Grafstein, B. Mechanism of spreading cortical depression. *J. Neurophysiol.,* 1956, **19,** 154–171.(a)

Grafstein, B. Locus of propagation of spreading cortical depression. *J. Neurophysiol.,* 1956, **19,** 308–316.(b)

Grafstein, B. Neuronal release of potassium during spreading depression. In M. A. B. Brazier (Ed.), *Brain function,* Vol. I, UCLA Forum in Medical Science, Berk- eley: Univ. of California Press, 1963.

Gray, E. G. Axo-somatic and axo-dendritic synapses of the cerebral cortex. An elec- tron microscope study. *J. Anat.,* 1959, **93,** 420–433.

Grundfest, H. Electrical inexcitability of synapses and some consequences in the central nervous system. *Physiol. Rev.,* 1957, **37,** 337–361.

Hild, W., & Tasaki, I. Morphological and physiological properties of neurons and glial cells in tissue culture. *J. Neurophysiol.,* 1962, **25,** 277–304.

Iwama, K., & Jasper, H. H. The action of gamma-aminobutyric acid upon cortical electrical activity in the cat. *J. Physiol. (London),* 1957, **138,** 365–380.

Jasper, H. H. Recent advances in our understanding of ascending activities of the reticular system. In, H. H. Jasper *et al.* (Ed.), *Reticular formation of the brain.* Boston: Little, Brown, 1958. Pp. 319–331.

Javrishvili, T. Fast and slow potential responses of the cortex (in Russian). *Sechenov Physiol. J.*, 1965, **51**, 27–36.

John, E. R. Higher nervous functions; brain functions and learning. *Ann. Rev. Physiol.*, 1961, **23**, 451–484.

Krnjević, K., Randic, M., & Straughan, D. Cortical inhibition. *Nature*, 1964, **201**, 1294–1296.

Leão, A. A. P. Spreading depression of activity in cerebral cortex. *J. Neurophysiol.*, 1944, **7**, 359–390.

Libet, B., & Gerard, R. W. Steady potential fields and neurone activity. *J. Neurophysiol.*, 1941, **4**, 438–455.

Libet, B., & Gerard, R. W. An analysis of some correlates of steady potentials in mammalian cerebral cortex. *Electroenceph. clin. Neurophysiol.*, 1962, **14**, 445–452.

Magoun, H. W. *The waking brain.* Springfield, Ill.: Charles C Thomas, 1958.

Marshall, W. H. Spreading cortical depression of Leão. *Physiol. Rev.*, 1959, **39**, 239–279.

Matsunaga, M. Firing level of Betz cells in relationship to direct cortical responses of the sensori-motor cortex. *Fed. Proc.*, 1963, **22**, 457.

Matsunaga, M., Suzuki, H., & Ochs, S. Control of Betz cell excitability by direct cortical stimulation. *Physiologist*, 1962, **5**, 179.

Merlis, J. K. Excitability cycle of the direct cortical response studied with minimal stimuli and response averaging. *Electroenceph. clin. Neurophysiol.*, 1965, **18**, 118–123.

Monakhov, K. K., Fifková, E., & Bureš, J. Vertical distribution of the slow potential change of spreading depression in the cerebral cortex of the rat. *Physiol. Bohemoslov.*, 1962, **11**, 269–276.

Morrell, F. Electrophysiological contributions to the neural basis of learning. *Physiol. Rev.*, 1961, **41**, 443–494.

Myers, R. E. Interocular transfer of pattern discrimination in cats following section of crossed optic fibers. *J. comp. physiol. Psychol.*, 1955, **48**, 470–473.

Myers, R. E. Function of corpus callosum in interocular transfer. *Brain*, 1956, **79**, 358–363.

Nakamura, Y., Nakajima, S., & Grundfest, H. The action of tetrodotoxin on electrogenic components of squid giant axons. *J. Gen. Physiol.*, 1965, **48**, 985–996.

Ochs, S. The direct cortical response. *J. Neurophysiol.*, 1956, **19**, 513–523.

Ochs, S. Effects of spreading depression on direct cortical response studies with an island technique. *J. Neurophysiol.*, 1958, **21**, 159–179.

Ochs, S. Organization of visual afferents shown by spike components of cortical response. *J. Neurophysiol.*, 1959, **22**, 2–15.(a)

Ochs, S. Curare and low blood pressure effects on direct cortical responses. *Amer. J. Physiol.*, 1959, **197**, 1136–1140.(b)

Ochs, S. Analysis of cellular mechanisms of direct cortical responses. *Fed. Proc.*, 1962, **21**, 642–647.(a)

Ochs, S. The nature of spreading depression in neural networks. *Int. Rev. Neurobiol.*, 1962, **4**, 1–69.(b)

Ochs, S. Cortical potentials and pyramidal cells—a theoretical discussion. *Perspectives*, 1965, **9**, 126–136.(a)

Ochs, S. *Elements of neurophysiology.* New York: Wiley, 1965.(b)

Ochs, S., & Booker, H. Spatial and temporal interaction of direct cortical responses. *Exp. Neurol.*, 1961, **4**, 70–82.

Ochs, S., & Hunt, K. Apical dendrites and propagation of spreading depression in cerebral cortex. *J. Neurophysiol.*, 1960, **23**, 432–444.

Ochs, S., & Ng, M. H. Tetrodotoxin on direct cortical responses. *Fed. Proc.*, 1966, **25**, 637.

Ochs, S., and Smith. 1966. In preparation.

Ochs, S., & Suzuki, H. Transmission of direct cortical responses. *Electroenceph. clin. Neurophysiol.*, 1965, **19**, 230–236.

Ochs, S., Hunt, K., & Booker, H. Spreading depression using chronically implanted electrodes. *Amer. J. Physiol.*, 1961, **200**, 1211–1214.

Olds, J. Spreading depression and hypothalamic behavior mechanisms. *Fed. Proc.*, 1962, **21**, 648–658.

O'Leary, J. L., & Goldring, S. Changes associated with forebrain excitation processes: d.c. potentials of the cerebral cortex. In J. Field, H. W. Magoun, and V. E. Hall (Eds.), *Handbook of physiology.* Sect. 1. *Neurophysiology.* Vol. 1. Washington, D. C.: American Physiological Society, 1959. Pp. 315–328.

O'Leary, J., & Goldring, S. D-C potentials of the brain. *Physiol. Rev.*, 1964, **44**, 91–125.

Pappas, G. D., & Purpura, D. P. Fine structure of dendrites in the superficial neocortical neuropil. *Exp. Neurol.*, 1961, **4**, 507–530.

Purpura, D. P. Observations on the cortical mechanisms of EEG activation accompanying behavioral arousal. *Science*, 1956, **123**, 804.

Purpura, D. P., & Grundfest, H. Nature of dendritic potentials and synaptic mechanism in cerebral cortex of cat. *J. Neurophysiol.*, 1956, **19**, 573–592.

Purpura, D. P., Girado, M., & Grundfest, H. Selective blockade of excitatory synapses in the cat brain by gamma-amino butyric acid. *Science*, 1957, **125**, 1200–1202.

Ross, R. B., & Russell, I. S. Lateralization and one-trial interhemispheric transfer of avoidance conditioning. *Nature* 1964, **204**, 909–910.

Russell, I. S., & Ochs, S. One trial interhemispheric transfer of a learning engram. *Science*, 1961, **133**, 1077–1078.

Russell, I. S., & Ochs, S. Localization of a memory trace in one cortical hemisphere and transfer to the other hemisphere. *Brain*, 1963, **86**, 37–54.

Schadé, J. P. On the contribution of neuroglia to the function of the cerebral cortex. In *Neurological and electroencephalographic correlative studies in infancy.* New York: Grune & Stratton, 1964.

Sholl, D. A. *The organization of the cerebral cortex.* New York: Wiley, 1956.

Sloan, N., & Jasper, H. H. The identity of spreading depression and "suppression." *Electroenceph. clin. Neurophysiol.*, 1950, **2**, 59–78.

Smith, S. M., Brown, H. O., Toman, J. E. P., & Goodman, L. S. The lack of cerebral effects of d-tubocurarine. *Anesthesiology*, 1947, **8**, 1–14.

Spencer, W. A., & Kandel, E. R. Electrophysiology of hippocampal neurons IV. Fast prepotentials. *J. Neurophysiol.*, 1961, **24**, 272–285.

Sperry, R. W. Cerebral organization and behavior. *Science*, 1961, **133**, 1749–1757.
Sperry, R. W. The great cerebral commissure. *Sci. Am.*, 1964, **174**, 2–12.
Suzuki, H., & Ochs, S. Laminar analysis of direct cortical responses. *Fed. Proc.*, 1962, **21**, 350.
Suzuki, H., & Ochs, S. (1964) Laminar stimulation of direct cortical responses from intact and chronically isolated cortex. *Electroencephal. clin. Neurophysiol.*, 1964, **17**, 405–413.
Terzuolo, C. A., & Araki, T. An analysis of intra- versus extra-cellular potential changes associated with activity of single spinal motoneurons. *Ann. N.Y. Acad. Sci.*, 1961, **94**, 547–558.
van Harreveld, A. Changes in the diameter of apical dendrites during spreading depression. *Amer. J. Physiol.*, 1958, **192**, 457–463.
van Harreveld, A. Compounds in brain extracts causing spreading depression of cerebral cortical activity and contraction of crustacean muscle. *J. Neurochem.*, 1959, **3**, 300–315.
van Harreveld, A. Water and electrolyte distribution in central nervous tissue. *Fed. Proc.*, 1962, **21**, 659–664.
van Harreveld, A. *Brain tissue electrolytes.* London and Washington, D. C.: Butterworth, 1966.
van Harreveld, A., & Bogen, J. E. Regional differences in propagation of spreading depression in the rabbit. *Proc. Soc. exp. Biol. Med.*, 1956, **91**, 297–302.
van Harreveld, A., & Ochs, S. Cerebral impedance changes after circulatory arrest. *Amer. J. Physiol.*, 1956, **187**, 180–192.
van Harreveld, A., & Ochs, S. Electrical and vascular concomitants of spreading depression. *Amer. J. Physiol.*, 1957, **189**, 159–166.
van Harreveld, A., & Schadé, J. P. Chloride movements in cerebral cortex after circulatory arrest and during spreading depression. *J. cell. comp. Physiol.*, 1959, **54**, 65–84.
van Harreveld, A., & Schadé, J. P. On the distribution of movements of water and electrolytes in the cerebral cortex. In D. B. Tower & J. P. Schadé (Eds.), *Structure and function of the cerebral cortex.* Amsterdam: Elsevier, 1960. Pp. 239–256.
van Harreveld, A., Terres, G., & Dernburg, E. A. Cortical discontinuity and propagation of spreading depression. *Amer. J. Physiol.*, 1956, **184**, 233–238.
Weiss, T., & Fifková, E. The use of spreading depression to analyse the mutual relationship between the neocortex and hippocampus. *Electroenceph. clin. Neurophysiol.*, 1960, **12**, 841–850.
Whitlock, D. G., Arduini, A., & Moruzzi, G. Microelectrode analysis of pyramidal system during transition from sleep to wakefulness. *J. Neurophysiol.*, 1953, **16**, 414–429.

CHAPTER 3

Neural Processing of Visual Information*

RUSSELL L. DE VALOIS

Department of Psychology,
Indiana University,
Bloomington, Indiana

I. INTRODUCTION

The question of how we see has been studied by people of many professions from many points of view over the last century. The approaches which have been made to the problem might be divided up into four general areas as follows:

* This work was supported by USPHS Grant No. NB-02274, and NSF Grant No. 3764.

1. One area of study is the nature and function of the supporting structures of the eye. Among these structures are the muscles which move the eyes, the iris which regulates the size of the entrance pupil and thereby the amount of light entering the eye, and the optical system which focuses the light rays on the retina. The most important role of the visual system is to analyze the spatial characteristics of the environment. To do this it must have information on the direction of the light rays reflected by objects. The vertebrate visual system accomplishes this by knowledge of the eye position, and by forming an image of the environment on the retina with the cornea and lens.

2. Another series of problems revolve around the photopigments in the receptors and the initiation of neural activity. To be effective, light must be absorbed by the receptor photopigments, and this absorption of light must lead to neural activity. The chemical nature of the various receptor pigments, their spectral sensitivities, how they recover from past light absorptions, and how they initiate neural activity constitute some of the most interesting and important problems of vision.

3. The information contained in the absorption of various amounts of light by different receptors must be processed by the nervous system. At each of the multiple synapses in the retina, thalamus, and cortex there is some sort of analysis of this information; it is modified in some way before being passed on to the next stage.

4. The end result of the operation of the whole mechanism is that an individual sees certain changes in the visual environment. The nature of these visual percepts and how they vary with environmental changes are the basic phenomena of vision which we would like to understand from the photochemical and neural points of view.

In this chapter, we will concentrate on selected aspects of (3) above, the neural processing of information. Some general principles of neural activity will be discussed, and then an attempt will be made to understand certain psychophysical relationships on the basis of the operation of these principles.

II. NATURE OF NEURAL ACTIVITY

Before discussing the way in which information is processed by the nervous system, it would be well to examine some of the general characteristics of neural behavior and the capabilities for data processing possessed by the nervous system.

A. Axonal and Synaptic Transmission

The nervous system is comprised of individual cells which extend various distances through the body and end in the vicinity of other cells. Information must be transmitted both down the length of the neuron and across the synaptic gap between neurons; quite different mechanisms operate in the two cases. Long distance transmission of information down the length of the neuron's axon is by means of the all-or-none spike, the depolarization of each region of membrane electrically triggering the response of the neighboring region. This sort of transmission is very reliable: Once started, an impulse is highly likely to reach the other end of the axon. But this very property makes it an unlikely mechanism for neural processing, which must involve change. Transmission across the synaptic gap is chemical, with the exception of one particular type of electrical synapse which is sometimes found. The axon endings release little packets of transmitter chemical which produce graded changes in the postsynaptic membrane. The effect may either be that of depolarizing or of hyperpolarizing the postsynaptic membrane, thus increasing or decreasing, respectively, the probability of the second neuron reaching the threshold depolarization level and thus firing a nerve impulse. The fact that synaptic transmission is somewhat uncertain—indeed, the chemicals released by a single impulse are generally insufficient to set off the second neuron—means that there must be an integration of different events at the synapse and thereby an analysis of the incoming information.

B. Spontaneous Activity

The nervous system is constantly active; neurons fire periodically in the absence of any specific stimulation, whether the animal is awake or asleep. This continuing activity is doubtless partly due to the fact that sensory stimulation is never completely absent, but it is also partly due to reverberatory activity in a nervous system which is highly interconnected and to the inherent instability of a system which is designed to be easily triggered. In any case, sensory information comes into the nervous system against a level of background activity. The spontaneous firing rate of a neuron can be either increased or decreased by the action of another neuron. Thus information can be transmitted by either of two changes in firing. The interplay of excitation and inhibition provides the means by which information is processed by the nervous system.

C. Excitation

Nerve impulses coming down an axon ending produce a discharge of synaptic chemical proportional to the impulse rate. At an excitatory synapse, this secretion depolarizes the postsynaptic membrane to an extent proportional to the amount of the transmitter chemical. The excitatory postsynaptic potential tends to fire the neuron at a rate proportional to its size. Thus, in general, the second neuron will be fired at a rate proportional to the first. However, there is generally a considerable decrement in the system so that more than one active axon ending is required to activate the second neuron; transmission will thus occur only with a summation of inputs. This summation can either come from several different neurons and/or from multiple endings of a single neuron. Since generator potentials decay with time, however, such multiple inputs must occur with near simultaneity.

D. Inhibition

Impulses arriving at some axon endings liberate a transmitter chemical which hyperpolarizes rather than depolarizes the postsynaptic membrane. This hyperpolarization inhibits the neuron by making it less likely that the threshold depolarization will be reached. An inhibitory input acting alone will decrease the firing rate of the neuron from the spontaneous level; the addition of an inhibitory input to an excitatory one will act to decrease or cancel the excitation. Such postsynaptic inhibition is nonspecific in that it decreases all excitatory inputs, and it has the effect of subtracting a certain number of impulses from the spontaneous firing or from the effects of excitatory inputs.

A second type of inhibition, presynaptic inhibition, may also occur. This is accomplished by the inhibitory neuron ending on the presynaptic axon ending and there producing a partial depolarization. This depolarization is insufficient to produce a release of much transmitter chemical but is enough to decrease the likelihood of the impulse reaching the axon ending where it can produce a release of the excitatory transmitter. Presynaptic inhibition is clearly specific to the particular axon ending being inhibited rather than having a general effect on all the inputs to a neuron as is the case with postsynaptic inhibition. It also differs from postsynaptic inhibition in that it acts to divide the excitatory input rather than subtract a certain amount from it. For instance, a strong presynaptic inhibition might decrease the probability of an impulse reaching the axon end from 100 to 50%; this would divide this particular input in half.

E. Excitatory-Inhibitory Interaction

As can be seen, the characteristics of excitation and inhibition discussed above give the nervous system the capability of performing several different types of operations. If two neurons each have excitatory connections to a third neuron, this latter neuron will *add* together the outputs and report the sum by a certain increase in its firing rate. The same addition would occur if both neurons had postsynaptic inhibitory connections to the third; the sum of their activity would now be reported as a certain decrement in firing from the spontaneous level. It is unlikely that these additions would be completely linear, but the postsynaptic firing rate would be proportional to the sum of the two presynaptic rates.

If one neuron ended on the third with an excitatory connection, and the other with a postsynaptic inhibitory connection, the latter neuron will *subtract* the one output from the other and report the difference as a certain change in firing rate. Since the neurons are spontaneously active, the difference can be reported in either direction as an excess of excitation over inhibition or vice versa. Finally, presynaptic inhibition allows a neuron to *divide* one input by another and report the ratio of the two.

Although these are simple properties by which to explain the enormous complexities of visual perception, it should not come as a surprise in this age of computers that very complex analyses can be performed by a large number of simple elements appropriately interconnected.

F. Some Structural Characteristics of the Visual System

In the retina, the receptors connect to the bipolar cells, which in turn synapse with the ganglion cells. The ganglion cell axons lead to the lateral geniculate nucleus of the thalamus, in the principal pathway, to end on cells whose axons in turn go to the visual cortex. Within the visual cortex are numerous further synapses. In addition, there are laterally interconnecting cells in the retina: horizontal cells at the receptor-bipolar synapse and amacrine cells at the bipolar-ganglion cell synapse. Also, there may well be direct contacts between receptors and perhaps between bipolar cells.

A human retina contains about 120 million receptors (mainly rods), a few million bipolars, and about one million ganglion cells. It is thus quite apparent that there must be a considerable convergence of information from many receptors to one ganglion cell. It is this convergence which allows data processing to take place. The average amount of convergence is actually far more than the 120:1 suggested above, for superimposed on this convergent organization is a large divergent organization. One receptor is connected to many bipolars, which in turn feed into an even greater number of ganglion cells. The receptive field of a single ganglion cell—the receptor area, stimulation of which can modify its activity—may thus extend over some thousands of receptors, particularly in the periphery of the eye. The receptive field may be further extended by the presence of the laterally connecting horizontal and amacrine cells.

Overwhelming evidence has been recently accumulated to indicate that the normal human receptors contain a total of four different photopigments, one in the rods and three in the cones. The photopigments are each sensitive to a broad spectral range; the maximum sensitivity of the rod photopigment, rhodopsin, is about 500 nm, and the cone pigment maxima are approximately 440, 535, and 570 nm (Marks, Dobelle, & MacNichol, 1964). Since each cone contains only one of the photopigments, we may for convenience refer to blue cones containing the 440 pigment, green cones the 535 pigment, and red cones the 570 pigment.

III. NEURAL PROCESSING OF VISUAL INFORMATION

Let us now examine a few selected aspects of vision to see to what extent the different types of neural processing discussed above can provide an understanding of how we see as we do. We will start with some simple considerations, adding complexity— and realism—as we go along.

A. *Brightness*

The brightness of a flash of light at a constant adaptation level is obviously related to its intensity. This might well be expected since the arrival at a receptor of a large number of photons per unit time should lead to a large receptor potential, which would produce increased excitation of the bipolar cells, etc. However, it can be shown that an increased amount of light will lead to increased brightness even when it hits not the same but neighboring receptors. It therefore appears that while there is an addition of the responses to increasing numbers of photons, the addition need not take place within the receptors but can occur at some later cell which receives an input from several receptors. Whether or not this addition takes place across different types of receptors can be determined by examining the spectral sensitivity of the visual system. The brightness of a light depends on the wavelength as well as the intensity of the light, light from the middle of the visible spectrum being brighter than that from the spectral extremes. Under very dim light conditions, the spectral sensitivity corresponds to the spectral absorption of rhodopsin, the rod photopigment; under bright light conditions it is displaced toward the long wavelengths and is too broad to correspond to the spectral absorption of any one cone pigment; while at intermediate light levels the curve falls between these two values. It would thus appear that the brightness of a light must be dependent upon the addition of the outputs of different types of photoreceptors at higher than scoptic levels.

Recordings made of the activity of single cells in the visual system support the above deductions from psychophysical experiments. Cells have been found which have a broad spectral sensitivity corresponding to the luminosity or brightness function (De Valois, 1966; Granit, 1955; Jacobs, 1964). One can show that such cells have the outputs of several different receptors, rods as well as cones, feeding into them: Selective adaptation allows one to demonstrate the presence of more than one cone type; dark adaptation of the eye reveals a rod input to the same cell also.

Contrary to what might be expected is the fact that roughly half of the cells of this type seen in the primate visual system have an excitatory input from the receptors, showing an increase in firing to the onset of light, whereas the other half have an inhibitory receptor input and show a decrease in firing to the onset of light (De Valois, 1965; Jacobs, 1964). In both cases, however, there is a *summation* of information from the different receptors to provide the organism with information about the brightness of a patch of light.

The visual receptors have attained the ultimate in sensitivity: A single photon of light absorbed by a single rod is sufficient to activate it. However, such an event is not sufficient to activate the later neural elements: At least two such elementary events must occur together to produce a percept of light. Since it is not until quite high light levels that a single receptor is likely to be struck by two photons simultaneously, the importance of summation across different receptors is clear. The larger the number over which the summation occurs, the lower the threshold. It is likely that the far greater sensitivity of the rod system compared with the cone system is only to a minor extent attributable to greater sensitivity of rod than cone receptors (Weale, 1958); rather it is largely the result of differences in the extent to which addition of receptor output occurs in the neural analysis of information from rods as opposed to cones. The rod system derives its greater sensitivity from addition over a far larger number of receptors: the receptive fields of ganglion cells receiving from the central cone-rich area are much smaller than the receptive fields of peripherally related ganglion cells which pick up mainly from rods. A two-photon absorption is much more likely to take place somewhere among a group of, say, ten thousand receptors than among a group of five thousand receptors. A second advantage, for sensitivity, of the rod system is that the summation can take place over a longer time than it can for the cones. The two photons do not actually have to be absorbed exactly simultaneously in order for summation to take place; the time period over which summation occurs is considerably longer for rods than for cones. Finally, it is likely that more than two—perhaps as many as ten—near-simultaneous photon captures must occur within the receptive field of a ganglion cell in the cone system to activate it. All of these different conditions taken together account for the far higher sensitivity of the rod system. The rod-related neural organization maximizes the amount of summation to gain sensitivity, but pays for it by a loss of information as to exactly where and when the light absorptions occurred, i.e., a loss of visual acuity.

It should be reemphasized that while we have for the moment ignored adaptation and lateral interaction effects, these factors must eventually be taken into account to give a complete picture of how the brightness system functions.

B. Color

If one superimposes two patches of light which differ in wavelength, the brightness will be some sum of the brightnesses of the components, as we have just seen. In fact, to a first approximation, the sum of two equally bright lights of different wavelengths will be as bright as the sum of two equally bright lights of the same wavelength. The color of the lights in this experiment, however, will be found to follow quite different rules. The superposition of two colored lights produces a color which differs qualitatively from the components, and in degree, or saturation, is equal to or less than the components, but never more as was the case with their brightness. In fact, one can find highly colored lights, of complementary wavelength, which when added together give a light which is gray or without color at all. These are all well-known facts, but they raise the question of what sort of neural analysis takes place in processing color information; it clearly must be of a different sort than was the case with brightness.

Studies of the neural organization of the visual system indicate the nature of these two different sorts of neural analysis. As mentioned above, some cells are found in the primate visual system which are clearly summing—through addition of excitation or through addition of inhibition—the outputs of the different receptor types; the spectral sensitivity of these cells corresponds to the relative brightness of different spectral regions. But in addition to these cells—and much more prevalent among the visual cells connected with the central retina—there are cells which are clearly subtracting the output of different classes of receptors rather than adding them together (De Valois, Smith, Kitai, & Karoly, 1958). These cells have been termed *spectrally opponent* cells because they have mechanisms of different spectral sensitivity feeding into them in opposite ways, one excitatory and the other inhibitory. Although there are a wide variety of such cells, they can be reasonably classified into four types, depending upon which parts of the spectrum produce excitatory and which inhibitory effects: +R−G (red excitatory, green inhibitory), +Y−B (yellow excitatory, blue inhibitory), and their respective mirror images, +G−R and +B−Y. In the case of the +R−G cells, for instance, long wavelength (red) light shone into the eye produces an increase in firing; short wave-

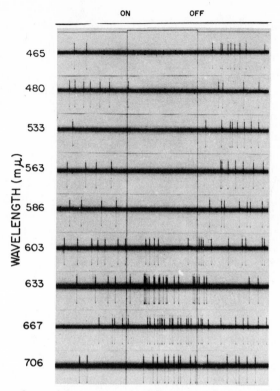

FIG. 1. Recordings of the responses to different wavelengths of light of a +R—G cell in the macaque LGN. The responses to the various wavelengths (equated for energy) have been lined up with respect to the one-second-long light stimulus. Note that this cell, which is firing spontaneously, is excited by red light and inhibited by green light. (LGN, lateral geniculate nucleus.)

lengths of the region which is seen as yellow produces little or no change in firing; and still shorter wavelengths produce a decrease in firing. An example of the respones of such a cell can be seen in Fig. 1.

Such an opponent cell clearly has both excitatory and inhibitory inputs; one would presume that the origin of these are in the cones containing different classes of photopigment. To verify this one would like to isolate the excitatory and inhibitory components and compare their spectral sensitivities with the spectral absorptions of the photopigments. Although these components cannot be completely isolated, they can be separated to a great extent by the use of chromatic adaptation. A very long wavelength light will stimulate primarily the red receptors; if left on, therefore, such an adaptation light will depress the excitability of the red receptors much more than it will that of the green or blue receptors. If one does this while recording from a +R−G cell, one finds that all regions of the spectrum now produce inhibition, including wavelengths which had previously excited the cell. Prior to adaptation of the red system the maximum inhibition occurred at about 500 nm; during adaptation it is found to come from light of about 530 nm. The spectral sensitivity curve determined in the presence of such a red adapting light reveals a good agreement to the "green cone" pigment curve. A short wavelength adapting light which selectively depresses the short wavelength inhibitory mechanism reveals excitation to all spectral regions, the maximum excitation coming from light of about 570–590 nm. The spectral sensitivity of this isolated excitatory component closely resembles that of the "red cone" pigment. It thus appears that the +R−G cells have an excitatory input from red cones and an inhibitory input from the green cones (De Valois, Jacobs, & Jones, 1963). Since the absorption curves of the red and green photopigments overlap across much of the spectrum, light of most wavelengths will be absorbed by both types of receptors. Most wavelengths thus produce both excitatory and inhibitory inputs to a +R−G cell, which then shows a firing rate dependent on the relative amounts of excitation and inhibition. It is therefore subtracting the output of the green cones from that of the red cones.

If the same selective adaptation experiment is performed with the +G−R cells, the same spectral sensitivity curves are found in the components, but now excitation and inhibition are reversed. An example of one such adaptation experiment is given in Fig. 2. The +G−R cells are approximate mirror images of the +R−G cells. However, since the slopes of the excitatory and inhibitory processes are not identical, the +R−G and +G−R cells are not complete mirror images. There is thus some additional information about the stimulus available to an organism which possesses both of these cell types rather than just one.

Similar chromatic adaptation experiments reveal that the +B−Y cells are connected with "blue cones" in an excitatory way and with either red or red plus green cones in an inhibitory way; vice versa with the +Y−B cells. Although the experiments described here

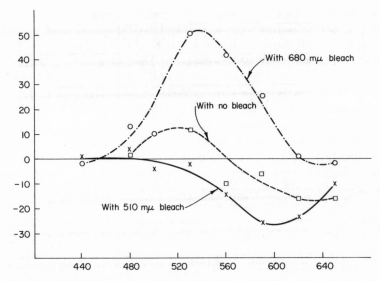

FIG. 2. A plot of the number of spikes fired by a +G−R cell in response to different wavelengths of light (equal energy) under three adaptation conditions. With no adaptation, it fires to green and inhibits to red. With a green adaptation field, which desensitizes the excitatory input, the cell is inhibited by all wavelengths; with a red adaptation, which desensitizes the inhibitory input, the cell is excited by all wavelengths. Note also the resulting shifts in peaks of the excitatory and inhibitory components.

were performed with cells in the lateral geniculate nucleus of the thalamus—the fourth-order cells in the visual pathway, located in the projection from the eye to the cortex—experiments with other animals strongly suggest that the site of these interactions is very early in the visual pathway. These experiments will be discussed later.

It can now be seen how this opponent organization provides an organism with the ability to differentiate different wavelengths of light independent of their relative intensity, which is what is meant by possessing color vision. The retina contains cones whose photopigment spectral sensitivity curves are overlapping but have different peak absorptions. The feature which distinguishes different spectral regions is not the amount that different wavelengths stimulate one or more of these receptors—which different intensities of the same wavelength will do—but the extent to which one as opposed to another receptor is activated. This is exactly the

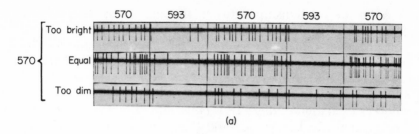

(a)

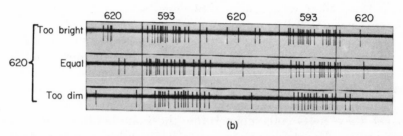

(b)

FIG. 3. Recordings of the responses of a macaque +G−R cell to shifts in the wavelength of light to the eye. (a) Wavelength shifts between 570 and 593 nm. In the middle, the 570 and 593 lights are equally bright, differing only in color; in the top line the 570 light is 0.5 log units too bright; in the bottom line the 570 is too dim. Note that in each case the cell fires to 570 and inhibits to 593, clearly responding to the color of the lights, not their brightness. (b) Same experiment, same cell, but a shift between 593 and 620 nm. The cell again responds to the color, not the brightness of the lights. Note also that the cell now fires to 593 and inhibits to 620, indicating that it is the relative wavelengths which are being signaled.

information which the subtractive opponent-cell organization is extracting from the receptors. For example, the extent to which the +R−G cells will be excited is dependent on the amount of activation of the red cones as opposed to the green cones, not upon the absolute amount of activation of either. If both cone types are activated to an equal extent, the excitation and inhibition will cancel out to produce no change in firing, regardless of intensity. Light of a given wavelength will produce roughly the same amount of firing in these cells regardless of intensity because a higher intensity will produce more excitation and more inhibition, and these will tend to cancel each other out. The opponent cell pictured in Fig. 3, for instance, is very sensitive to wavelength differences but quite insensitive to intensity differences.

As to the relationship between the activity of these cells and what we see, we may speculatively postulate a one-to-one relationship between certain perceptual characteristics and the firing rate of these cells. Specifically, that the brightness is signaled by the activity rate of the nonopponent cells; that excitation of the +R−G cells, and inhibition of the +G−R cells, signals "red," whereas excitation of the +Y−B cells, and inhibition of the +B−Y cells, signals "yellow," etc.; and that if both opponent and nonopponent cells are active this will be perceived as a colored light which is desaturated. Let us examine some stimulus situations in which we know what a normal observer sees, and how these different types of cells respond, in order to see to what extent this parallel holds. Long wavelength light will activate both the +R−G and the +Y−B cells, while inhibiting both their mirror images. One would expect, therefore, that the purest red would be produced by a long wavelength light combined with a very short wavelength light which would suppress the +Y−B cells and thus leave the +R−G cells alone firing, the same holding true in the reverse case for the mirror images. This is indeed the case. As the wavelength is decreased from the long wavelength end of the spectrum, the activity of the +Y cells increases, while the +R cell rate begins to drop as the inhibition from the green component starts to come in. One thus sees a series of colors which are increasingly yellow. At about 580 nm the R and G components cancel each other to leave just the Y mechanism active; we see this light as pure yellow. Still shorter wavelengths start to activate the G component of the +R−G cells, and are thus seen as yellow mixed with more and more green, and so forth through the spectrum. It should be reemphasized that the color seen corresponds to which one, or ones, of the opponent cells is active, not to which receptor is active. Thus pure green is seen at about 500 nm, which is where the +G−R cells show their maximum activity; this does not correspond to the peak of the "green receptor," which is approximately 535 nm. Also red is seen at wavelengths beyond about 630 nm, which is where the +R−G cells are most active; there is no pigment with maximum sensitivity past 575 nm. The agreement between the hues seen in the spectrum and the activity rate of the various opponent cells can be seen in Fig. 4, in which the physiological and psychophysical data are directly compared.

White light is absorbed by all the cones and thus highly acti-

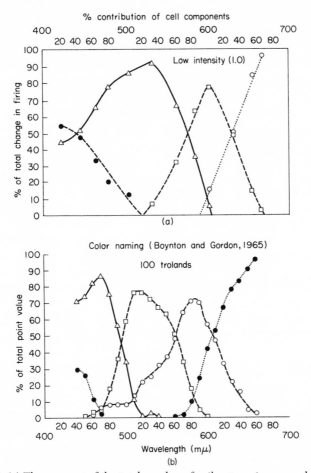

FIG. 4. (a) The per cent of the total number of spikes to a given wavelength contributed by each of the macaque opponent cell components: (O) +R&−R, (□) +4&−4, (△) +G&−G, and (●) +B&−B. (b) The hue of different spectral regions, plotted from Boynton and Gordon (1965). The per cent of total times each color name was used, in an experiment in which observers gave one of four color names to a flash of monochromatic light, is plotted at each wavelength: (△) blue, (□) green, (O) yellow, and (●) red.

vates the nonopponent cells which add together the outputs of all the cones. Such equal activation of the cones, however, leads to little or no response from the opponent cells which are subtracting the outputs of the different receptor types. Thus white light has no hue but a lot of brightness. One can also predict from this organi-

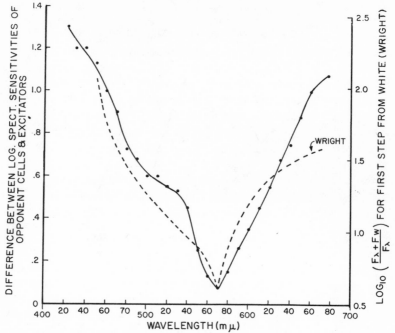

FIG. 5. Saturation function. Solid line represents relative saturation of different spectral lights (after Wright, 1947). Data points and solid line represent the difference between the spectral sensitivity of the opponent and nonopponent macaque cells. At the spectral extremes, which are highly saturated, the opponent cells are more responsive relative to the nonopponent cells than in region of 570 nm, which is highly desaturated.

zation that monochromatic light from different spectral regions will have differential saturation (De Valois, Abramov, & Jacobs, 1966). Very long or short wavelengths will strongly activate the +R—G and +B—Y cells, respectively (and inhibit their mirror images, of course). Such a light will also affect the nonopponent cells to some extent and will thus be desaturated to that extent. On the other hand, light from the middle of the spectrum will evoke little more opponent cell activity, while producing much more nonopponent cell activity, and should be seen, as it is, as less saturated. The spectral region around 570 nm, in particular, should be highly desaturated, as it is, because neither the +R—G or +G—R cells is responding here, leaving only the +Y—B opponent cells to fire, while the nonopponent cells are maximally responsive to this part of the spectrum. This comparison is shown in Fig. 5.

A further consequence for perception of the subtractive type of organization of the opponent cells is that some colors must be mutually exclusive. Since, for instance, in the $+G-R$ cells green is being signaled by excitation and red by inhibition, and since a cell cannot both increase and decrease its firing at the same time, a color cannot be both red and green at once. Since yellow is being signaled by a different type of cell, however, a color can be both red and yellow or green and yellow at once. Such mutually exclusive categories would be expected, if one can generalize from this data, in other sensory systems where a subtractive analysis takes place by means of combined excitation and inhibition; an example might be the temperature-sensing system which signals the temperature in either direction from the adaptation level by excitation or inhibition to form the mutually exclusive categories of hot and cold.

C. Adaptation

The accounts of brightness and color analysis given above are vastly oversimplified because only the effect of a light flash at one intensity superimposed on some particular adaptation level was considered. It is time to examine more general cases, for the brightness and color of a light flash depend on the amount and wavelength of the background light present at the time as well, and upon that which had been present in the near past. Stars radiate the same amount of light to the eye day and night; but they are seen as very bright on a dark night, dim at dawn, and totally invisible in daylight, as the intensity of the background light varies. An examination of the relation between the "test flash" and the background reveals that the increment in intensity ΔI needed to see the flash is roughly proportional to the background level I, so that the ratio $\Delta I/I$ is a constant—Weber's law. A related phenomenon is the way in which the visual system responds to different intensities of stimulation over a small range from a given adaptation level. The capture of photons must be linear except at blindingly high levels of illumination since there are many millions of photopigment molecules and only a few photons of light arriving at ordinary light levels. However, the brightness does not increase in a linear way with intensity, but rather in a quasi-logarithmic fashion. Recordings at the single cell level (Granit, 1955; Hartline & Graham, 1932; and many others) show the same logarithmic relationship in the firing rate. It can be seen that this is the same as the effect of background illumination discussed above. If one flash is I, then the ΔI needed to perceive another flash as brighter is found to be a constant ratio of I, so $\Delta I/I$ is constant.

The brightness varies not only as a function of present background illumination but is also dependent on the illumination in the near past. If one steps from a brightly lit room into the dark night, the stars would be initially invisible as a result of the preceding light adaptation and would become gradually brighter as one adapted to the dark. One can consider this as a special case of the same phenomenon if the preceding light adaptation is considered as producing an effect which is equivalent to a present background light which is becoming gradually dimmer as dark adaptation proceeds (Barlow & Sparrock, 1964). In an analogous, if somewhat more complicated fashion, the color of a light depends on the color of the background light and upon the preceding light.

It might appear that one could account for these adaptational phenomena by postulating that the receptors become less efficient when they are absorbing light too fast, perhaps because an excessive amount of their photopigment is broken down, and that they regain their high sensitivity and effective output as the photopigments are gradually regenerated during dark adaptation. Although photochemical processes doubtless play a crucial role in this, such a simple explanation is untenable. The background light which can render a given patch of retina relatively insensitive is so dim that few photopigment molecules are bleached. Furthermore, the adaptation light does not even have to shine on the receptors being tested with the flash at all; it is equally effective if it falls only on the neighboring receptors (Lipetz, 1962; Pirenne, 1958). The adaptational effect is thus certainly not the result of the mere inactivation of those receptors which receive the light, and what inactivation occurs must be a neural change rather than a matter of photochemical depletion.

The adaptation level must be determined by summing the extent to which a group of receptors has been activated, so that the breakdown of photopigments in any of the group will lead to a relative inactivation of them all. Direct experimental evidence is lacking on either the anatomical structure which collects the background intensity information from the receptors or about the type of neural interaction involved in the resulting desensitization. Some indirect evidence is available, however, as to the site of the interactions, and one can speculate about the process.

Results which are discussed later strongly suggest that the adaptational interactions must take place very early in the neural pathway, probably before the bipolars. It is possible that the mechanism is that of presynaptic inhibition. Such inhibition, summoned over a group of receptors and fed presynaptically into the pathway to the bipolar or ganglion cells, would have the effect of dividing the output of all of the receptors by a certain amount; the net result would be that the effective signal would be proportional to the total background, which it is. The explanation of the log transformation and the lateral adaptation by such presynaptic inhibition would appear to be precluded by the evidence that potentials attributed to the receptors themselves (Brown & Murakami, 1964a) show a logarithmic relation to the light intensity, thereby implying that the log transformation takes place in the receptors before interactions occur. In such a case, the output of the various receptors would be summed and fed postsynaptically into the pathway. However, one should note that Brown and Murakami (1964b) found evidence for some spatial interaction in the late receptor potential. Electron microscopy of the receptors (Cohen, 1963; Sjöstrand, 1953) reveals evidence for horizontal cell synapses within the receptor pouches, and of interreceptor contacts; either of these structures would provide a possible basis for presynaptic inhibition.

The slow increase in sensitivity during dark adaptation could be accounted for by much the same mechanism if one assumed that the receptors which have captured photons of light were to continue to feed an output into the desensitizing adaptation circuit for as long as their photopigments were still unregenerated (Barlow & Sparrock, 1964; Rushton, 1965).

Under photopic conditions, the cones are the principal active receptors, and there are three different classes of cones. Does the adaptational network described above take into consideration these differences, or does it sum across all the receptor types? That is, does a red light just desensitize the red system in the neighborhood in which it hits, or does it also desensitize the green and blue (and rod systems)? There is good evidence that under threshold conditions, at least, the effectiveness of the red receptors alone is changed by the activity of the red receptors (Alpern & Rushton, 1965). Light absorbed by the red receptors renders them relatively insensitive and also reduces the effectiveness of neighboring red receptors while not in the least changing the sensitivity of the green and blue receptors. It is this property which permits the isolation of different receptor spectral sensitivity functions with the increment threshold technique (Stiles, 1949): A red adapting field sufficiently reduces the sensitivity of the red receptors to enable one to examine the sensitivity of the green receptors to long wavelength light. Such a receptor-specific adaptational system would also account for many of the phenomena of simultaneous color contrast. A doughnut-shaped patch of long wavelength light will not only reduce the signal from the red receptors in the area hit by the light but also in the area covered by the hole in the middle. White light on this center area which previously affected red and green receptors equally will now be responded to more by the green than the red receptors. It will thus appear slightly greenish instead of white.

The fact that the adaptational interaction was shown by Alpern and Rushton (1965) to be specific to a single class of cones gives evidence as to the location of the effect: It must occur before the different cone types interact to form the opponent cells, for once the red and green cones have interacted to form the +R−G and +G−R cells it is no longer possible to extract the spectral sensitivity curves of the components from any interaction. That is to say, if the +R−G cells were to inhibit the neighboring +R−G cells the amount of inhibition from different spectral regions would correspond to the spectral sensitivity of the +R−G cells, not to that of the "red" photopigment. The maximum inhibition, for instance, would be produced by light of approximately 640 nm, not 570 nm as found by Alpern and Rushton.

The physiological evidence is that the interaction between different types of cones to form the opponent cells occurs somewhere in the region of the bipolar cells. Svaetichin (1956) and Svaetichin and MacNichol (1958) have recorded slow, graded potentials in the fish retina which are produced by some structure in the region of the inner nuclear layer, which contains the cell bodies of the horizontal, bipolar, and amacrine cells, and that of the glial Müller cells. These graded potentials respond to light of different wavelengths in a fashion analogous to the opponent ganglion cells (which fire spike discharges) found in the same animal: Light of some wavelengths produces depolarization and other wavelengths produce hyperpolarization, to produce a spectral response curve similar to that of the ganglion cells. Some units give a curve that may be described as +R−G, others, a +Y−B, etc. Although corresponding studies have not been made in the primate retina, it may be presumed from the other similarities between fish (MacNichol, 1964) and monkey (De Valois, 1965) visual systems that the interactions between *unlike* cones occurs at the bipolar level in the primate. If so, the adaptational interactions studied by Alpern and Rushton must occur at the receptor or horizontal cell level.

Additional evidence, which can be similarly interpreted to indicate that the adaptational interactions take place at an earlier stage of analysis than the interactions involved in the analysis of brightness and color information, comes from a psychophysical study by T. N. Cornsweet and Teller (1965) who showed that brightness and increment thresholds can vary independently. The increment threshold was found to depend solely on the stimulus luminance and the adaptational conditions in the immediate neighborhood. Brightness, while also affected by these factors, is in addition modified by spatial interactions which do not affect the increment threshold. These data can be interpreted as indicating that the spatial interactions over long distances take place at a later stage than the adaptational interactions, which alone are relevant for the increment threshold.

It is clear that insofar as adaptation occurs, the relationship stated earlier between brightness and light intensity will not hold. In fact, it does not: The brightness of a light is virtually independent of its intensity once the observer is adapted to it (Wright, 1947). While the transient initial response to a change in illumination signals some absolute intensity information, the longer term response does not. The same is true in the case of color vision: The color of a prolonged stimulus tends to disappear. The physiological response underlying this can be seen in the more or less rapid drop of the firing rate of both opponent and nonopponent cells approximately to the spontaneous level with prolonged stimulation (De Valois, 1965).

What is the possible functional significance of an adaptation process which produces a loss of absolute brightness and color information? Two clear advantages can be seen from a consideration of the physiological processes involved. One is that adaptation greatly extends the intensity range over which the visual system can operate while at the same time preserving a high sensitivity to change. Neurons in the visual system only fire for extended periods within the range of 0–200 or so spikes per second. The intensity difference between bright sunlight on a beach and a dark night may be well over 1,000,000,000 to 1. If this whole intensity range had to be signaled by the limited number of different spikes per second, it is obvious that small intensity differences could not be encoded. In actuality, the visual system has a dynamic range not of the 9 log units mentioned above, but only of about 1 to $\frac{1}{2}$ log units on either side of the adaptation level; flashes at a greater intensity difference than this in either direction from the adaptation level completely saturate the system (De Valois, 1965; Jacobs, 1964). Over this restricted range, the spectrally nonopponent brightness cells can signal very fine intensity variations. An analogy can be seen between this mechanism and a condensor-coupled voltmeter, which is very sensitive to small transient voltage difference. A large maintained voltage change might initially overdrive the meter, but it will soon drop back to the zero level from which it can again signal small transient changes about the new voltage level. Adaptation thus provides the mechanism for covering the whole 9 log range at different times, despite the limited response range at any given time: The portion of the total range covered varies from time to time depending on the over-all brightness, which defines the adaptation level.

Adaptation not only allows for better intensity discrimination but also better color discrimination. Wavelength discrimination takes place, as discussed above, by means of opposing excitatory and inhibitory processes which have their origin in receptors containing different photopigments. The best discrimination occurs when the excitation and inhibition are balanced; in the limiting case where there is only excitation or only inhibition (where only one cone type is responding) there is no color discrimination at all. Two wavelengths which both affect one photopigment much more than the others may be indiscriminable. With adaptation to the color, however, the more sensitive system will drop in sensitivity until a point of approximate balance between excitation and inhibition is reached. The wavelengths can now be discriminated.

As a result of the presence early in the visual pathway of achromatic and chromatic adaptation, the effective visual stimulus is not some intensity or wavelength of light, but rather some intensity or wavelength contrast. That is to say, one cannot predict the response which a visual stimulus will evoke from a ganglion cell from a knowledge of just the intensity and wavelength of the light, but can predict the response if one knows what the intensity or wavelength contrast is. The cells should thus be thought of as contrast detectors.

D. Contours

As a simplification, an object may be considered to be made up of an extended uniform area, with a border or contour separating it from the surround. In our discussion so far, we have examined some of the events which take place in the uniform area as a result of diffuse illumination of a section of the retina with light of different intensities and wavelengths under various adaptation conditions. The effect of a surround has also to some extent been considered; let us now examine the role of the contour between. This raises questions about the spatial aspects of vision, which we have largely ignored even though this is the most important aspect of visual activity.

The vertebrate visual system, with its millions of receptors and multiple interactions at several retinal synapses, is enormously complicated and hard to understand even under the simple conditions of uniform diffuse illumination. It would be highly advantageous to disentangle some of the basic mechanisms of spatial vision in a more simple visual system before adding these complexities to those we have already considered. The horseshoe crab, *limulus*, has a visual organization which forms a simple analog of the spatial organization of the vertebrate visual system. In this eye, which has been extensively studied by Hartline, Ratliff, and others (Ratliff, Hartline, & Miller, 1963), the receptors feed into eccentric cells (whose axons form the optic nerve without intermediate cells) that are analogous to vertebrate bipolar cells. They found that an eccentric cell was much more responsive to a pattern of light in which a contour appeared within the cell's receptive field than it was to uniform stimulation; the explanation for this was analyzed in a number of experiments.

It was found that there were mutual interactions among eccentric cells, and that the interactions were always inhibitory: Each fiber sends off collaterals to neighboring fibers and has an inhibitory effect on them. The amount of inhibition was found to be proportional to the activity rate of the inhibiting neuron, and the inhibition was strictly subtractive. The result of this mutual inhibition among neighboring fibers—which may well be similar to the lateral acting adaptation discussed earlier—was that uniform stimulation of the

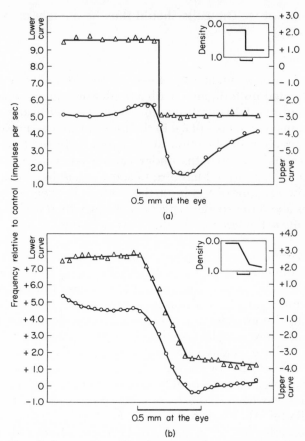

FIG. 6. The discharge of impulses from a single receptor unit in response to simple patterns of illumination in various positions on the retinal mosaic. (a) "Step" pattern of illumination. The demagnified image of a photographic plate was projected on the surface of the eye. The insert shows the relative density of the plate along its length as measured, prior to the experiment, by means of a photomultiplier tube in the image plane where the eye was to be placed. The density of the plate was uniform across its entire width at every point. The upper (rectilinear) graph shows the frequency of discharge of the test receptor, when the illumination was occluded from the rest of the eye by a mask with a small aperture, minus the frequency of discharge elicited by a small control spot of light of constant intensity also confined to the facet of the test receptor. Scale of ordinate on the right. The lower (curvilinear) graph is the frequency of discharge from the same test receptor when the mask was removed and the entire pattern of illumination was projected on the eye in various positions, minus the frequency of discharge elicited by a small control spot of constant intensity confined to the facet of the receptor. Scale of ordinate on the left. (b) A simple gradient of intensity (the so-called Mach pattern). Same procedure as in (a). (Reproduced from Ratliff & Hartline, 1959.)

whole receptive field led to little response, since each cell was inhibiting and being inhibited by each other. If half of the receptors were strongly illuminated and half dimly illuminated, those in the bright light inhibited those in the dim much more than the dimly lit ones inhibited them. This produced a larger difference in firing rate between the two halves of the field than there would have been in the absence of mutual inhibiton. This increase, however, held only for those cells at the border itself, as shown in Fig. 6. Units in the middle of the bright portion received much inhibition from all their highly lit neighbors and were therefore somewhat suppressed. Units at the edge of the bright area, on the contour, had a lot of inhibition from only one side and were therefore more active than other units in the brightly lit portion. Correspondingly, units in the uniformly dim area were subject to little inhibition from their dimly lit neighbors, but the units at the contour were strongly inhibited by the brightly lit cells on the one side, and would therefore show less activity than the other units in the dim region. The net result of these complex effects was that the border was highly emphasized in the firing pattern, one side of it by extra-high firing and the other side by extra-low firing; the uniformly stimulated areas, on the other hand, showed relatively little activity.

That similar interactions occur in human vision is indicated by the existence of Mach bands: areas seen as extra light and extra dark on either side of a visual border. These Mach bands correspond to the distribution of firing levels seen in the limulus experiments discussed above. As already mentioned, adaptation must also, in the human eye, involve lateral interactions; these may well be similar to those observed in limulus.

One way of analyzing the spatial organization of the visual system is by exploring the receptive field of a cell with a tiny spot of light to stimulate different ones of the receptors which feed into the cell. If the receptive field of a limulus eccentric cell were explored by a spot of light on a constant background, it would be found to be organized in a concentric fashion, as shown in the diagram of Fig. 7A. Stimulation of the eccentric cell's own ommatidium would produce excitation of the eccentric cell; stimulation of any of the surrounding ommatidia would inhibit it. If quantitative measurements were made of the amount of inhibition, it would be found to drop off gradually from the center, the greatest inhibition being from the immediately adjacent ommatidia. Kuffler (1952) recording from ganglion cells in the cat's eye, obtained similar

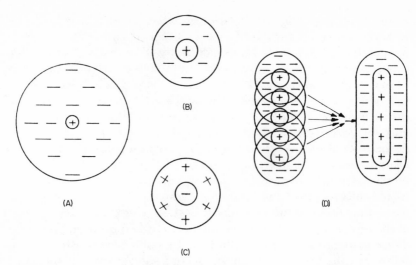

FIG. 7. Plots of the receptive fields of various cells, the plus symbolizes an excitatory response to a spot of light in that location, and the minus symbolizes an inhibitory response. (A) Limulus eccentric cell. Excitation comes only from its own ommatidium; all the surrounding ommatidia inhibit the cell. (B) and (C) Excitatory-center
and inhibitory-center cat ganglion cell plots. The receptive fields are similar to
limulus cells in being symmetrical and concentric but differ in that a number of
receptors are included in the center. (D) The receptive field of a cat simple cortical cell, to the right, along with the relation Hubel and Wiesel propose it has to
the concentric fields plotted in (B) and (C). Note that the optimal stimulus for this
cell would be a vertical line.

results from some of the cells, except that the excitatory portion
of the receptive field covered many receptors, so that the receptive field looked like that in Fig. 7B. Equally often exactly the same
organization was found except that excitation and inhibition were
reversed; the cells had an inhibitory center and excitatory surround
as shown in the diagram in Fig. 7C.

Both the inhibitory-center and the excitatory-center cells would
be very sensitive to spots of light or contours and would tend to
emphasize these points on a pattern just as limulus cells do.

As an aside, it might be interesting to compare some of the characteristics of these cells with those of the color cells discussed
earlier. Both types of cells have an opponent organization resulting
from an interplay of excitation and inhibition, with the cell reporting the difference in amount between the excitatory and the inhibitory inputs. In both cases there are certain types of cells and their
mirror images, e.g., $+R-G$ and $+G-R$ color cells, and excitatory-

center and inhibitory-center spatial cells. In both cases, activation of both excitatory and inhibitory mechanisms will tend to produce a cancellation resulting in little or no activity. In the color cells this occurs with white light stimulation; in the spatial cells with diffuse light stimulation. Finally, the color cells are very sensitive to a stimulus change which changes from a stimulus which produces excitation to one which produces inhibition, or vice versa, and are relatively insensitive to a stimulus change which leads from one amount of excitation to another; thus wavelength discrimination is best at the crosspoints from excitation to inhibition of the different cell types. Correspondingly, the spatial cells are relatively insensitive to a shift of the image from one portion of the excitatory part of the receptive field to another, but they are very sensitive to a shift from an excitatory to an inhibitory area. The same sort of neural analysis is being employed for two quite different ends in these different types of cells.

In the color and brightness experiments (De Valois *et al.*, 1963; De Valois *et al.*, 1966) and in the spatial experiments (Kuffler, 1952), different sets of stimulus parameters were being varied; one may inquire as to whether the cells found in the different series of experiments are really different types of cells or merely different aspects of the responses of the same cells. The answer to this question is not quite certain, but it would appear that the "brightness cells" seen in the diffuse light experiments are the same as the "concentric spatial cells" seen in the punctate light experiments. The center of the concentric receptive field is usually much more sensitive than the surround. Thus diffuse light, while less effective than a spot on the center, will nonetheless evoke the same pattern of response: excitation from an excitatory-center cell, and inhibition from an inhibitory-center cell. In the primate retina, containing different types of cones, these cells sum across the different cone types, and at the same time subtract the output of the cells in the surround from those in the center, to give the over-all brightness and an indication of the location of a spot or a contour. These cells, in short, are both brightness and space cells. The situation with the color cells is by no means as clear. While some of these may have a similar concentric spatial organization (Mac-Nichol, 1964; Hubel & Wiesel, 1964), others do not, at least to the same extent. But in general it can be said that the spatial and color-brightness organizations coexist, superimposed upon each other.

Although much more activity is evoked by a spot of light or a contour than by regions of uniform illumination, this activity will also die out in time as a result of adaptation. Therefore, an object steadily fixated should disappear, something which we know from ordinary experience does not occur. However, experiments indicate that the reason fixated objects do not disappear is that the eyes cannot be held steady, as much as one tries to do so. The eye fluctuates continuously in tiny rapid oscillations resulting from the eye's unstable mounting and the continuous activation of the eye muscles in a random fashion as they maintain fixation. Similar oscillations, which can be easily observed, are those of the finger tip when one tries to point steadily with the index finger.

There are, however, a number of ways by which an image can be truly stabilized on the retina; if that is done the percept of the image does soon fade out and disappear. One way to accomplish such a stabilization is to fixate in such a way that the image of a small object falls some distance out on the periphery of the eye. Visual acuity is very poor in the periphery; that is to say, an image must be displaced some distance on the peripheral retina for it to be perceived as being in a new location. Since the microfluctuations of the eye are too small to displace the image that far, the image is in effect always in the same location—and it disappears in a second or two (Troxler's effect). Another way to accomplish fixation of an image on the retina is by getting an afterimage of a bright light. The source of the afterimage is of course fixed on the retina and moves with it. The aftereffects of a bright adaptation light may persist for half an hour, as seen in the change in sensitivity of this area, but the afterimage soon disappears. The most versatile technique for image stabilization is by use of a close-fitting contact lens which moves with the eye, as first developed by Riggs, Ratliff, J. D. Cornsweet, & T. N. Cornsweet (1953) and Ditchburn (1958). The light source may be attached directly to the contact lens, or the image may be seen through a telescope after being reflected off the contact lens. In either case the image moves with the eye, and soon fades and disappears.

The net effect of adaptation and lateral interaction combined with the microfluctuations of the eye is to enhance considerably the role of the border or contour. The activity initially evoked by broad areas of uniform stimulation soon dies out, but the microfluctuations together with lateral interaction maintain a state of high activity at the contour region. The information signaled to the brain thus emphasizes these regions of the visual environment.

E. Form

When we look at a scene we see not flashes of light of different colors and brightness in different locations in the visual field, but objects having a particular shape or form. The various components of the visual stimulus are not kept and perceived as separate but are grouped into larger, coherent wholes. Can we find any hints as to the mechanism by which this very complex analysis takes place?

The receptive field of the cat ganglion cell, with its concentric areas of excitation and inhibition, responds much more to a contour in the field than to uniform illumination, as we have seen. However, the most effective stimulus of all in evoking activity (excitation in a plus center cell, and inhibition in a minus center cell) is a small round spot which just fills the center of the receptive field. Such a stimulus affects one mechanism, either excitation or inhibition depending on the cell type, almost in isolation from the countereffects of the opponent mechanism. As a result, one can state in a quite nontrivial sense that this ganglion cell can discriminate in a primitive way the shape of the visual stimuli in its part of the retina. If the object is round and of a particular size, the cell will fire more than to any other shape and size of object; to a considerable extent this will be independent of the intensity or any other aspect of the stimulus.

The cells at the cat lateral geniculate nucleus have much the same spatial organization as cat ganglion cells, but those in the visual cortex have receptive field organizations which differ in interesting ways from this. Cells with concentric receptive fields are not seen in the visual cortex; a considerable proportion instead have receptive fields with a long narrow central area—excitatory or inhibitory in about equal proportion in the now familiar mirror-image arrangement—with a surround of the opposite polarity (Hubel & Wiesel, 1959; Hubel & Wiesel, 1965). For such a cell, the optimal stimulus is a line of a particular width, oriented in the appropriate plane in the visual field, and in the correct location. Such a stimulus would just fill the center of the cell's receptive field but not its opponent surround; it would thus evoke the maximum response. A round stimulus would be much less effective since it would stimulate both the center and the surround and the

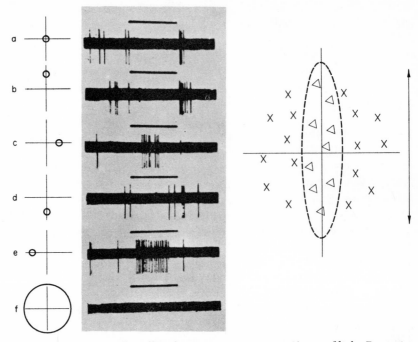

FIG. 8. Responses of a cell in the cat striate cortex to a 1° spot of light. Receptive field located in the eye contralateral to the hemisphere from which the unit was recorded, close to and below the area centralis, just nasal to the horizontal meridian. No response evoked from the ipsilateral eye. The complete map of the receptive field is shown to the right. (x) areas giving excitation; (△) areas giving inhibitory effects. Scale, 4°. Axes of this diagram are reproduced on left of each record. a, 1° (0.25 mm) spot shone in the center of the field; b–e, 1° spot shone on four points equidistant from center; f, 5° spot covering the entire field. Background illumination 0.17 log m.c. Stimulus intensity 1.65 log m.c. Duration of each stimulus 1 second. Positive deflections upward. (Reproduced from Hubel & Wiesel, 1959.)

opposing processes would tend to cancel. A line with the wrong orientation would also stimulate some of the center and some of the surround and thus be less effective than one having the correct orientation, see Fig. 8.

Hubel and Wiesel have found a great number of cells of this type in the cat visual cortex, with the "optimal orientation" of the cells varying in a systematic fashion across the cortical surface. All cells in a particular column down from the cortical surface have the same receptive field orientation, but the cells in an adjacent column will have a slightly different orientation. Lines in the visual field in different planes will therefore activate cells in different cortical loci.

It is not possible to be certain of how these cortical cells are related to the concentric-receptive-field cells in the lateral geniculate, but Hubel and Wiesel (1959) have offered a very plausible theory about the relationship. If a particular cortical cell gets an input from a group of earlier cells whose receptive fields all lie in a line, the receptive field of the cortical cell would be a composite of that of the earlier cells, as shown in the diagram in Fig. 7D.

A correctly oriented line would stimulate the receptive field centers of each of the lateral geniculate cells and thus add to a very large activation of the cortical cell. Here we see again, as in the retinal organization, a convergence of inputs, with the cortical cell summing the outputs of certain lateral geniculate cells.

An axon from the lateral geniculate runs parallel to the surface after reaching the cortex and gives off axon endings through a considerable region of the visual cortex. It will thus make contact with, and help activate, dozens of different columns of cells in a divergent organization. In one column it will activate a cortical cell in combination with a group of lateral geniculate cells whose receptive fields lie along one plane; in another column the same axon will be joined by axons of geniculate cells whose receptive fields lie along a different plane with reference to it. Which cortical column will be most effectively activated will depend on which line of neighboring geniculate cells are also stimulated, which in turn depends on the orientation of the visual stimulus.

In addition to finding these cells with long narrow receptive fields, responsive to lines of a particular orientation and location with respect to the retina, Hubel and Wiesel (1965) have found more complex cells in the same cortical areas and in other cortical areas to which the striate visual cortex projects. These complex cells appear to be later elements in the sequential analysis of visual information. One such cell may respond to a vertical line regardless of its location within a large area of the visual field. A cell could have such a response capability as a result of adding together the outputs of a group of simple cortical cells each of which had a vertical receptive field, but each component receptive field slightly displaced with respect to the others. A vertical line anywhere within a considerable retinal area would therefore stimulate one or more of these geniculate cells and thus activate the cortical cell.

Such a cortical cell might be the first unit in the line which was responsive to a shape regardless of its location.

Still more complex cells are found in the later visual areas; for instance, cells which respond to a vertical line, but only one which is of a particular length and stops at one or both ends within the visual field. Such a cell may be particularly sensitive to an angle (Hubel & Wiesel, 1965). Hubel and Wiesel suggest that such a cell may be receiving inputs from complex cells whose preferred orientations are at right angles to each other.

It is not known to what lengths this sort of analysis might be carried in the successive analyses of visual information through many synapses, but one can see that the principle involved, that of addition of inputs converging from the previous stage plus divergence to allow for parallel analysis, would allow cells to respond in a more and more specific way to forms.

F. Movement

A moving object is a very powerful visual stimulus: It is more likely to be attended to than a stationary object. How does the organism detect the presence and direction of movement? This might simply be "explained" on the basis of an object moving across the visual field stimulating a row of retinal receptors in succession which would produce the successive activation of a row of cortical cells. Such a statement, even if it were true, would merely shift the problem from the retina to the cortex, leaving the question of how the successive activation of cortical cells is detected by the nervous system. Recent physiological experiments have provided insights as to how this can occur through the interaction of excitation and inhibition.

Lettvin, Maturana, McCulloch, and Pitts (1959), recording from the axon endings of frog ganglion cells, found that most units were highly sensitive only to moving stimuli. Some units responded preferentially to objects of a particular size and shape (that of a small bug!) but only if it moved in the visual field. They did not explore possible retinal organizations that might have led to such complex capabilities.

Barlow, Hill, and Levick (1964) have found that certain ganglion cells in the rabbit retina also respond in a sustained manner only to a moving stimulus. A stationary flash of light or darkness evokes only a very brief response regardless of its shape, location, or wave-

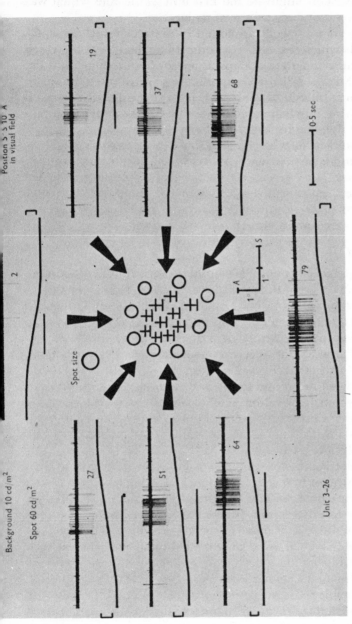

FIG. 9. Responses of a directionally selective unit (axon recording) to motion in different directions. Map of receptive field in center. Each pair of records shows (lower trace) movement of a spot of light right through the receptive field in the direction of the adjacent arrow and (upper trace) the response elicited. Conventions are as follows: (±) reponse to stationary spot at both on and off and (O) no response. There were no responses outside the ring of O's. Anterior A and superior S meridians in the visual field are shown together with 1° calibration marks. All records read from left to right. In upper trace, electrode positivity is downward; the number of spikes is shown immediately after each response. For lower trace, vertical calibration bar shows 5° displacement of light spot; horizontal bar indicates approximately when the spot was within the receptive field. (Reproduced from Barlow et al., 1964.)

length. If the spot is moved across the cell's receptive field in a particular direction, however, a large maintained response results. Movement in the opposite direction inhibits the cell, and other directions of movement evoke intermediate amounts of excitation or inhibition. An example of the responses of such a cell is seen in Fig. 9. It can be seen that movement down and to the right results in a long burst of firing, whereas a movement up and to the left inhibits the cell to produce a lower than spontaneous firing rate. This cell, then, responds in an opponent manner to different directions of movement, just as color cells give opponent responses to different wavelengths. Many of the same consequences would be expected to pertain.

The various movement cells found in the rabbit differ in the direction of movement to which they are most responsive, so that an image moving in any direction within a given retinal area will activate some cell which has that as its optimal direction, plus other cells to a lesser extent.

A cell with a concentric inhibitory-excitatory receptive field, such as the cat ganglion cells discussed earlier, will respond to a moving stimulus: A spot of light moving from the inhibitory surround to the excitatory center will fire an on-center unit; moving the spot in the opposite direction, from the center to the surround, will inhibit the cell. However, the movement-sensitive cells differ in significant ways from the cells with concentric receptive fields, and cannot be explained on that basis. First of all, the concentric cells are not movement-sensitive in the true sense for they respond equally well to a stationary spot of light in the appropriate part of their receptive field, whereas the movement cells do not. Second, the response of the concentric-receptive field cell to movement is not really directional: An on-center cell will fire to a light coming toward the center from any direction and inhibit to light going away from the center in any direction. The movement cells fire to movement in a particular direction anywhere in the receptive field and inhibit to movement in the reverse direction anywhere in the receptive field. Third, a plot of the responses of a movement-sensitive cell to stationary flashes in various loci in the receptive field do not show a concentric organization to the field. Instead, brief on-off responses are given to flashes anywhere in the field, as seen in Fig. 9. Finally, the response of movement-sensitive cells is quite independent of the intensity or contrast of the moving object, or whether it is a dark object on a light ground or vice versa

(Barlow *et al.*, 1964; Lettvin *et al.*, 1959). This is not the case with the cells with concentric receptive fields: They respond in an opposite way to a light object moved across the field as to a dark object moved in the same plane.

Barlow, Hill, and Levick suggest that an interaction of excitation and inhibition which is not concentrically organized, but rather unilateral, could account for many of the characteristics of these movement-sensitive cells. Suppose that, as Barlow *et al.* suggest, an element at some level in the retina (*a*) had rapid adaptation (perhaps through recurrent inhibition, but in any case resulting in a lack of response to steady stimulation), (*b*) exerted an inhibitory effect on the elements to the right of it, say, and was itself inhibited by elements to its left, and (*c*) that inhibitory effects had a longer time delay than the excitatory effects. Then an object moving to the right would successively stimulate elements which had been inhibited by the prior stimulation of elements to their left. The inhibition would cancel the straight-through excitatory effects of the stimulation, and the cell would be quiescent. An object moving to the left, however, would successively encounter elements which were not inhibited (for the inhibition would be going the opposite direction) and which were not desensitized by adaptation, so a large sustained response would be produced.

Such a mechanism should operate properly only for a certain range of speeds of movement. If an object moved too slowly in the inhibitory direction it would arrive after the inhibition had dissipated and thus fire the cell; if it moved too fast it would arrive before the inhibition had arrived and would also activate the later cell. Such indeed was found to be the case in the responses of the rabbit movement cells (Barlow *et al.*, 1964).

Such a mechanism could account for apparent as well as real movement—apparent movement being the case in which an object appears at point A, then some time later at point B some distance away, and is perceived to have moved continuously from A to B. If the lateral inhibition extends some distance across the retina, stimulation of one point then another distant point at the appropriate later time (depending upon the rate of conduction of the inhibitory effect) should have the same effect as continuous movement across the same region.

No direct evidence is available as to the precise nature of this unilateral excitatory-inhibitory interaction in the rabbit—and, presumably, frog—retina, nor as to which retinal structures are involved. However, the interaction must clearly occur before the ganglion cell level. It is unlikely, for several reasons, that a direct inhibition of one set of receptors by other receptors is involved. For one thing, if that were the case, the same receptors could not be used for the detection of movement in different directions, or used for any other sort of visual task. It would appear very probable, therefore, that the site of the interactions is in the region of the bipolar cells.

On the other hand, it is doubtful if any movement analysis takes place before the cortex in primate or other higher mammals. No cells have been found in the cat or monkey lateral geniculate nucleus which are specifically sensitive to movement (Hubel, 1963*); such cells have, however, been found in the cat visual cortex (Hubel & Wiesel, 1959). Although detailed studies are lacking, it is quite possible that the basic mechanism operating may be the same. Human psychophysical evidence (Barlow & Brindley, 1963) also points to the cortex as the likely locus of movement analysis.

It may appear strange that the higher animals take longer to do a certain type of data processing than do the more primitive frog and rabbit. While there are good reasons, discussed later, why this may well be a general rule of neural organization, in the specific case of movement detection a special consideration enters in, namely, eye movements. A rabbit moves its eyes but little and a frog almost not at all; both animals tend also to keep their bodies motionless for long periods of time. Movement of light across their retinae, therefore, is usually the result of an object moving in the visual environment. The same is certainly not true in primates: They are highly active and their eyes are highly mobile, so that a movement of light across the retina is more likely to be produced by eye or body movements than by movements in the environment. The analysis of movement information by the visual system must— and does—take into account the presence and extent of eye and other body movements. Only those displacements on the retina which are not attributable to body movements are perceived as moving objects. Now the relevant pieces of information for this calculation are the commands sent out to the eye and other body muscles, which originate in the cortex, and the retinal loci of activity, which are projected topographically to the cortex. In the

---

* W. R. Mead, personal communication. Results supported those of Hubel.

primate, therefore, the logical place to perform an analysis of movement, which involves coordinating these two kinds of information, would be at the cortex.

IV. SUMMARY

The basic sensory neural process which we have seen to operate in the visual system is that of an interaction among the various excitatory and inhibitory inputs which converge onto a cell. Depending upon the nature of the inputs, on whether both excitation and inhibition or just one or the other are involved, on whether the inhibition is presynaptic or postsynaptic, and on whether the origin of the input is symmetrical, unilateral, or recurrent, a vast number of different kinds of analyses can take place, resulting in the vast complexities of our perceptual behavior. The convergence of several excitatory inputs, or of several inhibitory inputs, produces a summation of the different inputs. This is used in the visual system to increase sensitivity to dim light, to average over a number of units to reduce variability, and to provide a measure of the average light level (adaptation level). Summation is also used to produce a kind of coincidence meter, in which the later neuron fires, if and only if, certain preceding neurons are active, thus providing the basis for neurons only responsive to certain shapes, for instance. The convergence of both excitation and inhibition onto a neuron provides the mechanism for subtracting quantities, of dividing one thing by another, and differentiating sharply among various stimulus conditions. We have seen how this process is used in the visual system to provide for vision over a wide intensity range through adaptation, the response of a receptor being divided by that of surrounding receptors before being passed on to subsequent stages. Such interaction between excitation and inhibition also produces neurons sensitive to particular colors, to movement, and to the presence of contours in the visual field.

The neural activity evoked in the visual receptors by light passes through two or more synapses in the retina, one or more in the thalamus, and a dozen or more in the cortex. At each of these synapses there is a convergence of inputs and some sort of processing of the visual information. By the time the light stimuli are perceived and responded to, the information has passed sequentially through a great many stages of analysis. This fact is not generally considered in theories of vision, which often hypothesize in effect one or, at most, two stages of analysis. The types of data processing which take place at successive stages in the sequence can be investigated by single-cell recording from different levels in the visual system; it can also be tackled in psychophysical experiments in which successively more complex stimuli and responses are involved. Our discussions of some of these experiments indicate that in the primate visual system one of the earliest, if not the first, stages involves the inhibition of each receptor by every other receptor of its type in the vicinity (adaptation and contrast). We know that in addition there is within the retinal portion of the visual system the summation of neighboring receptors of all types (brightness), the subtraction of the output of receptors of one class from the output of receptors of another class (color), and a simple concentric inhibitory and excitatory spatial organization of nearby cells. The more complex transformations which take place in the primate cortex are less well known but must involve processing with respect to form and movement, as we have mentioned.

It has been emphasized that at each stage of analysis there is a convergence of information from many earlier elements. Each analysis also involves a loss of information: A neuron acts in effect as a filter which allows certain events to pass through and excludes others. For instance, a brightness system summing across many receptors loses information on which particular receptors were stimulated; a concentric spatial organization with combined excitation and inhibition throws away information on the absolute amount of activity, reporting just the extent to which the activity in one area exceeds that in another, etc. Once the receptor output has been analyzed in one way or another, it is not possible to retrieve the information as to what the initial receptor output had been. It would therefore not be possible at some later point in the neural pathway to process the information for a different sort of relationship among the receptors; sequential processing along different parameters is not possible. Multiple channels in parallel are clearly needed in order to have information about many different aspects of the visual image; the receptor output can then be analyzed for several different types of information simultaneously at the same level. Anatomical divergence, the connections which one receptor makes with several bipolars, and each bipolar with several ganglion cells, provides for such parallel information analysis. Processing the receptor output in different ways along parallel channels, in which each cell leads to several others, these in turn each connecting to still others, soon demands a great number of cells. The cerebral cortex of higher mammals has doubtless evolved into a vast network containing billions of cells to serve just this need.

An animal such as man, possessing such a great capacity for data processing, would presumably do only the most general preliminary sorts of analyses early in the sensory pathway since, as we have seen, analyzing for one thing involves throwing away information about others. Apparently in the primate retina the receptor output is only processed in a few basic ways; the more complex and specific types of analyses await the multiple channels in the cortex. More primitive animals, lacking the multiplicity of neurons required for multiple analyses along many parameters, must specialize in certain types of visual information and process the receptor output rapidly. Thus movement analysis takes place in the frog (which has no cortex) at an early retinal level—but the penalty the frog pays for this early specialization is that of being virtually blind to any nonmoving object.

REFERENCES

Alpern, M., & Rushton, W. A. H. The specificity of the cone interaction in the after-flash effect. *J. Physiol. (London)*, 1965, **176**, 473–482.

Barlow, H. B., & Brindley, G. S. Inter-ocular transfer of movement after-effects during pressure blinding of the stimulated eye. *Nature*, 1963, **200**, 1347.

Barlow, H. B., & Sparrock, J. M. B. The role of afterimages in dark adaptation. *Science*, 1964, **144**, 1309–1314.

Barlow, H. B., Hill, R. M., & Levick, W. R. Retinal ganglion cells responding selectively to direction and speed of image movement in the rabbit. *J. Physiol. (London)*, 1964, **173**, 377–407.

Boynton, R. M., & Gordon, J. Bezold-Brücke hue shift measured by color-naming technique. *J. opt. Soc. Amer.*, 1965, **55**, 78–86.

Brown, K. T., & Murakami, M. Biphasic form of the early receptor potential of the monkey retina. *Nature*, 1964, **204**, 739–740.(a)

Brown, K. T., & Murakami, M. Receptive field organization of s-potentials and receptor potentials in light and dark adapted states. *Fed. Proc.*, 1964, **23**, 517.(b)

Cohen, A. I. Vertebrate retinal cells and their organization. *Bio. Rev. Camb. phil. Soc.*, 1963, **38**, 427–459.

Cornsweet, T. N., & Teller, D. Y. Relation of increment thresholds to brightness and luminance *J. opt. Soc. Amer.*, 1965, **55**, 1303–1308.

De Valois, R. L. Behavioral and electrophysiological studies of primate vision. *Contr. sensory Physiol.*, 1965, **1**, 137–178.

De Valois, R. L. Analysis and coding of color vision in the primate visual system. *Cold Spr. Harb. Sympos. quant. Biol.*, 1966, **30**, 567–579.

De Valois, R. L., Smith, C. J., Kitai, S. T., & Karoly, A. J. Response of single cells in monkey lateral geniculate nucleus to monochromatic light. *Science*, 1958, **127**, 238–239.

De Valois, R. L., Jacobs, G. H., & Jones, A. E. Responses of single cells in primate red-green color vision system. *Optik*, 1963, **20**, 87–98.

De Valois, R. L., Abramov, I., & Jacobs, G. H. Analysis of response patterns of LGN cells. *J. opt. Soc. Amer.*, 1966, in press.

Ditchburn, R. W. Eye-movements in relation to perception of colour. In National Physical Laboratory Symposium, *Visual problems of colour*, Vol. 11, No. 8. London: H. M. Stationery Office, 1958.

Granit, R. *Receptors and sensory perception.* New Haven, Conn.: Yale Univer. Press, 1955.

Hartline, H. K., & Graham, C. H. Nerve impulses from single receptors in the eye of Limulus. *Proc. Soc. exp. Biol. Med.*, 1932, **29**, 613–615.

Hubel, D. H. Integrative processes in central visual pathways of the cat. *J. opt. Soc. Amer.*, 1963, **53**, 58–66.

Hubel, D. H., & Wiesel, T. N. Receptive fields of single neurons in the cat's striate cortex. *J. Physiol. (London)*, 1959, **148**, 574–591.

Hubel, D. H., & Wiesel, T. N. Receptive fields and functional architecture in two nonstriate visual areas (18 & 19) of the cat. *J. Neurophysiol.*, 1965, **28**, 229–289.

Hubel, D. H., & Wiesel, T. N. Read at *Int. Organ. Pure Applied Biophys., Paris and Orsay, 1964*; Harmon, L. D., & Snell, F. M. *Science*, 1964, **146**, 278.

Jacobs, G. H. Single cells in squirrel monkey lateral geniculate nucleus with broad spectral sensitivity. *Vision Res.*, 1964, **4**, 221–232.

Jacobs, G. H., & De Valois, R. L. Chromatic opponent cells in squirrel monkey lateral geniculate nucleus. *Nature*, 1965, **206**, 487–489.

Kuffler, S. W. Neurons in the retina: organization, inhibition and excitation problems. *Cold Spr. Harb. Sympos. quant. Biol.*, 1952, **17**, 281–292.

Lettvin, J. Y., Maturana, H. R., McCulloch, W. S., & Pitts, W. H. What the frog's eye tells the frog's brain. *Proc. Inst. Radio Engrs. N.Y.*, 1959, **47**, 1940–1951.

Lipetz, L. E. A neural mechanism of the Purkinje shift. *Am. J. Optom.*, 1962, **39**, 188–194.

MacNichol, E. F., Jr. Retinal mechanisms of color vision. *Vision Res.*, 1964, **4**, 119–133.

Marks, W. B., Dobelle, W. H., & MacNichol, E. F., Jr. Visual pigments of single primate cones. *Science*, 1964, **143**, 1181–1183.

Pirenne, M. H. Some aspects of the sensitivity of the eye. *Ann. N.Y. Acad. Sci.*, 1958, **74**, 377–384.

Ratliff, F., & Hartline, H. K. The responses of *limulus* optic nerve fibers to patterns of illumination on the receptor mosaic. *J. gen. Physiol.*, 1959, **42**, 1241–1255.

Ratliff, F., Hartline, H. K., & Miller, W. H. Spatial and temporal aspects of retinal inhibitory interaction. *J. opt. Soc. Amer.*, 1963, **53**, 110–121.

Riggs, L. A., Ratliff, F., Cornsweet, J. D., & Cornsweet, T. N. The disappearance of steadily fixated visual test objects. *J. opt. Soc. Amer.*, 1953, **43**, 495–501.

Rushton, W. A. H. The Ferrier Lecture, 1962. Visual adaptation. *Proc. roy. Soc.*, *1965*, **B162**, 20–46.

Sjöstrand, F. S. The ultrastructure of the inner segments of the retinal rods of the guinea-pig eye as revealed by electron microscopy. *J. cell. comp. Physiol.*, 1953, **42**, 45–70.

Stiles, W. S. Increment thresholds and the mechanisms of colour vision. *Docum. Ophthal.*, 1949, **3**, 138–165.

Svaetichin, G. Spectral response curves from single cones. *Acta physiol. Scand.*, 1956, **39,** Suppl. 134, 19–46.

Svaetichin, G., & MacNichol, E. F., Jr. Retinal mechanisms for chromatic and achromatic vision. *Ann. N.Y. Acad. Sci.*, 1958, **74**, 385–404.

Weale, R. A. Retinal summation and human visual thresholds. *Nature*, 1958, **181,** 154–156.

Wright, W. D. *Researches on normal and defective colour vision.* St. Louis: Mosby, 1947.

CHAPTER 4

Visual Mechanisms beyond the Striate Cortex

MORTIMER MISHKIN

Section on Neuropsychology,
National Institutes of Mental Health,
Bethesda, Maryland

I. Introduction

A monkey that has been trained to discriminate between a pair of visual patterns will lose this ability, and will have great difficulty reacquiring it, after bilateral removal of cortex along the inferior edge of the temporal lobe. The lesion does not encroach on striate cortex, and it need not invade the optic radiations; yet, except for the absence of visual field defects, the resulting deficit is often difficult to distinguish from the effects of just such damage to the visual system. Discrimination of two-dimensional patterns is perhaps most severely impaired visual ability, but impairment has also been demonstrated in the discrimination of object quality, in color, size, and brightness discrimination, and in critical flicker frequency. While the effect would appear from this to be widespread within vision, it does not seem to extend beyond it. Experiments have failed thus far to uncover any deficits analogous to the visual deficits in other sensory modalities.

The evidence leads to the puzzling conclusion that a cortical region some distance removed from the primary visual area, and having no known direct connections with it, is the site of an important focus for visual functions. This chapter describes a search for a neural explanation of this phenomenon. Specifically, the goal was to identify the pathway mediating the presumed interaction between the inferotemporal area and the visual system. Before turning to these recent experiments, however, it would be well to review briefly the history of the problem, beginning with the discovery of a "visual area" in the temporal lobes.

II. LOCALIZATION STUDIES

Two lines of evidence led to the discovery. The first was the report by Klüver and Bucy (1939) of some dramatic changes in the behavior of monkeys following bilateral temporal lobectomy. Perhaps the most striking effect of the operation was the defect which Klüver and Bucy referred to as "psychic blindness," connoting an inability of their monkeys to recognize objects by vision alone. However, symptoms of agnosia were not limited to vision, nor was the temporal lobe syndrome confined to symptoms of agnosia; there were many other complex changes such as increased tameness, changes in dietary habits, and hypersexuality. Klüver (1952) considered the visual disturbance to be but one manifestation of a more profound disturbance in behavior, and he cautioned against the hypothesis that the component symptoms could be independently produced.

The second line of evidence stemmed indirectly from Lashley's (1948) study in monkeys of the effects of preoccipital lesions. In this investigation, Lashley failed to obtain any support for the classical view that the prestriate cortex serves "visuopsychic" or visual associative functions. Partly as a result of these negative findings, Blum, Chow, and Pribram (1950), working in Lashley's laboratory, turned to an investigation of the effects of a more radical removal; their lesion included the preoccipital area, but it also extended anteriorly into other parietal and temporal areas without invading any of the primary sensory projection fields. Using a battery of tests ranging from simple through complex visual, tactual, auditory, and gustatory discriminations, these authors found consistent deficits on the visual problems together with less consistent deficits on the others. Again, as with Klüver's interpretation of the temporal lobe syndrome, Lashley (1950) attributed the effects of the extensive neocortical removal to a basic disorder in behavior which could probably not be fractionated further.

Nevertheless, an attempt to locate a more circumscribed area selectively related to visual functions was carried on by a number of investigators (Chow, 1951; Mishkin, 1954; Mishkin & Pribram, 1954). The impetus for the search came from a comparison between the two sets of earlier results which suggested that such an area might be contained in the region of overlap between the temporal lobectomies and the large neocortical lesions. The later experiments confirmed the suggestion and they led, by a series of approximations, to a delineation of the focus as the inferior temporal convexity comprising the middle and inferior temporal convolutions: Lesions of this area consistently resulted in visual impairments; lesions of the same size sparing this area had either negative or negligible effects. Regions in which damage was found to be relatively ineffective included the superior temporal convolution, the temporal pole, subcortical structures such as the amygdala and hippocampus, the posterior parietal cortex, and, according to some investigators but not all, the prestriate area. The conflicting evidence regarding the effects of prestriate lesions will be considered in detail shortly.

III. Behavioral Analyses

It is important to make clear that the deficit produced by inferotemporal removals is not the dramatic derangement in visually guided behavior that had been observed after the larger ablations. Monkeys with the selective lesion do not display the signs of visual agnosia, such as repeated and indiscriminate examination of objects, or loss of fear reactions to previously aversive stimuli, seen in animals with temporal lobectomy; nor do they exhibit the signs of spatial disorientation sometimes seen after the extensive posterior neocortical ablations. To gross observation, the inferotemporal monkey is indistinguishable from the normal; its visual discrimination impairment becomes evident only in more formal training situations. In view of the relatively subtle nature of the disorder, the results of the localization studies left open the possibility that inferotemporal lesions had a generalized, cross-modal effect similar to that of the larger lesions but one that would take careful testing to detect.

As already indicated, however, the deficit has turned out on further investigation to be surprisingly specific. Tactual, auditory, and olfactory discrimination, evaluated by methods analogous to those used in evaluating visual discrimination, are apparently unaffected by the lesion (Brown, 1963; Brown, Rosvold, & Mishkin, 1963; Pasik, T. Pasik, Battersby, & Bender, 1958; H. Pribram & Barry, 1956; Weiskrantz & Mishkin, 1958; M. Wilson, 1957). It is unlikely that these negative findings in inferotemporal monkeys reflect the use of insensitive or otherwise inadequate tests of discrimination ability, since the same tests have yielded positive findings in monkeys with other cortical lesions. Of particular interest is the fact that discrimination losses in audition and olfaction have been obtained from lesions placed immediately dorsal and rostral, respectively, to the inferotemporal area (Rosvold & Mishkin, 1966; Rosvold, Vest, Mishkin, & Brown, 1966). The absence of such losses after inferotemporal lesions, despite severe and often permanent visual losses, presents a striking contrast indicative of a high degree of functional specialization.

The apparent selectivity of the impairment poses the difficult problem of defining precisely what role this area plays in visual functions. Because the disorder generally is reflected as a failure to retain visual discriminations or as a retardation in acquiring them, it might appear, superficially at least, that the inferotemporal cortex is the locus of visual habit formation. However, as pointed out repeatedly by Lashley (1950), the undeniable complexity of even the simplest memory trace makes it improbable that a small area of association cortex could serve as the storehouse for specific habits or engrams. The anti-localizationist positions of Lashley and Klüver, alluded to earlier, were adopted perhaps more in opposition to this aspect of the classical doctrine than to the view that small cortical fields might turn out to be highly specialized in their functions.

At the opposite extreme from the notion that the inferotemporal cortex contains the engrams for visual habits is the possibility that it contributes significantly to basic sensory processes. However, there is little reason to suppose that an area outside the primary visual system would be fundamentally involved in such functions, and in this instance there is direct behavioral evidence against the supposition. Sensory disturbances such as field defects, acuity losses, or markedly raised visual thresholds have not been demonstrated in inferotemporal animals (Cowey & Weiskrantz, 1963; Mishkin & Weiskrantz, 1959; Weiskrantz & Cowey, 1963; W. A. Wilson & Mishkin, 1959). Furthermore, animals having such defects, as a result, for example, of partial removals of the striate cortex, have been found to be less impaired than inferotemporal animals on a variety of visual tasks (Butter, Mishkin, & Rosvold, 1964; W. A. Wilson & Mishkin, 1959).

These considerations serve to narrow somewhat the limits within which it may be profitable to speculate, but they do not directly suggest a positive formulation of the impairment. Nor have further attempts at behavioral analysis yielded results which provide convincing support for one interpretation over others (Chow & Orbach, 1957; Ettlinger, 1959b; Ettlinger, 1962; Mishkin & Hall, 1955; T. Pasik, P. Pasik, Battersby, & Bender, 1958; Pribram & Mishkin, 1955; Pribram & Mishkin, 1956; Stepien, Cordeau, & Rasmussen, 1960). This difficulty in defining the nature of the inferotemporal area's contribution to vision may reflect, at least in part, the tendency to frame hypotheses in terms of traditional psychological categories such as perception, attention, recent memory, and the like—categories which, just as habit formation, may correspond better to the integrated function of a widespread neural system than to the specific contribution made by a discrete area of the cortex. Should this prove to be the case, it may be extremely difficult to develop the proper behavioral concept without some understanding of the underlying neural mechanisms. Even if such information is not a prerequisite, a description of inferotemporal function is likely to remain imprecise until the particular mechanism by which the function is accomplished has been specified. As a first step toward unraveling these neural processes, the mystery surrounding the inferotemporal area's participation in vision must be resolved. This, too, has proved to be a difficult problem, but one that now seems close to a satisfactory solution.

IV. POSSIBLE NEURAL PATHWAYS

Earlier studies explored the possibility that the interaction between the inferotemporal area and the visual system might be critically dependent on certain subcortical structures. For example, the pulvinar nucleus of the thalamus, which has long been thought to receive direct or indirect visual afferents, sends a projection to the temporal neocortex (Chow, 1950). The temporal neocortex, in turn, sends a projection to the superior colliculus (Whitlock & Nauta, 1956), an important mesencephalic visuomotor center. However, studies designed to evaluate their roles as essential subcortical relays failed to demonstrate any visual discrimination impairment as a result of damaging these two structures, either singly (Chow, 1954; Rosvold, Mishkin, & Szwarcbart, 1958) or in combination (Rosvold & Mishkin, 1966). Because total destruction of these nuclei was not achieved, the negative findings are not necessarily conclusive. At the same time, it may be pointed out that negative results were obtained in cases in which the damage was estimated to be 80% complete. The existence of an essential subcortical relay is placed further in doubt by a recent report (Chow, 1961) that partially undercutting the inferior temporal convexity so as to sever most of its direct subcortical connections leaves visual discrimination performance unaffected.

The evidence presented above against a subcortical pathway is only slightly more convincing than that which may be adduced against a cortical pathway. Although the inferotemporal area does not appear to receive a direct projection from the striate cortex, or to send such a projection to it, data from neuroanatomical (Clark, 1942; Mettler, 1935a; Mettler, 1935b) and strychnine neuronographic studies (Bailey, Von Bonin, Davis, Garol, & McCulloch, 1944; Petr, Holden, & Jirout, 1949; Von Bonin, Garol, & McCulloch, 1942) suggest that the two areas may be interconnected indirectly through prestriate cortex. However, the possibility that the prestriate region mediates the interaction between the inferotemporal area and the visual system was rendered unlikely, even before it became an issue, by the negative results of Lashley's prestriate study referred to earlier. Furthermore, subsequent experiments involving more extensive prestriate destruction than in Lashley's study likewise failed to reveal impairments on visual tasks (Chow, 1952; Evarts, 1952; Meyer, Harlow, & Ades, 1951; Riopelle, Harlow, Settlage, & Ades, 1951; M. Wilson, Wilson, & Chiang, 1963). Intermixed with these negative findings, however, are several reports indicating that prestriate removals may produce visual impairments under special conditions (Ades, 1946; Ades & Raab, 1949; Riopelle & Ades, 1953; M. Wilson & Wilson, 1962). Thus, discrimination deficits have been observed in naive animals but not in sophisticated animals, or in postoperative learning but not in retention. These findings have been extremely difficult to interpret. If the prestriate cortex were an essential link in a striate-inferotemporal pathway, damaging this link would be expected to yield effects approximately equivalent to those produced by damaging the areas it interconnects. Instead, prestriate lesions appear to produce, at most, comparatively mild effects, suggesting that the prestriate region is only marginally involved in visual discrimination functions. Even this degree of participation is open to question since such deficits as have been reported could easily have arisen not from the intended lesion, but from encroachment on striate or inferotemporal tissue adjacent to the prestriate area, or on the visual radiations coursing directly below it. Viewed in any of these ways, the findings would seem to argue strongly against a striate-prestriate-inferotemporal pathway.

However, in the absence of any evidence pointing to an alternative pathway, still another interpretation of these minor deficits should be considered. It is conceivable that prestriate cortex is characterized, at least with respect to a relay function, by a high degree of equipotentiality. According to this notion, extensive but subtotal damage would impair transmission without disrupting it completely. A similar proposal might be advanced in favor of a subcortical pathway, except that, as already noted, not even minor deficits have been reported after extensive damage to potential subcortical relays. Although the argument was a tenuous one, it indicated that a cortical pathway could not yet be entirely ruled out and that the hypothesis merited reexamination.

V. CROSSED-LESION EXPERIMENT

To attempt once more to interrupt cortico-cortical connections by ablating the prestriate region seemed unprofitable in view of the difficulty of destroying this area completely without critically damaging surrounding visual structures. An alternative approach was therefore adopted (Mishkin, 1958; Mishkin, 1962) which involved the combination of lesions shown in the diagram of Fig. 1. The first stage of the operation consisted of a unilateral inferotemporal resection, followed in the second stage by a contralateral occipital lobectomy. If in such a preparation there is a *cortical* interaction between the intact striate area of one hemisphere and

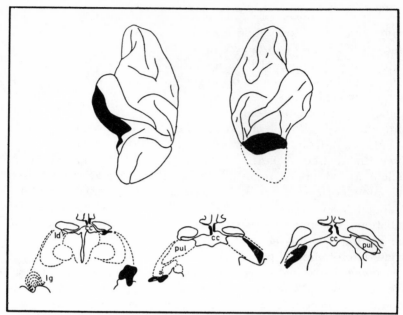

FIG. 1. Reconstructions of the cortical lesions and cross sections through the corpus callosum and thalamus of an experimental animal. Lesions and retrograde degeneration are shown in black. Note the complete degeneration of the lateral geniculate nucleus on the side of the occipital lobectomy, and the degeneration in the posterior tip of the pulvinar on the side of the inferotemporal resection.

the intact inferotemporal area of the other, then this interaction should be completely disrupted by sectioning the corpus callosum in the third stage. The advantage of the method was that it offered the possibility of severing an essential visual pathway without endangering the primary visual system.

The three-stage experiment was performed in the following way. Unoperated monkeys were trained in a Wisconsin General Test Apparatus (Harlow, 1949) on a simultaneous visual pattern discrimination. The stimuli consisted of a plus sign (the positive cue) and an outline of a square (the negative cue), each a white paper cutout mounted on a 3 by 3 in. gray cardboard plaque. The two plaques served as covers for food wells spaced 14 in. apart, and the positions of the plaques were interchanged from trial to trial in accordance with a Gellerman (1933) series. Training was presented for 30 trials a day to a criterion of 90 correct responses in 100 trials; this was followed two weeks later by a retention test presented to the same criterion. The animals were then given the first-stage lesion—either a unilateral inferotemporal resection or, as a control, a unilateral frontal resection—allowed two weeks to recover, and then retested. Assuming that each striate area has indirect cortical connections with both inferotemporal areas, the first stage of the experiment may be viewed as a test of the effects of destroying two of these four connections. As illustrated in Fig. 2, and in line with results obtained earlier in animals with unilateral inferotemporal lesions (Mishkin & Pribram, 1954), this amount of damage to the system had no detectable effect.

After a two-week interval and another retention test, the animals were subjected to the second-stage lesion. The operation involved a partial occipital lobectomy followed by a resection of all the striate cortex spared by the lobectomy, including that portion

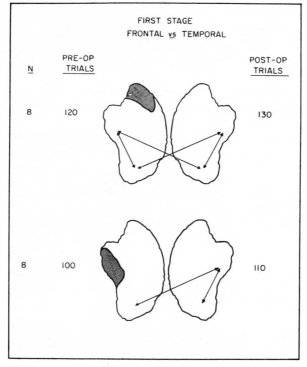

FIG. 2. Discrimination retention before and after the first-stage lesion. In this and in the following figures, N equals number of animals; arrows denote hypothetical connections left intact by the lesions; scores are group medians and include the 100-trial criterion run; an underlined score denotes impairment; and F indicates failure to relearn within the limits of training.

buried in the rostral part of the medial calcarine sulcus. In half
the animals of each of the original groups this second lesion was
placed on the same side as the first, while in the others it was placed
on the opposite side. The hypothetical cortical connections remaining after the complete unilateral striate removals are shown in the
diagrams of Fig. 3. As may be seen by the postoperative retention
scores, those control animals in which the lobectomy was presumed
to have reduced four connections to two showed little or no impairment. Even a single connection proved adequate provided that it
was intrahemispheric. By contrast, when the residual connection
crossed from one hemisphere to the other, as was assumed to be
the case in the experimental group, a marked impairment appeared.

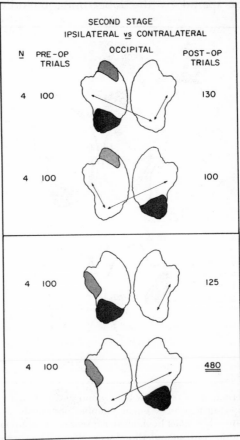

FIG. 3. Discrimination retention before and after the second-stage lesion.

A differential result at this stage of the experiment had not been anticipated. What it seemed to suggest was that crossed striate and inferotemporal areas were less well integrated than uncrossed, and, by implication, that the interaction between the two cortical areas was indeed of considerable importance. However, whether such interaction was mediated by a cortical pathway remained to be determined in the third stage.

To insure that all groups were performing satisfactorily prior to the callosal transection they were given another two-week rest followed by another retention test. As shown in Fig. 4, all groups,

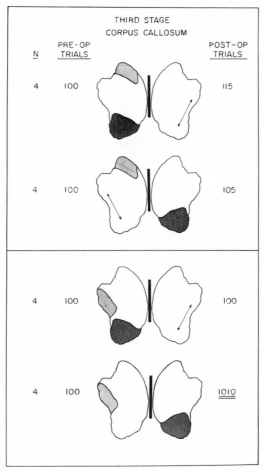

FIG. 4. Discrimination retention before and after the third-stage lesion.

including the experimental group, reattained criterion within the minimum number of trials before the final operation. Furthermore, the three control groups, now left with but one ipsilateral connection each, continued to perform at the same high level after operation. Nevertheless, sectioning the corpus callosum in the experimental animals had the effect of disrupting their performance completely.

The severity of the effect is shown graphically in Fig. 5. The final result is particularly striking in that, first, all animals had been given identical lesions at this stage, and second, all had met the discrimination criterion several times before. Overtraining to this extent is known to attenuate the effects of bilateral inferotemporal lesions (Chow & Survis, 1958; Orbach & Fantz, 1958), and it undoubtedly accounts for the gradual improvement in performance shown by the control animals over the course of the present study. Despite the overtraining, however, and despite a combination of lesions which differed only slightly from that given each of the three control groups, the experimental animals showed a stepwise deterioration in performance until at the last they had difficulty in

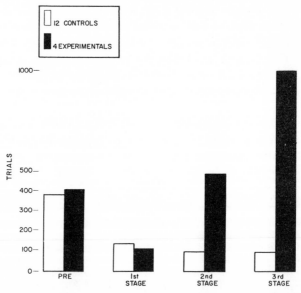

FIG. 5. Recapitulation of results, comparing the experimental animals with all others on initial learning (pre) and on retention after each of the three lesions.

relearning the discrimination at all. The result strongly supported the view that the callosal transection in the experimental group had isolated the inferotemporal area from the visual system by cutting its last cortical connection with the striate area.*

VI. CONTROL EXPERIMENTS

Because this positive finding followed the long series of negative findings described earlier, it seemed especially important to examine the new evidence critically for possible experimental artifacts. One such possibility was suggested by the unanticipated group differences that had been found after the occipital lobectomy. The experimental animals had sustained their first loss at this stage, and although they then showed an apparently complete and lasting recovery, it was conceivable that their discrimination habit was now a fragile one, vulnerable to any additional brain damage—not to callosal damage alone. To explore this question further, another group of animals was trained and operated through the second stage according to the same procedures as those used for the experimental group in the original study. A comparison was then made of the effects of three different third-stage lesions: unilateral ablation of the cingulate gyrus, transection of the anterior third of the corpus callosum, and transection of the posterior third. The results, shown in Fig. 6, indicated that the critical lesion was limited not only to the corpus callosum but to its posterior segment, a finding in keeping with the probable route of an interhemispheric visual pathway.

The evidence for a posterior callosal pathway was also compatible, however, with still another interpretation of the deficit, this one related to the unilateral visual neglect resulting from an occipital lobectomy. Although they were free to move about the testing cage, and might thus have been expected to compensate quickly for their hemianopia, the animals with crossed temporal and occipital lesions persisted in responding to the stimulus plaque

* In an experiment undertaken independently of the one reported here, Ettlinger (1959a) found a severe deficit in visual pattern discrimination in monkeys given combined callosal transection, unilateral inferotemporal ablation, and (in place of a contralateral occipital lobectomy) complete section of the contralateral optic tract. Ettlinger's results complement those described above and strengthen the argument for the proposed cortical pathway.

which fell in their intact visual field. As a result of this position preference, they may have in effect spontaneously converted the simultaneous "go left–go right" discrimination into a successive "go–no go" discrimination, a task to which even normal animals have difficulty in transferring after having just been trained to respond on every trial (Pribram & Mishkin, 1955). In the case of the

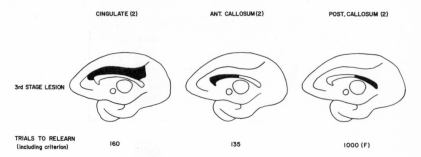

CINGULATE (2)   ANT. CALLOSUM (2)   POST. CALLOSUM (2)

3rd STAGE LESION

TRIALS TO RELEARN
(including criterion)   160   135   1000 (F)

FIG. 6. Discrimination retention following differential third-stage lesions.

crossed-lesion animals, reacquisition of the discrimination habit in the second stage of the experiment presumably involved learning, in successive steps, to refrain from responding to their preferred side when the negative stimulus was presented there, to shift to their nonpreferred side to obtain the reward, and finally, to examine the stimulus on their nonpreferred side before making a choice. If learning to look toward their blind field involved bilateral integration of the eye movement functions of the prestriate area (Crosby & Henderson, 1948; Wagman, Krieger, & Bender, 1958), a speculative but perhaps not an unreasonable proposal, then sectioning the posterior portion of the corpus callosum may have impaired their discrimination performance simply because it interfered with this compensatory visuomotor mechanism. In support of such an analysis, the callosal transections in the crossed-lesion animals resulted in even stronger position habits than were observed before.

The line of reasoning outlined above led to the following test. A new group of monkeys was trained from the beginning to perform a successive go–no go discrimination, that is, to respond or not within five seconds depending on whether the single food well being used was covered by the positive or by the negative pattern.

Half of the animals were trained on this task using the food well that would fall postoperatively in their blind field (the other well was empty and uncovered), while the others were trained in the field that was to remain intact. In all other respects, the procedures were the same as those employed in the previous experiments. Figure 7 compares the results at the second stage of the new study

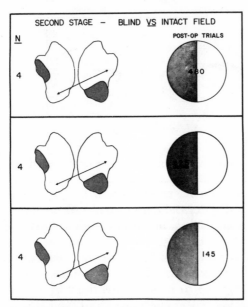

FIG. 7. Go–no go discrimination retention after the second-stage lesion—blind vs. intact field. Shaded half of circle represents defective field of vision. The group shown in the upper set of diagrams is the same as that shown in the lowest portion of Fig. 3.

with those obtained from the experimental group at the same stage in the initial study. Not only did the two new groups differ from each other in the expected direction, but also their scores fell on either side of the scores obtained by the original group, suggesting that the latter's performance on the simultaneous discrimination had indeed been affected by a unilateral visual neglect. It seemed at this point that an explanation in terms of visual neglect might prove adequate to account for all the results of the crossed-lesion experiments. As shown in Fig. 8, however, this did not turn out to

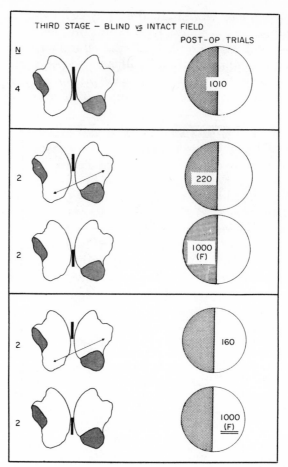

FIG. 8. Go–no go discrimination retention after the third-stage lesion—blind vs. intact field. Shaded half of circle represents defective field of vision. The group shown in the upper set of diagrams is the same as that shown in the lowest portion of Fig. 4.

be the case. Following posterior callosal transections, the animals that had been trained on their preferred side exclusively, and as a result had shown no difficulty in the earlier stages of the experiment, now exhibited a discrimination impairment as severe as that seen in animals trained on their nonpreferred side. Whether or not sectioning the posterior callosum exacerbated the symptom of neglect (a question which remains unanswered by these results), it was clear that a severe impairment in visual discrimination could be elicited as a completely independent effect.*

These several studies provided ample evidence that visual discrimination functions could be disrupted by a specific combination of lesions other than bilateral inferotemporal ablations. However, it was not yet clear how closely the deficits following these two types of brain damage resembled each other, and consequently, to what extent the results of the crossed-lesion experiments could be attributed to a functional ablation of the intact inferotemporal cortex. In order to obtain some preliminary evidence on this problem, the animals with crossed lesions from the preceding experiment were trained on an extended series of two-choice object quality discriminations and their scores compared with those obtained on the same discriminations by animals with bilateral inferotemporal lesions and by unoperated controls. The data for the latter two groups, as well as the methods used in testing, have already been reported (Mishkin, 1964). As may be seen in Fig. 9, comparison among the learning-set curves for all four groups yielded a gradient of impairment consistent with the different degrees of

* Still other controls for visual neglect were contained in the original crossed-lesion experiment. For example, the four animals comprising each of the four groups were preselected to include two animals that used the left hand predominantly and two that preferred the right; further, the laterality of the lesions was so arranged that within each subgroup of two, one animal was made hemianopic in the field ipsilateral to its preferred hand and the other in the contralateral field. All eight animals with defective vision on the side of their initially preferred hand shifted handedness by the end of the experiment, while only one of the other eight animals did so. However, no differential effect of the various combinations of hand and field preferences was observed on discrimination performance at any stage of the experiment.

At the conclusion of the discrimination phase of the study, the animals were trained on a visual spatial delayed response problem using a procedure which has been described in detail elsewhere (Battig, Rosvold, & Mishkin, 1960). The task was employed because of its known sensitivity to the effects of frontal lesions. The median number of trials up to and including criterion on 5-second delayed response was 450 for the group with crossed *frontal* and occipital lesions as compared with a median of 250 to 280 trials for each of the other groups including the one with crossed *temporal* and occipital lesions. A more severe delayed-response deficit, following a more complete isolation of an intact frontal lobe from cortically relayed visual inputs, was recently reported by Glickstein, Arora, and Sperry (1963). In addition to providing another control for visual neglect, these results demonstrate the same double dissociation of deficits after crossed lesions combined with commissurotomy as has previously been demonstrated after bilaterally symmetrical frontal and temporal lesions.

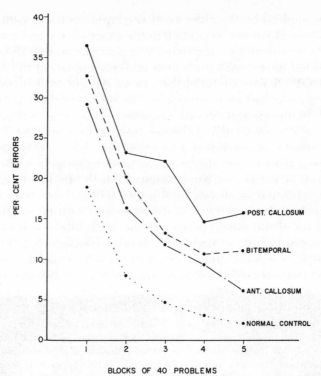

FIG. 9. Mean percentage of errors on a series of 200 11-trial object discriminations.

damage to the postulated visual system. Thus, the anterior callosal group, with an intact transcallosal pathway between one occipital lobe and the opposite inferotemporal area, though impaired relative to the normal animals, was somewhat less impaired than the bitemporal group. The bitemporal group, in turn, was somewhat less impaired than the posterior callosal group, a finding in line with the supposition that the performance of the latter reflected the combined effects of a unilateral occipital lobectomy *and* a functional bitemporal ablation. The fact that the scores of the two callosal groups differed nearly as much as the scores of the normal and bitemporal groups lends further support to the view that the posterior callosal transection effectively ended the participation of inferotemporal cortex in visual functions.

VII. THE PRESTRIATE RELAY

The behavioral evidence that had been gathered up to this point confirmed the existence of the indirect cortical pathway that had been implied by the older neuronographic and neuroanatomical literature. However, inasmuch as the exact source and termination of the connections comprising this pathway were still largely unknown, an anatomical study was undertaken, using the Nauta-Gygax (1954) silver stain technique, in an attempt to delineate the relevant connections more precisely. The results of the experiment have been reported in detail elsewhere (Kuypers, Szwarcbart, Mishkin, & Rosvold, 1965). Of major interest here was the finding that the striate area sends a projection not only to the banks of the lunate sulcus and to the preoccipital gyrus, that is, to the prestriate area as it has commonly been defined, but also to the annectant gyri in the depths of the parieto-occipital junction, to the caudal bank of the upper half of the superior temporal sulcus, and to the banks of the caudal portion of the intraparietal sulcus. This projection field of the striate cortex sends a projection, in turn, to an area in the temporal lobes which corresponds remarkably closely to the inferotemporal "visual area." An example of the cortical dis-

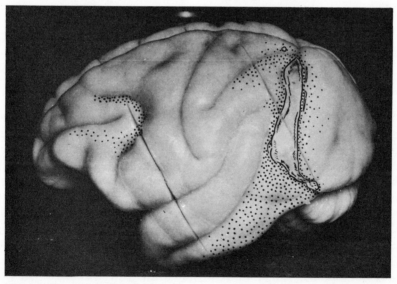

FIG. 10. Photograph of the brain of an operated monkey, showing the unilateral prestriate lesion (outlined) and the cortical distribution of degenerating fibers (stippled). In addition to heavy degeneration in the inferotemporal cortex, this preoccipital lesion led to degeneration in (a) the prefrontal area, particularly the prefrontal "eyefields," (b) intact portions of the prestriate region, including the area around the intraparietal sulcus, and possibly (c) the striate area, though only few scattered fibers were noted here.

tribution of preterminal fiber degeneration in an animal with a partial prestriate lesion is shown in Fig. 10.

The picture which emerges from these findings is that of a complex neural system in which each prestriate area serves as the essential link in a homolateral pathway, and, by virtue of their reciprocal connections across the posterior portion of the corpus callosum, as part of a dual link in the transcallosal pathway. The entire system is depicted schematically in Fig. 11 (top), while the

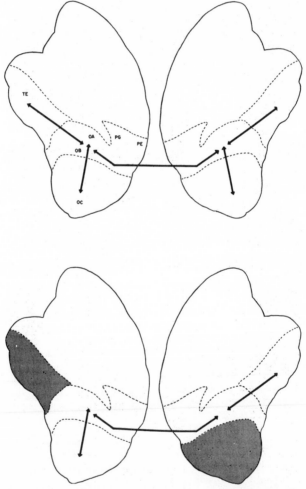

FIG. 11. Hypothetical pathways before and after a crossed striate-inferotemporal lesion. Letters refer to Von Bonin and Bailey's (1947) cytoarchitectural areas.

residual connection remaining after a crossed striate-inferotemporal lesion is shown in Fig. 11 (bottom). The schema suggests a further test of the proposed pathway, and, simultaneously, a new test of the relay function of the prestriate region. According to the schema, it should be possible to interrupt the critical connection in a third-stage lesion, not only by sectioning the posterior callosum but also by resecting the prestriate cortex on the side of the occipital lobectomy. The advantage of this method of investigating the postulated relay is that extensive prestriate ablations become possible, including complete destruction of the banks and depths of sulci, without the usual concern for incidental damage to the primary visual system.

That extensive prestriate ablations are necessary was made clear by the following experiments. In one group of crossed-lesion animals, the third-stage resection was limited largely to the preoccipital gyrus in an attempt to reproduce the prestriate lesions that had been performed in earlier studies. As may be seen in Fig. 12, neither a lesion of this type in the lobectomized hemisphere nor the addition of a symmetrical lesion in the opposite hemisphere had any detectable effect on the animals' performance. An impairment was observed, as in the earlier experiments, only when the posterior segment of the corpus callosum was cut. These results led to the attempt in a second experiment to remove not only the preoccipital gyrus but also the entire cortical area to which the striate cortex projects. When this more extensive lesion was made, the predicted effect appeared (see Fig. 13). Of particular interest was the finding that subsequent transection of the posterior callosum in this second series of animals had no additional effect. Taken together, the results of the two experiments demonstrate that negative or negligible effects of prestriate lesions can be traced to a failure to disrupt completely the critical striate-inferotemporal interaction. The difficulty in achieving complete disruption is in accord with the supposition made earlier that multiple pathways exist throughout the prestriate region, investing this area of association cortex with a high degree of equipotentiality. Nevertheless, the fact that an impairment can be produced by a sufficiently extensive ablation favors the view that the prestriate region is an essential part of the system.

In providing an explanation for the involvement of inferotemporal cortex in visual functions, this series of experiments has thus uncovered new evidence pointing to the importance for visual

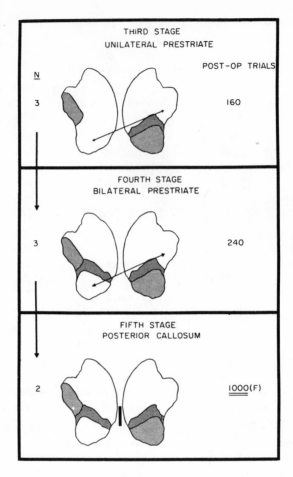

FIG. 12. Failure to interrupt the transcallosal pathway by partial prestriate lesions.

functions of the prestriate cortex. Indeed, the implication of the results is that the inferotemporal cortex cannot function without the prestriate. Although its role in vision has been overshadowed for many years by the more conspicuous role of the inferotemporal area, there is now reason to believe that it is the prestriate area which may provide the key to an understanding of inferotemporal function. In the context of the experiments described in this report, the prestriate region has been considered simply as a relay

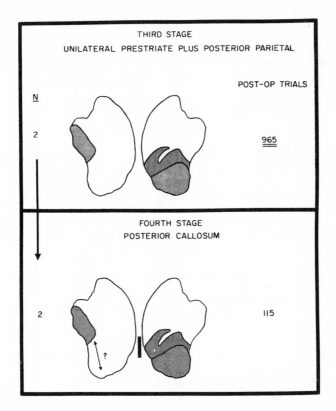

FIG. 13. Interruption of the transcallosal pathway by a unilateral lesion of the cortical projection of the striate area. The possibility that eventual recovery of the discrimination habit is mediated by the remaining prestriate area [a possibility indicated by the arrow in the lower diagram is currently being investigated.

for transmitting activity between the other components of the proposed cortical visual system. However, if, as now seems likely, the elaboration of visual mechanisms beyond the striate cortex begins in prestriate cortex, then it would seem that renewed efforts to investigate the function of this early stage in the system would yield some important clues to the contribution made by later stages.

ACKNOWLEDGMENT

The support and assistance of H. Enger Rosvold in all aspects of the work reported here are gratefully acknowledged.

REFERENCES

Ades, H. W. Effect of extirpation of parastriate cortex on learned visual discriminations in monkeys. *J. Neuropath. exp. Neurol.*, 1946, **5**, 60–65.

Ades, H. W., & Raab, D. H. Effect of preoccipital and temporal decortication on learned visual discrimination in monkeys. *J. Neurophysiol.*, 1949, **12**, 101–108.

Bailey, P., Von Bonin, G., Davis, E. W., Garol, H. W., & McCulloch, W. S. Further observations on association pathways in the brain of Macaca mulatta. *J. Neuropath. exp. Neurol.*, 1944, **3**, 413–415.

Battig, K., Rosvold, H. E., & Mishkin, M. Comparison of the effects of frontal and caudate lesions on delayed response and alternation in monkeys. *J. comp. physiol. Psychol.*, 1960, **53**, 400–404.

Blum, J. S., Chow, K. L., & Pribram, K. H. A behavioral analysis of the organization of the parieto-temporo-preoccipital cortex. *J. comp. Neurol.*, 1950, **93**, 53–100.

Brown, T. S. Olfactory and visual discrimination in the monkey after selective lesions of the temporal lobe. *J. comp. physiol. Psychol.*, 1963, **56**, 764–768.

Brown, T. S., Rosvold, H. E., & Mishkin, M. Olfactory discrimination after temporal lobe lesions in monkeys. *J. comp. physiol. Psychol.*, 1963, **56**, 190–195.

Butter, C. M., Mishkin, M., Rosvald, H. E. Stimulus generalization following inferotemporal and lateral striate lesions in monkeys. In D. Mostofsky (Ed.), *Stimulus generalization*. Stanford, Calif.: Stanford Univer. Press, 1964.

Chow, K. L. A retrograde cell degeneration study of the cortical projection field of the pulvinar in the monkey. *J. comp. Neurol.*, 1950, **93**, 313–340.

Chow, K. L. Effects of partial extirpation of posterior association cortex on visually mediated behavior in monkeys. *Comp. Psychol. Monogr.*, 1951, **20**, 187–217.

Chow, K. L. Further studies on selective ablation of associative cortex in relation to visually mediated behavior. *J. comp. physiol. Psychol.*, 1952, **45**, 109–118.

Chow, K. L. Lack of behavioral effects following destruction of some thalamic association nuclei in monkey. *A.M.A. Arch. Neurol. Psychiat.*, 1954, **71**, 762–771.

Chow, K. L. Anatomical and electrographical analysis of temporal neocortex in relation to visual discrimination learning in monkeys. In J. F. Delafresnaye (Ed.), *Brain mechanisms in learning*. Oxford, England: Blackwell, 1961.

Chow, K. L., & Orbach, J. Performance of visual discriminations presented tachistoscopically in monkeys with temporal neocortical ablations. *J. comp. physiol. Psychol.*, 1957, **50**, 636–640.

Chow, K. L., & Survis, J. Retention of overlearned visual habit after temporal cortical ablation in monkey. *A.M.A. Arch. Neurol. Psychiat.*, 1958, **79**, 640–646.

Clark, W. E. LeGros. The visual centers of the brain and their central connections. *Physiol. Rev.*, 1942, **22**, 205–232.

Cowey, A., & Weiskrantz, L. A perimetric study of visual field defects in monkeys. *Quart. J. exp. Psychol.*, 1963, **15**, 91–115.

Crosby, E. C., & Henderson, J. W. The mammalian midbrain and isthmus regions. Part II. Fiber connections of the superior colliculus. B. Pathways concerned in automatic eye movements. *J. comp. Neurol.*, 1948, **88**, 853–892.

Ettlinger, G. Visual discrimination following successive temporal ablations in monkeys. *Brain*, 1959, **82**, 232–250.(a)

Ettlinger, G. Visual discrimination with a single manipulandum following temporal ablation in the monkey. *Quart. J. exp. Psychol.*, 1959, **11**, 164–174.(b)

Ettlinger, G. Relationship between test difficulty and the visual impairment in monkeys with ablations of temporal cortex. *Nature*, 1962, **196**, 911–912.

Evarts, E. V. Effects of ablation of prestriate cortex in auditory-visual association in monkey. *J. Neurophysiol.*, 1952, **15**, 191–200.

Gellerman, L. W. Chance orders of alternating stimuli in visual discrimination experiments. *J. genet. Psychol.*, 1933, **42**, 206–208.

Glickstein, M., Arora, H. A., & Sperry, R. W. Delayed-response performance following optic tract section, unilateral frontal lesion, and commissurotomy. *J. comp. physiol. Psychol.*, 1963, **56**, 11–18.

Harlow, H. F. The formation of learning sets. *Psychol. Rev., 1949,* **56**, 51–65.

Klüver, H. Brain mechanisms and behavior with special reference to the rhinencephalon. *J.-Lancet*, 1952, **12**, 567–577.

Klüver, H., & Bucy, P. C. Preliminary analysis of functions of the temporal lobes in monkeys. *Arch. Neurol. Psychiat.*, 1939, **42**, 979–1000.

Kuypers, H. G. J. M., Szwarcbart, M. K., Mishkin, M., & Rosvold, H. E. Occipitotemporal corticocortical connections in the rhesus monkey. *Exp. Neurol.*, 1965, **11**, 245–262.

Lashley, K. S. The mechanism of vision: XVIII. Effects of destroying the visual "associative areas" of the monkey. *Genet. Psychol. Monogr.*, 1948, **37**, 107–166.

Lashley, K. S. In search of the engram. *Sympos. Soc. exp. Biol.*, 1950, **4**, 454–482.

Mettler, F. A. Corticifugal fiber connections of the cortex of Macaca mulatta. The occipital region. *J. comp. Neurol.*, 1935, **61**, 221–256.(a)

Mettler, F. A. Corticifugal fiber connections of the cortex of Macaca mulatta. The parietal region. *J. comp. Neurol.*, 1935, **62**, 263–291.(b)

Meyer, D. R., Harlow, H. F., & Ades, H. W. Retention of delayed responses and proficiency in oddity problems by monkeys with preoccipital ablations. *Amer. J. Psychol.*, 1951, **44**, 391–396.

Mishkin, M. Visual discrimination performance following partial ablations of the temporal lobe: II. Ventral surface vs. hippocampus. *J. comp. physiol. Psychol.*, 1954, **47**, 187–193.

Mishkin, M. Visual discrimination impairment after cutting cortical connections between the inferotemporal and striate areas in monkeys. *Amer. Psychologist*, 1958, **13**, 414. (Abstract)

Mishkin, M. A possible link between interhemispheric integration in monkeys and cerebral dominance in man. In V. B. Mountcastle (Ed.), *Interhemispheric relations and cerebral dominance*. Baltimore: Johns Hopkins Press, 1962.

Mishkin, M. Perseveration of central sets after frontal lesions in monkeys. In J. M. Warren & K. Akert (Eds.), *The frontal granular cortex and behavior*. New York: McGraw-Hill, 1964.

Mishkin, M., & Hall, M. Discrimination along a size continuum following ablation of the inferior temporal convexity in monkeys. *J. comp. physiol. Psychol.*, 1955, **48**, 97–101.

Mishkin, M., & Pribram, K. H. Visual discrimination performance following partial ablations of the temporal lobe: I. Ventral vs. lateral. *J. comp. physiol. Psychol.*, 1954, **47**, 14–20.

Mishkin, M., & Weiskrantz, L. Effects of cortical lesions in monkeys on critical flicker frequency. *J. comp. physiol. Psychol.*, 1959, **52**, 660–666.

Nauta, W. J. H., & Gygax, P. A. Silver impregnation of degenerating axons in the central nervous system. A modified technic. *Stain Tech.*, 1954, **29**, 91–94.

Orbach, J., & Fantz, R. L. Differential effects of temporal neo-cortical resections on overtrained and non-overtrained visual habits in monkeys. *J. comp. physiol. Psychol.*, 1958, **51**, 126–129.

Pasik, P., Pasik, T., Battersby, W. S., & Bender, M. B. Visual and tactual discrimination by Macaques with serial temporal and parietal lesions. *J. comp. physiol. Psychol.*, 1958, **51**, 427–436.

Pasik, T., Pasik, P., Battersby, W. S., & Bender, M. B. Target size and visual form discrimination in monkeys with bitemporal lesions. *Fed. Proc.*, 1958, **17**, 481. (Abstract)

Petr, R., Holden, L. B., & Jirout, J. The efferent intercortical connections of the superficial cortex of the temporal lobe in Macaca mulatta. *J. Neuropath. exp. Neurol.*, 1949, **8**, 100–103.

Pribram, H., & Barry, J. Further behavioral analysis of the parieto-temporo-preoccipital cortex. *J. Neurophysiol.*, 1956, **19**, 99–106.

Pribram, K. H., & Mishkin, M. Simultaneous and successive discrimination by monkeys with inferotemporal lesions. *J. comp. physiol. Psychol.*, 1955, **48**, 198–202.

Pribram, K. H., & Mishkin, M. Analysis of the effects of frontal lesions in monkey: III. Object alternation. *J. comp. physiol. Psychol.*, 1956, **49**, 41–45.

Riopelle, A. J., & Ades, H. W. Visual discrimination performance in rhesus monkeys following extirpation of prestriate and temporal cortex. *J. genet. Psychol.*, 1953, **83**, 63–77.

Riopelle, A. J., Harlow, H. F., Settlage, P. H., & Ades, H. W. Performance of normal and operated monkeys on visual learning tests. *J. comp. physiol. Psychol.*, 1951, **44**, 283–289.

Rosvold, H. E., & Mishkin, M. Effects of combined pulvinar and superior colliculus damage on visual discrimination in monkeys. Unpublished manuscript.

Rosvold, H. E., & Mishkin, M. Further analysis of the effects of frontal and temporal cortical lesions on auditory discrimination in monkeys. Unpublished manuscript.

Rosvold, H. E., Mishkin, M., & Szwarcbart, M. K. Effects of subcortical lesions in monkeys on visual-discrimination and single-alternation performance. *J. comp. physiol. Psychol.*, 1958, **51**, 437–444.

Rosvold, H. E., Vest, B., Mishkin, M., & Brown, T. S. Olfactory discrimination impairment after medial temporal cortical lesions in monkeys. Unpublished manuscript.

Stepien, L. S., Cordeau, J. P., & Rasmussen, T. The effect of temporal lobe and hippocampal lesions in auditory and visual recent memory in monkeys. *Brain*, 1960, **83**, 470–489.

Von Bonin, G., & Bailey, P. *The neocortex of Macaca mulatta*. Urbana, Ill.: Univer. of Illinois Press, 1947.

Von Bonin, G., Garol, H. W., & McCulloch, W. S. The functional organization of the occipital lobe. *Biol. Sympos.*, 1942, **7**, 165–192.

Wagman, I. H., Krieger, H. P., & Bender, M. B. Eye movements elicited by surface and depth stimulation of the occipital lobe of Macaca mulatta. *J. comp. Neurol.*, 1958, **109**, 169–193.

Weiskrantz, L., & Cowey, A. Striate cortex lesions and visual acuity of the rhesus monkey. *J. comp. physiol. Psychol.*, 1963, **56**, 225–231.

Weiskrantz, L., & Mishkin, M. Effects of temporal and frontal cortical lesions on auditory discrimination in monkeys. *Brain*, 1958, **81**, 406–414.

Whitlock, D. G., & Nauta, W. J. H. Subcortical projections from the temporal neocortex in macaca mulatta. *J. comp. Neurol.*, 1956, **106**, 183–212.

Wilson, M. Effects of circumscribed cortical lesions upon somesthetic and visual discrimination in the monkey. *J. comp. physiol. Psychol.*, 1957, **50**, 630–635.

Wilson, M., & Wilson, W. A. Intersensory facilitation of learning sets in normal and brain operated monkeys. *J. comp. physiol. Psychol.*, 1962, **55**, 931–934.

Wilson, M., Wilson, W. A., & Chiang, H. M. Formation of tactual learning sets. *J. comp. physiol. Psychol.*, 1963, **56**, 732–734.

Wilson, W. A., & Mishkin, M. Comparison of the effects of inferotemporal and lateral occipital lesions on visually guided behavior in monkeys. *J. comp. physiol. Psychol.*, 1959, **52**, 10–17.

CHAPTER 5

Physiological Mechanisms in Attention *,†

RAÚL HERNÁNDEZ-PEÓN

*Instituto de Investigaciones Cerebrales, A.C., Moras 445,
Mexico City, Mexico*

I. INTRODUCTION

The world in which we live is different for each of us. The reason for this difference stems from two well-known facts: (*a*) The perception of our physical environment is limited, and (*b*) The selection of the items perceived varies among different individuals according to their past experiences and to their present motivations.

* The preparation of this chapter was aided by the National Institute of Mental Health (U.S.P.H.S.) under Grant MH-10003-02.
† This chapter is not a review of the literature, but deals mainly with the author's contributions to the topic.

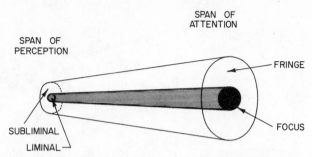

FIG. 1. Diagram showing the relationship between the span of attention and the span of perception. The objects located in the focus of attention are better perceived than those situated in the fringe of attention. (From Hernández-Peón, 1964b.)

Since attention is a necessary requirement for sensory perception and for all its behavioral consequences, perhaps it is not exaggerated to state that our own world and all our life experiences depend on selective states of attention. We can consider attention as the primary process underlying sensory perception, memory, and thinking, without which human life would be comparable to that of lower organisms.

Attention involves the selective passage of relevant sensory information to consciousness with simultaneous exclusion of insignificant signals. The selection of sensory signals accomplished by attention implies that the final integrative mechanisms involved in sensory perception can only handle a limited amount of sensory information at any given time. This limitation in the span of perception was well known by earlier psychologists many years ago, and it is closely related with the accuracy of perception. The finer our sensory discrimination by enhancement of attention, the smaller our span of perception. As illustrated schematically in Fig. 1, attention can be compared to a beam of light in which illumination is brighter in the center, *focus* of attention, than in the periphery, *fringe* of attention. Therefore, only the objects which occupy the focus of attention elicit a well-defined sensory perception, whereas the items located in the surrounding fringe produce a less accurate experience.

II. SENSORY INHIBITION

The question arises as to which are the neurophysiological mechanisms responsible for the limitation of the span of attention and of sensory perception. According to traditional concepts which

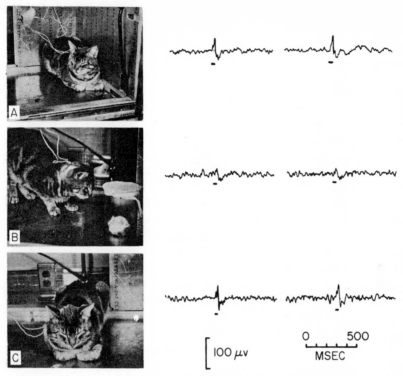

FIG. 2. Blocking effects of distraction upon click-evoked potentials recorded from the dorsal cochlear nucleus. When the cat appeared attentively looking at a pair of mice placed inside a jar, the auditory potentials were significantly reduced as compared to those recorded during relaxed wakefulness. (From Hernández-Peón *et al.*, 1956a.)

ascribed exclusive privileges to the cortex in all mental processes, the exclusion of irrelevant signals and the facilitation of relevant sensory information during attention would take place exclusively at the cortex. However, this concept is no longer tenable in the light of recent experimental evidence. Electrophysiological recordings made in awake animals with electrodes permanently implanted in their brains have permitted the exploration of sensory transmission at different levels of the various afferent pathways during the wakefulness continuum. The pioneer experiments of Hernández-Peón and Scherrer (1955) and of Hernández-Peón, Scherrer, and Jouvet (1956a) demonstrated significant changes of afferent signals in specific sensory pathways at a level as far down as the first sensory synapse. Figure 2 illustrates the effect of distraction upon click-evoked potentials recorded at the dorsal cochlear nucleus in an awake relaxed cat. When the cat was attentively looking at a pair of mice in a jar, the auditory-evoked potentials from the cochlear nucleus were significantly reduced. The auditory potentials recovered their original amplitude when the cat became relaxed again. Therefore, granting that the evoked potentials represent volleys of auditory impulses, the conclusion is warranted that most of those impulses did not reach the neuronal circuits involved in consciousness and perception. This finding explains similar situations often experienced by ourselves. For instance, we may not hear a loud noise behind us when we are reading an interesting book.

The above-mentioned effect, observed at the lowest level of the central auditory pathway during distraction, led us to explore whether the same phenomenon occurs in other afferent pathways. Indeed, similar results were obtained at the first synapse of the visual pathway (Palestini, Davidovich, & Hernández-Peón, 1959). By recording photic potentials evoked by flashes of light in the optic tract, which represents the axons of the ganglion cells of the retina, it was found that those potentials had a stable magnitude when the cat was in a state of relaxed wakefulness. However, when the animal was distracted by introducing fish odor into the cage, the potentials diminished, and they recovered when the cat was no longer sniffing. For exploring sensory transmission in the somatic paths, bipolar electrodes were implanted in the lateral columns of the spinal cord (Hernández-Peón, 1959; Hernández-Peón, 1961; Hernández-Peón & Brust-Carmona, 1961a). Tactile stimuli, single electric shocks of mild intensity, were applied when the cat was relaxed. Then, a rat inside a jar was presented to the cat, and at this moment the evoked potentials diminished or disappeared. A few seconds later, the rat was removed from the cat's sight, and, when the latter became relaxed again, the potentials recovered their original amplitude. It is evident that if the tactile impulses did not ascend through the spinal cord, they did not reach the supraspinal structures involved in conscious sensory perception. Therefore, it may be concluded that the tactile stimuli were not perceived by the cat when it was looking at the rat.

In another study, tactile- or nociceptive-evoked potentials were simultaneously recorded at the lowest and upper synapses of the trigeminal pathway by applying single electric rectangular pulses

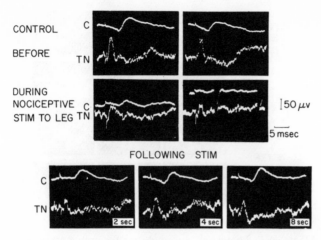

FIG. 3. Simultaneous recordings from the spinal trigeminal sensory nucleus *TN* and from the face area of the somatic sensory cortex *C*. The potentials were evoked by single shocks of mild nociceptive intensity applied to the skin of the face in a cat. The figure shows (from above downward) the potentials recorded during relaxed wakefulness, during the application of a series of painful electric shocks to a leg of the animal, and after the end of the latter stimulus. The potential was incompletely recovered 8 seconds after the end of the nociceptive stimulus.

to the skin of the face (Hernández-Peón, 1959; Hernández-Peón, 1961). After a control period of relaxed wakefulness, a train of electric shocks was applied to a limb of the cat which then presented a typical behavioral reaction to pain. Immediately after the end of the nociceptive stimuli, the potentials both in the bulbar synapse and at the cortex were considerably reduced. As shown in Fig. 3, several seconds elapsed before the potentials recovered. Therefore, reflex inhibition at the first sensory synapse can explain, at least partially, the suppression of a mild pain produced by another more painful stimulus arising in any other region of the body.

From the preceding experiments, it is evident that sensory impulses are blocked at the lowest levels of central sensory pathways when attention is focused upon a stimulus of a different sensory modality more significant than the test stimulus. But selective inhibitory mechanisms within a given sensory pathway must also function when attention is focused upon another stimulus of the same modality. We all have had the experience that when attending a motion picture we do not ordinarily perceive the frame of the screen. This psychological observation finds an explanation in the

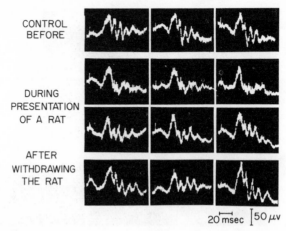

CONTROL
BEFORE

DURING
PRESENTATION
OF A RAT

AFTER
WITHDRAWING
THE RAT

20 msec |50 μv

FIG. 4. Photic-evoked potentials recorded from the optic tract in a cat with electrodes permanently implanted. Immediately after presentation of a rat, the late
waves were practically abolished (second row) and reappeared when the cat was
no longer attentive to the rat (third row). (From Palestini *et al.*, 1959).

following experimental results. By recording retinal photic-evoked
potentials in cats with electrodes permanently implanted in the
optic tract, Palestini *et al.* (1959) have observed that the potentials
were reduced, especially in the late waves, when a white rat, which
did not interfere with the intensity of the testing flash, was presented to the cat. After several seconds, the cat lost its interest in
the rat. In those circumstances, even though the physical conditions
were exactly the same, the potentials recovered a similar shape and
magnitude to that found when the cat was completely relaxed in
the absence of the rat. Figure 4 shows the sequence of changes
which occurred in the evoked potentials.

All these observations made in cats with electrodes permanently
implanted may raise doubts about whether these mechanisms also
exist in the human brain. Furthermore, only in the human being is
it possible to study some other varieties of attention which cannot
be studied in animals, such as voluntary attention to selected mental processes. With this aim, Hernández-Peón and Donoso (1957;
1959) recorded, in a few patients with deep electrodes, photic-
evoked potentials from the optic radiations. The electrodes were
implanted one or two days prior to the recordings; the potentials
were evoked by strong flashes of light. It was observed that the
size of the evoked potentials were significantly reduced during

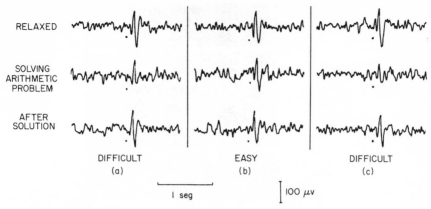

RELAXED

SOLVING
ARITHMETIC
PROBLEM

AFTER
SOLUTION

DIFFICULT   EASY   DIFFICULT
(a)   (b)   (c)

⊢ I seg ⊣   ⌶ 100 μv

FIG. 5. Photic-evoked potentials recorded subcortically from the visual radiations of a human subject. During the solution of an arithmetic problem which required concentration of attention, the evoked potentials were significantly reduced. (From Hernández-Peón & Donoso, 1959.)

arithmetic calculations. When the subject reached the solution, i.e., when his attention was no longer concentrated on the mental task, the evoked potentials recovered. This phenomenon was not only consistent in different subjects, but it was confirmed that the reductions of the evoked potentials were related to the degree of attention focused on the arithmetic problem. Figure 5 shows how this effect appeared in the recordings. When the individual was given a difficult problem which required attention, the evoked potentials were significantly reduced, but when he was presented with an easy problem which did not require a high concentration of attention, the potentials remained unchanged. A similar effect was observed in the visual-evoked subcortical responses during emotional excitement, which, undoubtedly, involved distraction from our testing photic stimulus. Figure 6 shows the photic potentials of a woman when she was relaxed and when she was emotionally excited. More recently, R. Guerrero-Figueroa and Heath (1964) and E. Guerrero-Figueroa, R. Guerro-Figueroa, and Heath, (1964) have confirmed the effects of attention and distraction on visual- and acoustic-evoked potentials recorded from specific and polysensory pathways in humans with depth electrodes. Furthermore, they have observed that the postsynaptic component of thalamo-hippocampal-evoked responses were inhibited during mental calculations. Both presynaptic and postsynaptic interhippocampal

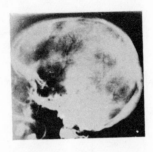

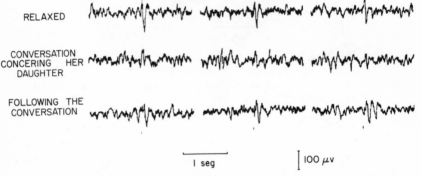

RELAXED

CONVERSATION
CONCERING   HER
DAUGHTER

FOLLOWING THE
CONVERSATION

I seg $\bigg\rvert$ 100 μv

FIG. 6. Blocking of photic-evoked potentials recorded from the visual radiations of a woman during emotional excitement elicited by conversation about her daughter. (From Hernández-Peón & Donoso, 1959.)

impulses were affected by distraction (R. Guerrero-Figueroa & Heath, 1965).

However, the opportunities for direct recordings of sensory signals at the specific sensory pathways in the human brain are limited. It is not always possible to find cases with clinical indications for implanting electrodes in the brain, and therefore it became necessary to record the evoked sensory signals from the scalp. This was achieved by averaging cortical-evoked potentials with a photoelectronic technique based on a principle described by Kozchevnikov (1958) and modified by Handler, Vanzulli, Bogacz, and Garcia-Austt (1960). The evoked activity modulated the intensity of the beam of the oscilloscope. The successive sweeps were photographed on a moving film at a slow speed, and then the film was scanned and explored by a light of constant intensity passing through a lens to a photomultiplier which, in turn, was connected to the Y axis of the oscilloscope. The successive stages involved

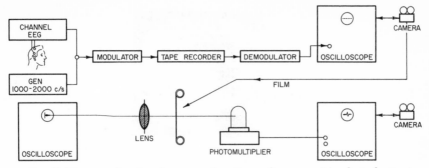

FIG. 7. Diagram showing the successive stages of an averaging photoelectronic technique used for recording evoked potentials from the scalp of human subjects.

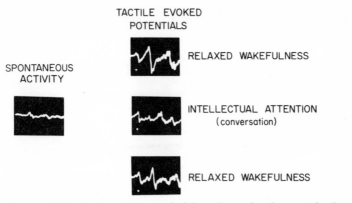

FIG. 8. Averaged electrical activity recorded from the scalp of a normal subject. Each picture represents the average of 40 successive sweeps. Potentials were evoked by tactile stimuli (short trains of rectangular pulses) applied to the skin of the forearm. The somatic-evoked potentials were significantly reduced during conversation on a topic of interest to the subject.

are shown in the diagram of Fig. 7. In this way, it was possible to average the potentials evoked by a number of successive stimuli. In the particular experiments to be presented, 40 successive evoked responses were averaged.

In normal subjects we have confirmed that the potentials evoked by tactile stimuli, single shocks of mild intensity which are felt as a slight touch, applied to the skin of the forearm were significantly reduced during the distraction. In the recordings shown in Fig. 8, distraction was accomplished by conversation on a matter of interest to the subject. The potentials recovered when the subject

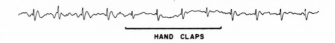

HAND CLAPS

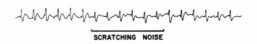

SCRATCHING NOISE

I SEC.

FIG. 9. Potentials recorded from the basolateral region of the amygdaloid complex and evoked by single shocks applied 1 mm apart from the recording site. The amygdaloid-evoked potentials were reduced when the cat was distracted by handclaps or by scratching the wall of the cage. (From Hernández-Peón and R. Guerrero-Figueroa, *Acta neurol. latinoamer* (in press).)

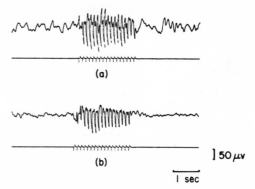

(a)

(b)

] 50 μv

I sec

FIG. 10. Recruiting cortical responses elicited by electrical stimulation of the nucleus ventralis anterior of the thalamus in a cat with electrodes permanently implanted: (a) asleep and (b) alert. The recruiting responses were smaller during alertness than during sleep.

became relaxed again. Therefore, both in lower mammals and in the highest primate, the transmission of sensory signals is modified during shifts of attention.

III. EXTRASENSORY INHIBITION

Not only synaptic transmission in the sensory pathways is modified during distraction but also many other central structures present changes of excitability during different states of wakefulness which can be detected with the technique of evoked potentials.

Hernández-Peón and R. Guerrero-Figueroa (1966) have recorded evoked potentials from the basolateral nuclei of the amygdaloid complex by applying single shocks to the vicinity of the recording electrodes. As seen in Fig. 9, during alertness elicited by handclaps the evoked potentials were reduced, and they recovered when distraction was over. Any other acoustic stimulus affecting the attention of the cat, such as a scratching noise in the wall of the cage, also elicited an immediate reduction of the evoked amygdaloid potentials. Similar effects have been observed in many other central structures. The author has confirmed the results of Evarts and Magoun (1957) concerning the effects of alertness upon thalamo-cortical recruiting responses. Figure 10 shows how the cortical responses evoked by stimulating the nucleus ventralis anterior of the thalamus were reduced when the cat became alert. R. Guerrero-Figueroa, Barros, De Balbian, and Verster (1963) reported a diminution or abolition of 3 per second spike and wave discharges propagated from thalamic epileptogenic foci during the transition from a state of relaxed wakefulness to a state of alertness.

IV. SENSORY FACILITATION

As mentioned above, attention involves the dominance of some sensory experiences with simultaneous exclusion of others. Therefore, the question arises whether, in addition to these general mechanisms which inhibit a great number of structures within the brain, there are also specific mechanisms which facilitate the activity of other central structures necessary for a particular physiological situation. Palestini *et al.* (1959) have approached this question experimentally by using the simple Pavlovian conditioning technique. By giving a series of four flashes of light at a rate of one per second, they recorded the photic retinal-evoked potentials at the optic tract. Following a control period, a nociceptive stimulus, an electric shock to the leg, was applied during the fourth flash of light. As illustrated in Fig. 11, after several associations, the photic-evoked potentials, particularly the fourth of each series, were enhanced and their recovery cycle was shortened. These results indicated that when the photic stimulus became meaningful to the cat, retinal excitability was increased by centrifugal influences. This effect may be independent of sensory facilitation occurring at higher levels of the sensory pathways (Hernández-Peón, 1960).

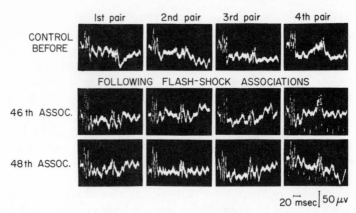

FIG. 11. Facilitatory effects of Pavlovian conditioning upon retinal excitability. The conditional stimulus consisted in 4 pairs of flashes presented at a rate of one per second. The painful unconditional stimulus presented during the fourth pair of flashes was an electric shock applied to a leg. After 45 associations, an enhancement was observed in the photic-evoked potentials recorded from the optic tract. (From Palestini *et al.* 1959.)

Another example of centrifugal sensory facilitation has been found in the olfactory bulb of the cat (Hernández-Peón, Alcocer-Cuaron, Lavin, & Santibañez, 1957; Hernández-Peón, Lavin, Alcocer-Cuaron, & Marcelin, 1960b; Lavin, Alcocer-Cuaron, & Hernández-Peón, 1959). If the animal were in a state of relaxed wakefulness and at a given moment a mouse was brought into the cage, bursts of rhythmic activity termed "arousal discharges" immediately appeared. The magnitude and number of the discharges increased in parallel with the degree of alertness. Correspondingly, they decreased and disappeared when the mouse was removed and the cat became relaxed again. This type of activity in the olfactory bulb appears to be related both to respiratory olfactory stimuli and to centrifugal efferent impulses.

V. SENSORY FILTERING

A. *Oscillations of Sensory Filtering*

The centrifugal influences in the various sensory pathways act in an oscillating manner. This can be shown by recording simultaneously the electrical activity of several afferent pathways, which Hernández-Peón, Brust-Carmona, Peñaloza-Rojas, and Bach-y-Rita (1961) have done in the olfactory bulb, the spinal fifth sensory nucleus, and the cochlear nucleus. Tactile stimuli and clicks were presented simultaneously in order to record the evoked tactile and auditory activity. Immediately after a mouse was presented to the cat, arousal discharges appeared in the olfactory bulb, the tactile trigeminal potentials were enhanced, and the auditory potentials were reduced. Therefore, the first effects were: facilitation in the olfactory and tactile trigeminal pathways, and inhibition in the auditory pathway. A few seconds later, when the cat focused its attention upon the mouse, the electrical activity of the olfactory bulb was further increased, the tactile potentials diminished, and the auditory potentials were further reduced. After removing the mouse from the cat's sight, all the background and evoked sensory activity recovered its original magnitude.

Fast oscillations in sensory transmission are very clearly observed when the animal is in a state of nonspecific alertness, i.e., in an anticipatory or exploratory attitude toward unfamiliar stimuli. In this situation, simultaneously with the arousal discharges in the olfactory bulb, the size of the auditory-evoked potentials in the cochlear nucleus vary greatly from second to second. These fluctuations of sensory activity probably represent the neural counterpart of the well-known psychological observations about oscillations of attention.

B. Central Regulation of Sensory Filtering

Accepting the existence of centrifugal mechanisms which inhibit or facilitate the entrance and transmission of sensory signals throughout the brain as well as the excitability of nonsensory structures during the various states of wakefulness, it is important to know how those mechanisms are regulated. Where do these influences arise?

Logical reasoning first leads us to consider the neural circuits involved in wakefulness and attention. Since the pioneer observations of Moruzzi and Magoun (1949) it has been know that arousal is elicited by high frequency electrical stimulation of a region located in the core of the brain stem extending from the medulla up to the ventromedial part of the thalamus. This region was termed by Magoun (1952) the "ascending reticular activating system." It was called "reticular" because anatomically the reticular formation represents an important part of the system. It was called "activating" because it was assumed to produce arousal by generalized activation of the cortex. It was called "ascending" because the assumed generalized activation of the cortex necessarily must involve ascending reticulocortical projections.

This original concept needs revision in the light of more recent experimental evidence. It has been found that the part of the brain stem essential for wakefulness and conscious experience (Fessard, 1954) is located in the mesodiencephalon (French & Magoun, 1952), and that it does not extend caudally beyond the rostral part of the pons. On the contrary, the myelometencephalic tegmentum in the caudal portion of the brain stem mainly contains antagonistic hypnogenic structures (Moruzzi, 1963). On the other hand, microelectrode recordings have revealed that many cortical neurons are inhibited during arousal and alertness (Jung, Kornhuber, & Da Fonseca, 1963; Ricci, Doane, & Jasper, 1957) and that the firing rate is greater during "desynchronized sleep" associated with a high arousal threshold than during "synchronized sleep" or wakefulness (Evarts, 1960; Evarts, 1962; Evarts, 1963; Evarts, 1964; Evarts, 1965). However, all these findings do not preclude the validity of the original discovery pointing toward the brain stem as the essential locus for wakefulness and consciousness.

The arousing neurons in the brain stem, which may be designated the *vigilance system*, receive corticofugal projections from certain cortical areas (French, Hernández-Peón, & Livingston, 1955), the electrical stimulation of which produces arousal and alertness (Segundo, Arana-Iñigue, & French, 1955). Therefore, there are two main pathways by means of which the vigilance system can be activated:

(1) by the specific sensory pathways which give off collaterals to the reticular formation, and

(2) by descending projections arising from the cortex.

It may be concluded that arousal can be produced either by sensory stimulation or by cortical activation. These two mechanisms are probably responsible for the two types of wakefulness described by Kleitman (1939) as "wakefulness of necessity" and "wakefulness of choice," and for the two varieties of attention known as "involuntary" and "voluntary."

Since transmission of sensory impulses is regulated during attention and distraction, it is of particular interest to find out whether the central region essential for wakefulness and conscious-

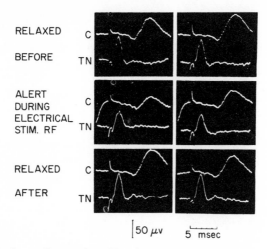

RELAXED
BEFORE

ALERT
DURING
ELECTRICAL
STIM. RF

RELAXED
AFTER

|50 μv   5 msec

FIG. 12. Blocking effect produced by electrical stimulation of the mesencephalic reticular formation on the potentials recorded both at the spinal trigeminal sensory nucleus *TN* and the cortex *C* evoked by electric single shocks of nociceptive intensity applied to the skin of the face.

ness is concerned with the regulation process. There is a great deal of experimental evidence showing that the midbrain reticular formation exerts both inhibitory and facilitatory influences at all levels of the specific sensory pathways (Hernández-Peón, 1961). Figure 12 provides examples of the effect elicited by electrical stimulation of the brain stem reticular formation upon tactile-evoked potentials recorded from the spinal fifth sensory nucleus and from the cortex in an awake cat with electrodes permanently implanted. During relaxed wakefulness, the evoked potentials from the spinal fifth sensory nucleus and from the cortex had a stable magnitude. When the mesencephalic reticular formation was briefly stimulated for 3 seconds, the cat became very alert, and, simultaneously, the bulbar and cortical potential were significantly reduced. There is a significant relationship between the magnitude of afferent volleys in the sensory pathways and the state of alertness elicited by direct electrical stimulation of the reticular formation in the midbrain.

Blocking effects upon nonsensory structures can also be observed following electrical stimulation of the mesencephalic reticular formation. As seen in Fig. 13, the local and propagated after-discharges elicited by repetitive electrical stimulation of the

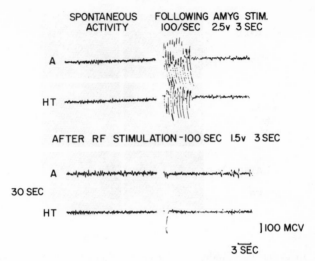

FIG. 13. The upper part of the figure shows the after-discharges recorded from the basolateral region of the amygdala *A* and from the posterior hypothalamus *HT* immediately after repetitive stimulation of the amygdala (100 per second, 2.5 volt) during 3 seconds. After stimulating the mesencephalic reticular formation, the same stimulus was ineffective in producing the after-discharge. (From Hernández-Peón and R. Guerrero-Figueroa, 1966.)

basolateral region of the amygdaloid complex were prevented by electrical stimulation of the mesencephalic reticular formation which elicited an alerting response.

Facilitatory effects upon the first sensory synapse of the olfactory pathway have been obtained by electrical stimulation of the midbrain reticular formation (Hernández-Peón *et al.*, 1960b). In experiments in which the electrical activity of the olfactory bulb and of the septal region in the vicinity of the anterior commissure were recorded simultaneously, the electrical stimulus applied for 3 seconds produced a state of alertness associated with desynchronization of the septal region and with the appearance of arousal discharges in the olfactory bulb.

It can be argued that electrical stimulation of the brain is an unphysiological procedure. However, the results obtained from studies involving experimental lesions support the physiological nature of the centrifugal inhibitory and facilitatory influences: Sensory-evoked potentials recorded from the spinal fifth sensory nucleus were significantly increased after a lesion was made in the midbrain tegmentum which rendered the cat unconscious

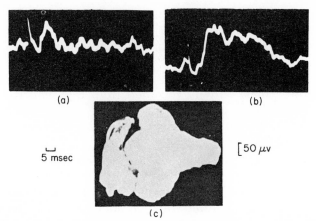

FIG. 14. Tactile-evoked potentials recorded from the lateral column of the spinal cord in a decerebrate preparation with the brain stem transected at the midcollicular level, before and immediately after transection of the spinal cord above the recording site (a) decerebrated, (b) spinal, and (c) hindbrain between transections. (From Hernández-Peón & Brust-Carmona, 1961b.)

(Hernández-Peón and Scherrer, 1955; Hernández-Peón *et al.*, 1956b). The evidence from such experiments supports the conclusion that, during wakefulness, a tonic descending influence of an inhibitory nature, which requires the midbrain tegmentum, decreases the excitability of sensory neurons at the first sensory trigeminal synapse. The nonessentiality of the cortex and the important participation of the brain stem in sensory inhibition were shown in decerebrate cats in which a complete transection was made at the rostral midbrain level (Hernández-Peón & Brust-Carmona, 1961b). In these preparations having only the lower part of the brain stem and the spinal cord, tactile-evoked potentials were recorded from the spinothalamic tract at the lateral column before and after transection of the spinal cord. As shown in Fig. 14a, remarkable enhancement of the spinal tactile potentials was observed immediately after a high spinal transection indicating that the tonic descending inhibitory influence does not arise from supramesencephalic levels of the central nervous system.

The corresponding sensory inhibitory neurons are very sensitive to barbiturates. Hernández-Peón *et al.* (1956b) have shown that the gracilis nucleus potentials evoked by stimulating the dorsal columns were enhanced during barbiturate anesthesia at the same time that the somatic-evoked potentials recorded from the mid-brain reticular formation were significantly depressed. Further evidence of a tonic inhibitory influence restraining sensory transmission at subcortical levels in the human brain has been provided by the experiments of Hagbarth and Höjeberg (1957), who showed that tactile-evoked activity recorded from the subcortical white substance in anesthetized patients decreased when the anesthesia became lighter, and that the same evoked activity increased when the anesthesia was deepened.

The role of the midbrain in centrifugal sensory facilitation has been demonstrated in the olfactory bulb where the arousal discharges disappeared completely after a lesion was made in the mesencephalic tegmentum which rendered the cat unconscious (Hernández-Peón et al., 1960b). In this state, even nociceptive stimuli became ineffective in producing an activation response.

However, the reticular formation is not the only source of efferent fibers which modify transmission of sensory impulses along the specific afferent pathways. From the description of earlier anatomists it is known that there are fibers of cortical origin relaying in the thalamus and in lower levels of specific afferent pathways. These fibers have been described in the auditory, visual, and somatic pathways. Therefore, we must accept the existence of two systems regulating sensory transmission: one, located in the vicinity of the ascending specific afferent pathway, may be termed the *paraspecific descending pathway;* the other is the *cortico-reticular-sensory pathway.* These pathways are shown in the diagram of Fig. 15. It seemed natural to wonder what the functional role of the paraspecific descending pathway is during different states of attention and distraction. In order to answer this question, Bach-Y-Rita, Brust-Carmona, Peñaloza-Rojas, and Hernández-Peón (1961) recorded auditory-evoked potentials from the cochlear nucleus in cats in which lesions had been made in the lateral part of the mesencephalon or in the internal part of the medial geniculate body, destroying the ascending specific as well as the descending paraspecific auditory pathways. As shown in Fig. 16, the auditory potentials from the cochlear nucleus were significantly reduced when the cat was distracted by visual stimuli, the same effect as that obtained in the intact animal. Therefore, sensory inhibition during distraction is present in the absence of

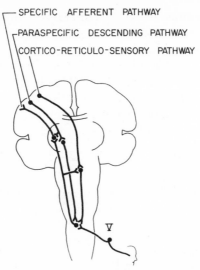

SPECIFIC AFFERENT PATHWAY

PARASPECIFIC DESCENDING PATHWAY

CORTICO-RETICULO-SENSORY PATHWAY

V

FIG. 15. Diagram showing the descending pathways which regulate sensory transmission along the specific afferent pathways.

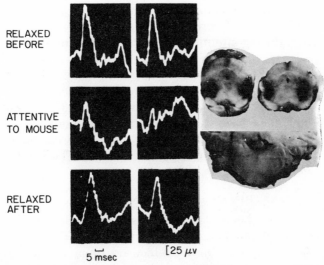

RELAXED
BEFORE

ATTENTIVE
TO MOUSE

RELAXED
AFTER

5 msec   [25 μv

FIG. 16. Blocking effects of distraction elicited by a mouse on the click-evoked potentials recorded from the dorsal cochlear nucleus in a cat with bilateral lesions in the lateral parts of the midbrain involving the ascending and descending auditory pathways.

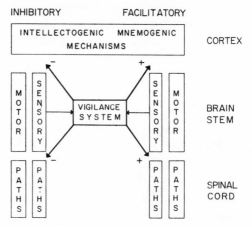

INHIBITORY   FACILITATORY

FIG. 17. Diagram showing the inhibitory and facilitatory influences arising from the rostral brain stem during attention. Both influences are exerted upon sensory and motor paths at all levels of the CNS as well as upon the central mechanisms concerned with memory and intellectual processes.

the paraspecific descending pathway. Although the latter must have an important functional role, it does not appear to be concerned with sensory filtering during attention.

In brief, during attention inhibitory and facilitatory influences act at all levels of the central nervous system and require the activity of a central station in the rostral brain stem. This station receives information of all sensory modalities and sends efferent impulses to sensory and motor pathways as well as to the neural systems involved in memory, emotions, and motivations. In turn, the central station controlling general excitability can be influenced by the neocortex, paleocortex, or archicortex. These relationships are shown in the diagram of Fig. 17.

VI. CLASSIFICATION OF ATTENTION

Attention has been classified in several varieties according to its origin, development, and object as given in Table I. According to its object, attentiom may be focused upon sensory stimuli or upon intellectual processes, and, therefore, may be termed *sensory attention* and *intellectual attention*. On the basis of its origin, attention may be *nonvoluntary, passive* or *reflex*, and *voluntary* or *active*. A better descriptive terminology may be *exo-evoked*

TABLE I

VARIETIES OF ATTENTION

Origin	Development	Object
Nonvoluntary (passive, reflex) exo-evoked	Immediate (direct)	Sensorial
Voluntary (active) auto-evoked	Derived (indirect)	Intellectual

and *auto-evoked* attention: In the case of the former it is evoked by activity outside the brain, and in the latter it is evoked by activity within the brain. Classified in terms of its temporal development, attention can be divided into *immediate* or *direct* and *derived* or *indirect* categories.

The neurophysiological mechanisms of the different varieties of attention are outlined in Fig. 18. A neural system in the rostral brain stem plays a central role regulating the activity triggered either by sensory stimuli or by memory tracings, which in turn feeds into the central system. Sensory attention requires the sensory pathways and the central system with or without the cortex. Intellectual attention involves complex higher circuits activated during remembering or thinking. Whereas the cortex is necessary for voluntary attention, involuntary attention requires only subcortical structures.

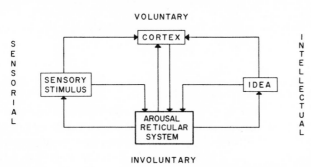

FIG. 18. Central mechanisms proposed for explaining the varieties of attention outlined in Table I.

VII. Sensory Transmission

A. Sensory Transmission During Sleep

In recent years, a growing interest in the neural mechanisms of sleep has been reawakened among neurophysiologists and psychologists (Hernández-Peón & Sterman, 1966). It is not only accepted that sleep is the result of active inhibition of the *vigilance system* originating in well-defined hypnogenic structures which have been termed the "sleep system" (Hernández-Peón, 1965a; Hernández-Peón, 1965b), but it is also well established that two typical patterns of electrophysiological indices often alternate during sleep. At the onset of sleep the electrical activity of the neocortex is characterized by high voltage slow waves, slow sleep (SS), which are later replaced by low voltage fast activity, rapid sleep (RS), when the arousal threshold is markedly raised. It is during periods of the latter kind, which are also accompanied by bursts of rapid eye movements, that the highest percentage of dreams are reported by human subjects (Dement & Kleitman, 1957). An important question for psychology is: How does the brain handle the arrival of sensory inflow during sleep, and particularly during the episodes associated with dreaming? In an experimental approach to this problem, Hernández-Peón, O'Flaherty, and Mazzuchelli-O'Flaherty (1965) recorded tactile-evoked potentials from the spinal trigeminal sensory nucleus during the sleep-wakefulness continuum monitored by several electrophysiological recordings. It was found that both the presynaptic and postsynaptic components of the trigeminal potentials increased during SS and diminished during the episodes of RS to a degree comparable to that recorded during alertness. Furthermore, all the changes observed during wakefulness and sleep disappeared completely after a midbrain tegmental lesion. From these results it is evident that the responsible inhibitory neurons filtering the entrance of afferent signals at the first somatic sensory synapse are not linked with the vigilance system nor with the hypnogenic neurons. Since the only common outstanding function of the waking and sleeping periods in which sensory filtering acts is that concerned with conscious experiences designated as sensory perception and dreaming, respectively, it seems logical to think that the sensory inhibitory neurons must be closely related with a specific neural mesodiencephalic neuronal system which may be designated the "conscious experience system" (Hernández-Peón, 1965c; Hernández-Peón, 1965d; Hernández-Peón, 1965e). According to this new concept, a functional dissociation exists between the latter and the vigilance system in spite of their anatomical overlapping.

B. Sensory Transmission during Hypnosis

In an attempt to obtain neurophysiological correlates of the fate of sensory input at the lowest level of the central nervous system during hypnosis, Hernández-Peón, Dittborn, Borlone, and Davidovich (1959; 1960a) recorded reflex spinal potentials evoked by electrical stimuli applied to the skin of the forearm. The potentials were significantly reduced during hypnotically suggested anesthesia and enhanced during hypnotically produced hyperesthesia, as compared to pre- and post-hypnotic wakefulness. These results indicate that verbal suggestions during hypnosis may produce correlative changes of excitability in the spinal cord. In a more recent study of averaged tactile-evoked potentials from the scalp, Stross, Hernández-Peón, Shevrin, and Remrick (1966) have found a statistically significant diminution of the late waves from the hypnotically anesthetized arm, indicating a functional blockade in some part of the polysensory system.

C. Pathological Alterations of Sensory Transmission

Our research has also led us to study pathological deviations of the attention mechanisms and of sensory transmission. Since attention is obviously deficient in mentally retarded subjects, we decided to gain a preliminary insight into those disturbances by recording from the scalp cortical tactile-evoked potentials in mentally retarded subjects (Hernández-Peón, 1964a; Hernández-Peón, 1964b). A deficiency was found in the triggering mechanisms for shifting of attention. Both the blocking effects of distraction and the facilitatory mechanisms of attention appeared with a considerable delay. If, after taking a series of evoked potentials during relaxed wakefulness, the subject was distracted or asked to focus his attention upon the test stimulus, the corresponding diminution or enhancement of the evoked potentials became evident with a latency of 40 seconds.

Sensory regulating mechanisms appear to be altered in cases of sensory hysterical disturbances. Hernández-Peón, Chavez-Ibarra, and Aguilar-Figueroa (1963) have recorded tactile-evoked potentials in one case of hysterical anesthesia. Whereas very clear double-evoked potentials were recorded by applying tactile stimuli to the normal right arm, no evoked activity was recorded by stimulating the anesthetic left arm. However, during Kemithal anesthesia, not only the evoked potentials from the normal arm became enhanced, but also a well-defined evoked activity appeared by stimulating the anesthetic arm.

It seems likely that many sensory and perceptual disturbances will be found to be associated with alterations of the neurophysiological mechanisms regulating sensory transmission.

REFERENCES

Bach-Y-Rita, G., Brust-Carmona, H., Peñaloza-Rojas, J., & Hernández-Peón, R. Absence of para-auditory descending impulses at the cochlear nucleus during distraction and habituation. *Acta neurol. latinoamer.*, 1961, **7**, 73–81.

Dement, W., & Kleitman, N. The relation of eye movements during sleep to dream activity: an objective method for the study of dreaming. *J. exp. Psychol.*, 1957, **53**, 339–346.

Evarts, E. V. Effects of sleep and waking on spontaneous and evoked discharge of single units in visual cortex. *Fed. Proc.*, 1960, **19**, 828–837.

Evarts, E. V. Activity of neurons in visual cortex of the cat during sleep with low voltage fast EEG activity. *J. Neurophysiol.*, 1962, **25**, 812–816.

Evarts, E. V. Neuronal activity in sensorimotor cortex during sleep and waking. *Fed. Proc.*, 1963, **22**, 637.

Evarts, E. V. Temporal patterns of discharge of pyramidal tract neurons during sleep and waking in the monkey. *J. Neurophysiol.*, 1964, **27**, 152–171.

Evarts, E. V. Neuronal activity in visual and motor cortex during sleep and waking. In M. Jouvet (Ed.), *Neurophysiologie des etats de sommeil*. Paris: C.N.R.S., 1965.

Evarts, E. V., & Magoun, H. W. Some characteristics of cortical recruiting responses in unanaesthetized cats. *Science*, 1957, **125**, 1147–1148.

Fessard, A. E. Mechanisms of nervous integration and conscious experience. In J. F. Delafresnaye (Ed.), *Brain mechanisms and consciousness*. Oxford: Blackwell, 1954. Pp. 200–236.

French, J. D., & Magoun, H. W. Effects of chronic lesions in central cephalic brain stem in monkeys. *A.M.A. Arch. Neurol. Psychiat.*, 1952, **68**, 591–604.

French, J. D., Hernández-Peón, R., & Livingston, R. B. Projections from cortex to cephalic brain stem (reticular formation) in monkey. *J. Neurophysiol.*, 1955, **18**, 74–95.

Guerrero-Figueroa, E., Guerrero-Figueroa, R., & Heath, R. G. Effects of attention and some chemical compounds upon trigeminal evoked potential. In R. G. Heath (Ed.), *The role of pleasure in behavior*. New York: Harper & Row, 1964.

Guerrero-Figueroa, R., & Heath, R. G. Evoked responses and changes during attentive factors in man. *Arch. Neurol.*, 1964, **10**, 74–84.

Guerrero-Figueroa, R., & Heath, R. G. Alterations of interhippocampal impulses in man during natural sleep and distraction. *Percept. mot. Skills,* 1965, **21,** 667–670.

Guerrero-Figueroa, R., Barros, A., & De Balbian Verster, F. Some inhibitory effects of attentive factors on experimental epilepsy. *Epilepsia,* 1963, **4,** 225–240.

Hagbarth, K. E., & Höjeberg, S. Evidence for subcortical regulation of the afferent discharge to somatic sensory cortex in man. *Nature,* 1957, **179,** 526–527.

Handler, P., Vanzulli, A., Bogacz, J., & Garcia-Austt, E. A photo-optic-electronic method for the detection and study of evoked potentials. *Acta neurol. latino-amer.,* 1960, **6,** 163–173.

Hernández-Peón, R. The centrifugal control of afferent inflow to the brain and sensory perception. *Acta neurol. latinoamer.,* 1959, **5,** 279–298.

Hernández-Peón, R. Neurophysiological correlates of habituation and other manifestations of plastic inhibition (internal inhibition). In H. H. Jasper and G. D. Smirnov (Eds.), *The Moscow colloquium on electroencephalography of higher nervous activity. Electroenceph. clin. Neurophysiol.* 1960, **13,** Suppl., 101–114.

Hernández-Peón, R. Reticular mechanisms of sensory control. In W. A. Rosenblith (Ed.), *Sensory communication.* New York: Wiley and Cambridge, Mass.: M. I. T. Press, 1961.

Hernández-Peón, R. Psychiatric implications of neurophysiological research. *Bull. Menninger Found.,* 1964, **28,** 165–185.(a)

Hernández-Peón, R. Attention, motivation and behavior. In R. G. Heath (Ed.), *The role of pleasure in behavior.* New York: Harper & Row, 1964.(b)

Hernández-Peón, R. Central neuro-humoral transmission in sleep and wakefulness. In K. Akert and J. P. Schadé (Eds.), *Progress in brain research.* Vol. 18. *Sleep mechanisms.* Amsterdam: Elsevier, 1965.(a)

Hernández-Peón, R. Die neuralen Grundlagen des Schlafes. *Arzneimittel-Forschung,* 1965, **15,** 1099–1118.(b)

Hernández-Peón, R. Neural systems in the brain stem involved in wakefulness, sleep and conscious experience. *Excerpta med.,* 1965, **93,** 123–124.(c)

Hernández-Peón, R. A neurophysiological model of dreams and hallucinations. *J. nerv. ment. Dis.,* 1965, **141,** 623–650.(d)

Hernández-Peón, R. Una teoria neurofisiologica de los procesos psiquicos conscientes e inconserentes. *APAL.,* 1965, **1,** 15–33.(e)

Hernández-Peón, R., & Brust-Carmona, H. Inhibition of tactile and nociceptive spinal evoked potentials in the cat during distraction. *Acta neurol. latinoamer.,* 1961, **7,** 289–298.(a)

Hernández-Peón, R., & Brust-Carmona, H. Functional role of subcortical structures in habituation and conditioning. In J. F. Delafresnaye (Ed.), *Brain mechanisms and learning.* Oxford: Blackwell, 1961.(b)

Hernández-Peón, R., & Donoso, M. Subcortical photically evoked activity in the human waking brain. Fourth International Congress of Electroencephalography and Clinical Neurophysiology. *Excerpta med.,* 1957, p. 155.

Hernández-Peón, R., & Donoso, M. Influence of attention and suggestion upon subcortical evoked electric activity in the human brain. *The first international congress of neurological sciences, Bruxelles, 1957.* Vol. III. New York: Macmillan (Pergamon), 1959.

Hernández-Peón, R., & Guerrero-Figueroa, R. Modifications of local amygdaloid evoked responses during wakefulness. *Acta neurol. latinoamer.,* 1966, in press.

Hernández-Peón, R., & Scherrer, H. "Habituation" to acoustic stimuli in cochlear nucleus. *Fed. Proc.*, 1955, **14**, 71.

Hernández-Peón, R., & Sterman, M. B. Chapter on Brain Functions. *Annu. Rev. Psychol.*, 1966, **17**, 363–394.

Hernández-Peón, R., Scherrer, H., & Jouvet, M. Modification of electric activity in cochlear nucleus during "attention" in unanaesthetized cats. *Science*, 1956, **123**, 331–332.(a)

Hernández-Peón, R., Scherrer, H., & Velasco, M. Central influences on afferent conduction in the somatic and visual pathways. *Acta neurol. latinoamer.*, 1956, **2**, 8–22.(b)

Hernández-Peón, R., Alcocer-Cuaron, C., Lavin, A., & Santibañez, G. Regulacion centrifuga de la actividad electrica del bulbo olfactorio. *Resúmenes Primera Reunion Cientifica Latinoamericana de Ciencias Fisiológicas*. Punta del Este, Uruguay, 1957.

Hernández-Peón, R., Dittborn, J., Borlone, M., & Davidovich, A. Changes of spinal excitability during hypnotically induced anesthesia and hyperesthesia. *Proceedings XXI international congress of physiological sciences, 1959*. p. 124.

Hernández-Peón, R., Dittborn, J., Borlone, M., & Davidovich, A. Modifications of a forearm skin reflex during hypnotic anesthesia and hyperesthesia. *Acta neurol. latinoamer.*, 1960, **6**, 32–42.(a)

Hernández-Peón, R., Lavin, A., Alcocer-Cuaron, C., & Marcelin, J. P. Electrical activity of the olfactory bulb during wakefulness and sleep. *Electroenceph. clin. Neurophysiol.*, 1960, **12**, 41–58.(b)

Hernández-Peón, R., Brust-Carmona, H., Peñaloza-Rojas, J., & Bach-Y-Rita, G. The efferent control of afferent signals entering the central nervous system. *Ann. N. Y. Acad. Sci.*, 1961, **89**, 866–882.

Hernández-Peón, R., Chavez-Ibarra, G., & Aguilar-Figueroa, E. Somatic evoked potentials in one case of hysterical anesthesia. *Electroenceph. clin. Neurophysiol.*, 1963, **15**, 889–892.

Hernández-Peón, R., O'Flaherty, J. J., & Mazzuchelli-O'Flaherty, A. L. Modifications of tactile evoked potentials at spinal trigeminal sensory nucleus during wakefulness and sleep. *Exp. Neurol.*, 1965, **13**, 40–57.

Jung, R., Kornhuber, H. H., & Da Fonseca, J. S. Multisensory convergence on cortical neurons. Neuronal effects of visual acoustic and vestibular stimuli in the superior convolutions of the cat's cortex. In G. Moruzzi, A. Fessard, & H. H. Jasper (Eds.), *Progress in brain research*. Vol. I. *Brain mechanisms*. Amsterdam: Elsevier, 1963.

Kleitman, M. *Sleep and wakefulness*. Chicago: Univer. of Chicago Press, 1939.

Kozchevnichov, V. A. Photoelectric method of selecting weak electrical responses of the brain. *J. Physiol. (USSR)*, 1958, **44**, 801–809.

Lavin, A., Alcocer-Cuaron, C., & Hernández-Peón, R. Centrifugal arousal in the olfactory bulb. *Science*, 1959, **129**, 332–333.

Magoun, H. W. The ascending reticular activating system. *Res. Publ. Ass. nerv. ment. Dis.*, 1952, **30**, 480–492.

Moruzzi, G. Active processes in the brain stem during sleeping. *Harvey Lect.*, 1963, **58**.

Moruzzi, G., & Magoun, H. Brain stem reticular formation and activation of the EEG. *Electronenceph. clin. Neurophysiol.*, 1949, **1**, 455–473.

Palestini, M., Davidovich, A., & Hernández-Peón, R. Functional significance of centrifugal influences upon the retina. *Acta neurol. latinoamer.*, 1959, **5**, 113–131.

Ricci, G., Doane, B., & Jasper, H. Microelectrode studies of conditioning: technique and preliminary results. 4th int. Congr. EEG clin. Neurophysiol. *Acta Med. Belg.*, 1957, 401–415. 43 rue des Champs-Elysées. Bruxelles.

Scherrer, H., & Hernández-Peón, R. Inhibitory influence of brain stem reticular formation upon synaptic transmission in trigeminal nucleus. *Fed. Proc.*, 1955, **14**, 71.

Segundo, J. P., Arana-Iñiguez, R., & French, J. D. Behavioral arousal by stimulation of the brain in the monkey. *J. Neurosurg.*, 1955, **12**, 601–613.

Stross, L., Hernández-Peón, R., Shevrin, H., and Remrick, R. Changes of cortical evoked responses with suggested anesthesia in hypnosis. *Science*, 1966, in press.

CHAPTER 6

Neural Processes during Learning *

E. ROY JOHN

Brain Research Laboratories,
Department of Psychiatry,
New York Medical College,
New York, New York

I. INTRODUCTION

This chapter is a survey of some phenomena believed to be related to the process of elaboration of a memory and to the process by which the information stored may be retrieved at some later time. These are processes basic to the acquisition and maintenance of behavior patterns upon which an organism's adjustment to its

* The work described in this paper was supported in part by Research Grant MY-2972 from the National Institute of Mental Health and Grant G21831 from the National Science Foundation.

environment depends. They are central to all systematic views about behavior. To understand the neural events involved would be an important step toward clarifying constructs, e.g., the "memory trace," which psychologists have felt compelled to introduce into their theoretical models of learning since the advent of modern experimental psychology.

We are still a considerable distance from possessing a full understanding of these neural events. Indeed, there will be other possible interpretations even of the data presented in the paragraphs to follow. Recent discoveries at the frontier in this area of research are, however, challenging in that they provide new suggestions about ways in which neural events may be involved in learning. The author's interest in the data reported herein is enhanced by the fact that he believes they are particularly relevant to the establishment of and the readout from memory. No pretense is made that this is an absolutely clear and unequivocal conclusion which all will share when the data have been presented.

II. PHASES OF LEARNING

There is appreciable evidence that in the process of learning one can distinguish, with relative clarity, two phases. The first, an early period—the so-called *consolidation phase*—is one in which the consequences of an experience seem to have a relatively labile form, so that interference with the remembering system by a drug, or by massive electrical input, or by severe disruptions of various sorts cancels out the contribution of that experience to the acquisition of a learned response. After this consolidation phase— estimates of its duration range from 20 minutes to as much as 3 hours depending on the technique employed—these same perturbing influences on the nervous system do not seem to disrupt the establishment of the learned response. There seems to be an interface, then, at approximately half an hour to an hour or two, between a process which represents past experience in a fashion which can be easily interfered with and a more durable process, which is associated with the *long-term storage of information* and with its use or *readout* by the organism. This latter process can last the greater part of a lifetime. Various theorists have suggested that during the so-called consolidation phase the representative activity which stands for the neural consequences of an experience may be electrical reverberation. Some evidence will be presented which supports this suggestion, along with some evidence believed relevant to the possible functional significance of electrical reverberations of this sort.

Of the experiments on consolidation, many of which have recently been well reviewed by Glickman (1961) and others, research by Westbrook and McGaugh (1964) on the ability of a rat to perform delayed alternation is of particular interest. With the technique employed in studying this kind of performance, it is possible to determine the length of time a rat can remember what he did last, when, at the next opportunity, he must do the opposite. The rat can perform this learned response with nonrandom accuracy with maximum delays of about half an hour. This can be regarded as the duration of the consequences of a single experience. McGaugh has observed that the administration of a number of generalized excitant drugs, including strychnine and metrazol, prolongs the period during which the rat can perform the alternation response at a nonrandom level to well beyond eight hours. It makes no difference whether the excitant is administered before or immediately following the learning experience itself. Clearly, investigation of the electrophysiological events going on in the central nervous system during this period would be of interest. One thing which does suggest itself is that the administration of the excitant after the experience sufficiently increases the excitability of neurons to prolong their participation in reverberatory activity and thereby extends the period in which this electrical reverberation can contribute to the synthesis of a more stable representational system. What is the nature of this system?

III. FREQUENCY SPECIFIC POTENTIALS

The electrical evidence comes mainly from investigations into electrophysiological changes in conditioning, using the *technique of intermittent conditioned stimuli*. The technique was first used for this purpose in the U.S.S.R. by Livanov and Polyakov (1945), whose experiment Killam and the author, unknowingly, essentially repeated in 1958, with the exception that a cat was used as the subject instead of a rabbit. The basic assumption in such an experiment is that, whatever the nature of the process by which the nervous system codes a stimulus impinging upon its sensory receptors, if the stimulus is presented regularly, it will be encoded regularly. Therefore, if one studies the electrical activity of the nervous system over a period of time during which an intermittent event in the environment acquires a meaning by conditioning procedures, one could justifiably assume that regions in the nervous system where electrical events appeared at the repetition frequency of the intermittent stimulus were places to which information about that peripheral event was arriving. Places which did not show such *frequency specific potentials* might also be involved in processing or receiving influences from the peripheral presentation. However, it is logically sufficient to conclude that a structure which produces potentials at the frequency of an external event is somehow being influenced by that event. Using this method to enhance the "signal-to-noise ratio" of recordings from implanted electrodes, we studied changes in the distribution of frequency specific potentials throughout the nervous system as the subject learned that certain intermittent events in his environment called for the performance of a particular response. Recordings showed rather massive changes in the distribution of such potentials, or harmonics thereof, throughout the nervous system. Places which initially showed no frequency specific potentials began to display them as the animal learned; some places which displayed them initially showed a diminution and then an enhancement; places which showed potentials at a harmonic changed to the fundamental; fundamentals changed to harmonics. Such complex changes, which have now been seen in many different species, appear almost every place one looks and indicate that the electrical response of the nervous system to a stimulus is altered when that stimulus becomes a conditioned stimulus. These observations are intriguing in one sense, but rather trivial in another. That such modifications of neural activity might occur had been suggested by others before these complex electrophysiological techniques were invented. Nonetheless, to have empirical verification for basic assumptions is important.

The fact that the changes described do occur is by itself neither remarkable nor very informative. One would like to go much further and, for example, ask whether it is possible to infer anything about the neural organization of a conditioned response from the configuration of electrical changes which are observed. First of all, certain anatomical relationships appear to hold true. It seems generally true that, as a stimulus acquires meaning for an animal, frequency specific potentials shift from sensory specific structures of the nervous system and extend quite massively through nonspecific structures. The consequences of the administration of a peripheral conditioned stimulus become very much more marked in regions of the brain which are not subservient to particular sensory modalities but receive many different kinds of inputs. This suggests an increased participation of nonspecific structures and, perhaps, even a diminution of the participation of specific structures. The elaboration of the anatomical characteristics of configurations and changes in configurations certainly merits further study. However, for the present it is wished to confine attention to results of this kind of experiment which appear to offer insights into some fundamental processes.

IV. ASSIMILATION

The first process which these studies reveal is one which Livanov and Polyakov (1945), who first observed it, called *assimilation*. The resting electrical activity of the brain of a naive animal in a conditioning situation generally is composed of low voltage fast activity of no conspicuous frequency. If one now starts to train the animal using a conditioned stimulus with a characteristic repetition frequency, as the learning ogive starts to develop, or shortly before, one can observe synchronous waves in the resting activity of the brain during the intertrial intervals. These appear at the frequency of the conditioned stimulus being used, or an harmonic thereof. The probability of occurrence of these assimilated rhythms increases as the conditioning progresses, and in the sharply rising portion of the ogival acquisition curve they tend to dominate the resting record of the animal during the intertrial intervals. If, at this stage, the animal is returned to his home environment and electrical potentials recorded there, the normal desynchronized record expected from an alert animal is observed. Bringing the animal back into the conditioning situation results in the reappearance of the frequency specific hypersynchrony. As the animal's performance asymptotes, these assimilated rhythms tend to disappear from the resting record. They reappear fairly frequently in the period 15 to 30 seconds after the animal makes an incorrect response and fails to achieve the expected outcome following the presentation of the conditioned stimulus. If the expected outcome occurs, these assimilated rhythms do not recur. It is interesting to note that these rhythms tend to appear simultaneously in a number of structures; spontaneous frequency specific rhythms tend

154   E. ROY JOHN

to arise in multiple places at the same time. They tend to arise earliest, be present most frequently, and persist longest in nonspecific regions of the brain. They are particularly easy to observe in the reticular formation, the hippocampus, and the intralaminar nuclei of the thalamus.

Figure 1 shows the development of assimilation in various regions of the brain. The top recordings were taken from the brain of a cat who was just beginning to learn to perform a conditioned

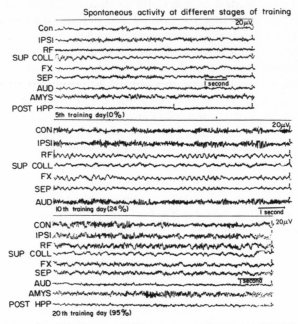

FIG. 1. Assimilated rhythms at different stages of training. CON, bipolar derivation between two electrodes, one on each visual cortex; IPSI, bipolar derivation between the two visual cortices; RF, mesencephalic reticular formation; SUP COLL, superior colliculus; FX, fornix; SEP, septum; AUD, auditory cortex; AMYG, amygdala; POST HIPP, dorsal hippocampus. (From John & Killam, 1958.)

avoidance response, a hurdle jump, to a 10 per second flickering light as the conditioned stimulus (CS). There is no characteristic rhythmicity to these recordings of the intertrial resting activity. The middle set of records was obtained when the animal was performing at the 24–25% level of accuracy, after training for ten days. The hypersynchronous discharges in this sample were at one-half the frequency of the conditioning stimulus. The bottom records were obtained from the fully trained animal, 95% correct in its performance. The rhythmicity is not nearly as apparent as before. Notice that the rhythms in the middle set of records appear with apparent simultaneity in the anatomical areas of the reticular formation, fornix and septum.

One can observe much more sustained and striking assimilation than this. A phenomenon similar to assimilation has been seen by Stern, Ulett, and Sines (1960) in a trace conditioning situation where they presented an intermittent stimulus, terminated it, and waited 5 seconds before the animal was permitted to make the response. The electrical activity during the 5-second waiting period was studied using a wave analyzer. Over a wide range of frequencies, they have shown that the CS frequency dominates the activity during the interval before the animal is permitted to make his response. K. L. Chow and E. R. John (unpublished observations, 1956) have seen a similar phenomenon in cortical conditioning experiments. If a flickering light is withheld after a series of regularly spaced presentations, at the appropriate time after the last flicker presentation, hypersynchrony at approximately the flicker frequency will appear in a number of structures. This is, as it were, cyclic conditioning to the regular spacing of an event, and the conditioned response is electrical activity at the frequency of the event.

Basically, assimilation phenomena show that neural processes, which generate potentials observable with macroelectrodes of this configuration and size, are capable of producing a temporal pattern of electrical activity reflecting the rhythmicity of a previously experienced event *in the absence of that event*. Several years ago, Killam and John (1959) suggested that this ability to sustain a prolonged frequency specific discharge in the absence of the initially effective stimulus might function in the elaboration of a representation of that event. The data presented in the following discussion indicate that not only does the nervous system have the capability of generating electrical activity similar to that which it has previously experienced, but that such electrical activity is reliably associated with certain behavioral events in a manner which implies that these spatiotemporal patterns may have a functional role.

V. GENERALIZATION

Perhaps the most striking kind of evidence suggesting a functional role for these frequency specific potentials occurs in tests of *generalization.* If an animal is trained to perform a conditioned response to an intermittent stimulus of a particular frequency, a very characteristic discharge is elicited in certain regions of the brain when the conditioned stimulus is presented and the animal performs correctly. If the fully trained animal is presented with a stimulus of the same modality as the CS but a different frequency, the animal will often generalize and perform the previously established conditioned response. Under such circumstances the electrical potentials in certain places in the nervous system display the frequency of the initially experienced conditioned stimulus rather than the frequency of the test stimulus actually present.

As an example, Fig. 2 shows a set of tracings from the brain of a cat who was taught to jump a hurdle on presentation of a 10 per

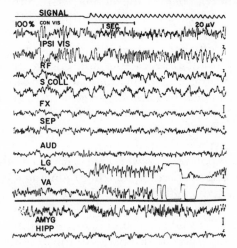

FIG. 2. Tracings from various regions of cat brain in response to 10 cps flicker CS after completion of avoidance training. Leads labeled as in Fig. 1; LG, lateral geniculate; VA, nucleus ventralis anterior. (From John & Killam, 1958.)

second flickering light and had reached perfect performance. Characteristically, animals beginning to learn avoidance will show potentials in the visual cortex at the frequency of the intermittent conditioned stimulus. Such animals will then go through a period in which potentials at three times the frequency of the conditioned stimulus are evoked in the visual cortex. When the criterion for learning is reached the cortical potentials usually stabilize at double the frequency of the conditioned stimulus. The basis for this sequence of changes, which has been seen in the rat as well as the cat, is not understood. Perhaps it is related to the number of pathways along which information converges upon the cortex at different stages of sophistication in the animal's learning. For our present purpose, it suffices to point out that the configuration of response in the visual cortex of a fully trained animal, upon the presentation of an intermittent CS at frequency F, is a potential at frequency $2F$: In the case illustrated here, the CS frequency was 10 per second and the frequency of the visual cortex response was 20 per second.

Shortly after this animal reached the criterion for acquisition, he was shown a flickering light at 7 per second. Figure 3 shows tracings obtained on the first presentation of the new stimulus. At the arrow the cat started to move toward the hurdle. Just before

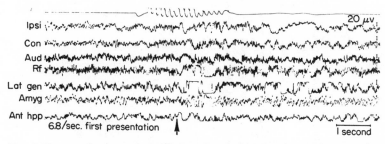

FIG. 3. Tracings from same animal as in Fig. 2, showing electrical activity during generalization as cat performs avoidance response upon presentation of 6.8 cps flicker. Arrow indicates hurdle jump. Leads as in Fig. 2. (From John & Killam, 1958.)

the behavioral response was initiated, a fast discharge appeared in the ipsilateral visual cortex. The frequency of that discharge was 20 per second: twice 10, which was the conditioned stimulus, rather than at the 7 per second rate of the new stimulus. After a number of repetitions of the new stimulus, the animal stopped generalizing and sat quietly. At this time, the visual cortex showed a 7 per second discharge on presentation of the new stimulus, and a 7 per second assimilated rhythm appeared. As can be seen in Fig. 4, presentation of the original 10 second CS now failed to elicit the CAR and the 20 per second cortical discharge was absent, replaced by a slower potential with a 7 per second component. After continued presentation of the 10 per second stimulus, under extinction conditions, the animal again started to perform the conditioned response. Twenty per second potentials then reappeared in the visual cortex.

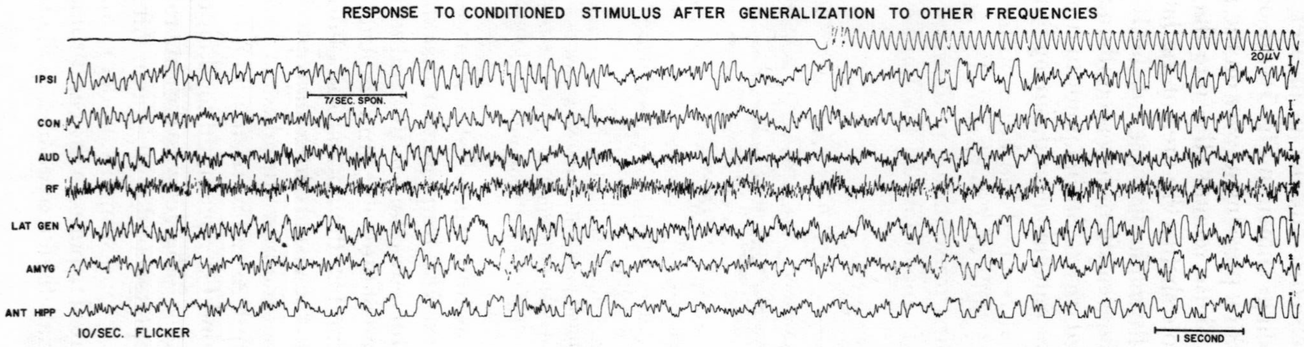

RESPONSE TO CONDITIONED STIMULUS AFTER GENERALIZATION TO OTHER FREQUENCIES

IPSI

CON

AUD

RF

LAT GEN

AMYG

ANT HPP

IO/SEC. FLICKER

7/SEC. SPON.

20 μV

I SECOND

FIG. 4. After repeated unreinforced presentation of the 6.8 cps flicker, generalization no longer occurred. The intertrial electrical record was observed to contain marked rhythmic waves at about 7 cps. These tracings illustrate the electrical response to presentation of the original 10 cps flicker CS, which now failed to elicit performance of the avoidance response. Note the contrast between these records and Fig. 2. (From John & Killam, 1958.)

We have recently obtained a number of clearer examples of this phenomenon. The tracings shown in Fig. 5 were obtained from a cat trained to avoid shock by pressing a lever on the presentation of a 4 per second flicker. These records illustrate the response to a 10 per second flicker. Note that in the area of the lateral genicu-late there was a frequency specific discharge at the 10 per second, with an occasional slower wave. After a few seconds, a marked slow wave appeared in the visual cortex. At this point in time the animal made its first overt muscular movement, and, during the subsequent

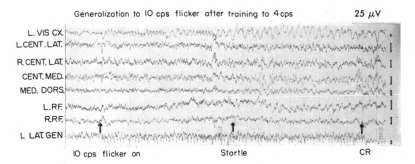

FIG. 5. Recordings obtained from another cat during generalization to 10 cps flicker after training to a 4 cps CS. At the first arrow, the CS was presented. At the second arrow, the cat stood up and slowly walked across the apparatus performing the avoidance response at the time indicated by the third arrow. Note the slow wave at about 4 cps in the visual cortex (L. VIS) and the reticular formation (L. RF), while the lateral geniculate (L. LAT. GEN.) continues to show clear 10 cps responses. (From John & Killam, 1958.)

interval, the conditioned response was performed quite leisurely. Throughout this period, slow potentials at about 4 per second were displayed in visual cortex. Traditionally electroencephalographers refer to slow waves as related to drowsiness and inhibition. These records are from an alert and tense animal, who is producing a slow wave while performing an avoidance response: Clearly, the slow wave cannot be attributed to drowsiness. We tend to believe that the slow wave is a function of the previous experience with the 4 per second aversive stimulus. Notice that in the reticular formation, where there is no conspicuous activity until movement begins, a slow wave emerges.

Figure 6, showing recordings obtained from a rabbit, was pub-lished in *Acta Physiological Polonica* in 1958 by Majkowski (1958), who later collaborated with Jasper at the Montreal Neurological Institute on further explorations of these phenomena. The rabbit had been trained to perform a leg flection to a 3 per second flickering light. The recordings shown were obtained at the very beginning of differentiation training. The animal was responding with a leg flection to a 5 per second light. The author has taken the liberty of adding time markers below the potentials of particular interest. In the visual cortex there is a 5 per second slow wave, the frequency of the stimulus as shown in the stimulus marker trace. In the motor

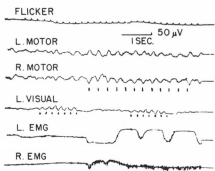

FIG. 6. An early example of the release of electrical waves at the frequency of the stimulus used in training during generalization to a new stimulus at a different frequency. MOTOR, motor cortex; VISUAL, visual cortex; EMG, electromyogram from foreleg of rabbit. (From Majkowski, 1958.)

cortex, a slow wave developed at 3 per second, which was the stimulus frequency used during training, and the leg flection was elicited. These data suggest that, in the motor cortex, a neural mechanism, which was established during training with the 3 per second flicker, was somehow triggered by the new stimulus but discharged with the customary frequency of the often-experienced CS.

Figure 7 shows further examples of this phenomenon, permitting more specific comments.* The top set of records is taken from an animal who has been trained to perform a lever press to a 4 per second flicker. When criterion was achieved, this animal would generalize very reliably on the presentation of a 10 per second flicker; the shock intensity which had been used was high enough so that he took no chances by not responding. The lateral geniculate

* These data are taken from an unpublished master's thesis by Marc Weiss, Department of Electrical Engineering, University of Rochester. Histological confirmation of electrode placement has not yet been obtained.

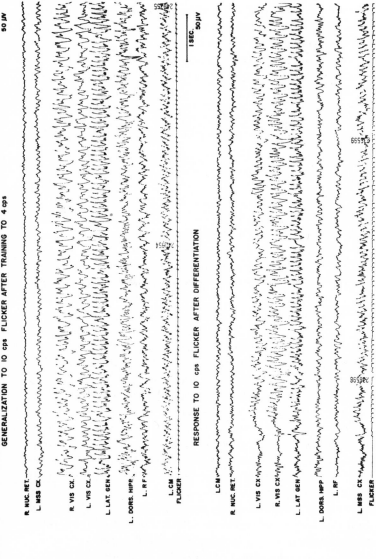

FIG. 7. Tracings from various brain structures of a cat after completion of avoidance training to 4 cps flicker. Top: During generalization to 10 cps flicker. Bottom: After differential training in which performance to the 10 cps flicker was punished. NUC. RET, nucleus reticularis; MSS, medial suprasylvian cortex; VIS, visual cortex; LAT. GEN, lateral geniculate; DORS. HIPP, dorsal hippocampus; RF, mesencephalic reticular formation; CM, nucleus center median. (From M. Weiss, 1962.)

body showed a very marked, regular 10 per second discharge on the presentation of the flicker. In the medial suprasylvian cortex there was a similar regular discharge. A small but regular discharge at 10 per second was initially displayed by the reticular formation, later a large slow wave appeared. Inspection of the visual cortex record showed that the frequency correspondence to the stimulus from this point on was quite poor. Left and right visual cortex showed slow waves on top of which could be seen spikelike peaks at a higher frequency. It might be commented, parenthetically, that this animal was being tested with what we call the "limp" technique. He had been trained using a steady 10 per second flicker. We wanted to know what portion of the electrical activity observed in the fully trained animal was endogenously generated by some kind of memory system. We proposed to approach this question by periodically deleting a flash of light and examining the records to see what structures displayed an evoked potential during the absence of the peripheral stimulus. Such potentials would allow us to infer an endogenous contribution in such a structure. There is not enough data to discuss this phenomenon in detail, but the record shows that, on some occasions when a flash was deleted, evoked potentials nonetheless appeared in the geniculate.

The bottom set of records in Fig. 7 was obtained after behavioral differentiation. The animal was taught that if he pressed the lever when 10 per second flicker was presented, he would be shocked; at the same time, if he failed to press the lever when a 4 per second flicker was presented, he would also be shocked. After differentiation was complete, 10 per second flicker was again presented. The visual cortical response no longer showed the large slow wave with spikes riding on it. Response now was at 10 per second, although there was still a slight amount of slow activity. The reticular formation displayed brief periods of 10 per second activity, but it no longer showed the big slow cusps. At this point the animal behaviorally treated a 10 per second stimulus as different from a 4 per second stimulus. As these recordings were obtained, the potentials were simultaneously processed using a four-channel average response computer. Essentially an average response computer is a device which enhances the signal-to-noise ratio for that portion of the electrical activity of a structure occurring in reproducible time relationship to an event which marks the beginning of a time period. The purpose in using this computer in conjunction with the

100 SWEEPS

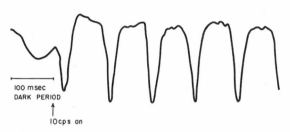

FIG. 8. Average response of lateral geniculate body during generalization to 10 cps flicker after training to 4 cps CS. Same animal as in Fig. 7. (From M. Weiss, 1962.)

electroencephalographic recordings was to determine whether a reliably produced, statistically significant event took place during the period when the flash was deleted. In order to contrast the amplitude and shape of this event with that produced by an actual light pulse, we had decided to average over a period of 625 msec, an interval sufficient for the dark period and a number of evoked responses to peripheral light flashes. The data gathered from the computer revealed something unexpected but probably much more interesting. The next figures show a number of average response computations. These may be viewed as the statistically reliable, reproducible, time-bound potential occurring in certain structures in coherent relation to the onset of a flash of light. Each computation was obtained under the same conditions: It was based on one hundred 625-msec samples; its statistical reliability was relatively high. The computer was triggered in each of these instances by the pulse emitted from the stimulator at the time that the deleted light flash would have occurred. The initial portion of the computation, then, was time in which there was no light flash. The first of these figures shows the average response computation obtained from the lateral geniculate of the animal whose records were shown in Fig. 7 during generalization to a 10 per second flash of light after previous training to 4 per second flicker. A word of explanation is needed before examining Fig. 8: In all of these computations the first evoked potential shape after a dark period was somewhat different from the subsequent ones; this was quite reliably observed and probably had something to do with the fact that this was the first flash after a dark interval. Figure 8, then, is the average of 100 times in which there was a dark period followed by a number of flashes of 10 per second flicker. During these 100 times the animal performed many generalized responses. Each time the behavioral response occurred, the stimulus was turned off, a period of time elapsed, and then a new trial took place. This was continued until 100 sweeps had occurred. In general, this would be between 10 and 15 behavioral trials, since this animal responded rapidly. Note that in this record from the lateral geniculate during generalization to a 10 per second flicker, there is a periodic event with a rhythmicity of 100 msec, or 10 per second. In center median, dorsal hippocampus, ventral hippocampus, nucleus reticularis, and medial suprasylvian cortex, a similar regular periodicity at 100 msec was observed during gen-

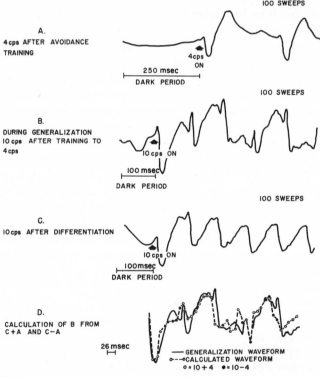

FIG. 9. Average response of visual cortex: (A) to 4 cps flicker CS after avoidance training; (B) during generalization to 10 cps flicker after completion of training to the 4 cps signal; (C) to the 10 cps flicker after completion of differential training; (D) comparison of actual waveform during generalization with calculated interaction waveform (calculation of B from C + A and C − A). Same animal as in Fig. 7. (From M. Weiss, 1962.)

eralization to a 10 per second flicker. However, at the same time that this regular waveform occurred in those structures, striking phenomena occur in other places.

Figure 9 illustrates the response of the visual cortex. Again, a series of average response computations are shown, all of these computations are based on 100 sweeps. The top one was obtained during presentation of the actual CS, flicker at 4 per second. Following avoidance training the animal was performing correctly. After this waveform, which we shall call waveform $A(t)$, was obtained, the animal was presented with 10 per second flicker to which he generalized very reliably. Whenever he generalized this computation could be obtained relatively reproducibly. The second computation is one of a number which were recorded during generalization; it came from the visual cortex at the same time that the very regular geniculate computation was obtained. Notice the complexity and irregularity of the waveform. Let us call this waveform $B(t)$. After differentiation, this animal would reliably refrain from pressing the lever to a 10 per second flicker, although he continued to perform consistently to a 4 per second stimulus. The third computation, $C(t)$, obtained during 10 per second flicker following differentiation was quite regular, with a periodicity of 100 msec. What interpretation might be attached to the change in the shape of the computed waveform after differentiation?

VI. COINCIDENCE DETECTION

Previous data and reasoning on assimilation and on the difference between correct responses and errors during differentiation performance have led to the argument that there was some kind of representational system elaborated in the brain by an experience. It was suggested that when an animal behaved as though a present event corresponded to some previously experienced event, some portion of the brain produced electrical activity corresponding to that which had been produced during the past event. One can, then, consider the second waveform in Fig. 9 as reflecting the activity of the visual cortex in an animal who is treating a 10 per second flicker as if it were 4 per second. How does an animal process a 10 per second flicker, which "reminds" him of a 4 per second flicker? The author does not have the faintest idea. But it might, somewhere in its brain, produce electrical activity representing what was *expected*, as well as the electrical activity evoked by what was present. That is, some place in its brain there ought to have been inter-action between a memory of past experience and a response to present experience. We and other research workers have suggested the necessity, in certain kinds of discrimination situations, for a *coincidence detection mechanism* which somehow compares the temporal sequence of events which occurred in the past with the temporal sequence of events occurring in the present. Discrimination must be based on the temporal sequence of events, since the individual constituent flashes in the flicker train are identical: Each individual flash of the 4 per second flicker is identical with the individual flashes of the 10 per second flicker. The difference between the two stimuli lies in their temporal sequence. To decide whether a flash is in a 4 or a 10 per second train, there must be some representation of time between events—and thus derives the argument for a comparator system.

If one assumes that the computation of cortical waveforms reveals a "memory" interacting with "reality," one wonders how waveforms interact. They might add or they might subtract. Should "memory" add or subtract from "reality"? We have no strong prejudices in this matter. The reader will agree that at this point it was appropriate for conservatism to reassert itself. It is not really known if memory would add or subtract from reality, so let us say that it might do both or either. Therefore, the point on each waveform marked by the arrow in Fig. 9 was defined as T_0 on a time scale and the voltage at that time as V_0 on a positive-negative voltage continuum. We then measured the voltage of each waveform, relative to V_0, at 5 msec intervals after T_0. Thus we constructed a digitalized description of each waveform in terms of numbers representing relative voltage at fixed times after the light flash. Let us call these sets of numbers: $A(t)$, response to a 4 per second conditioned stimulus; $B(t)$, response to a 10 per second stimulus during generalization; and $C(t)$, response to a 10 per second stimulus after differentiation. Now let us pose the question: Is it possible to construct the sequence, $B(t)$, by adding or subtracting $A(t)$ from $C(t)$? In Fig. 9 the bottom curve shows, as a solid line, the actual waveform of the potential recorded from visual cortex during generalization. The dotted line is the calculation $C(t) \pm A(t)$. The fit certainly appears to be nonrandom. It is exceedingly difficult to estimate the probability of obtaining such a fit across such an interval. Much time has been spent with applied mathematicians trying to derive a way to evaluate this, but the estimate is not satisfactory. However, the correspondence between the dotted line and the solid line is such that one must reject the null hypothesis that these two curves are unrelated.

The open circles on the dotted curve show where it was necessary to add the two waveforms to achieve the fit; the solid circles show where subtraction was required. It is approximately true that the phase of the 10 and 4 per second waveforms was similar when $A(t)$ and $C(t)$ were added; the phases were opposite when $A(t)$ was subtracted from $C(t)$. It was assumed that 10 per second was predominant, and the value of $C(t)$ was always taken as positive. Depending upon which manipulation yielded the best fit to the set of numbers $B(t)$, $A(t)$ was then either added or subtracted. The rules which describe what gave the best fit are represented by open or closed circles. It was not decided beforehand on what the rules would be, i.e., to add if $A(t)$ and $C(t)$ were in phase but subtract if they were not in phase, and thus generate these calculated curves. Had such been the fact, it could have been asserted unequivocally that the probability of obtaining the fit by chance is vanishingly small.

Figure 10 shows the results of an identical operation on the reticular formation waveforms. The first waveform, $A(t)$, is the response of reticular formation to 4 per second flicker; the second waveform, $B(t)$, is the response during generalization to a 10 per second flicker; and the third waveform, $C(t)$, is the response to a 10 per second flicker after differentiation. On the bottom line of the figure, the solid curve is the actual computed average response during generalization; the dotted curve is the calculation. In general it appears to be true that the rule for the best fit is opposite from that found for the visual cortex: if the phase of the responses to 10 per second flicker and to 4 per second flicker were alike it was necessary to subtract 4 from 10 to get the best fit; if the phases were not alike, it was necessary to add. Why "memory" should choose to interact with "reality" in this fashion is not clear. The fact that the rule for bipolar recordings from reticular formation should be somewhat different from the rule for monopolar derivations from the visual cortex is not surprising. The remarkable observation is that we can get such striking correspondence to the complex generalization waveform by algebraic manipulation of two waveforms obtained under different behavioral conditions. This has

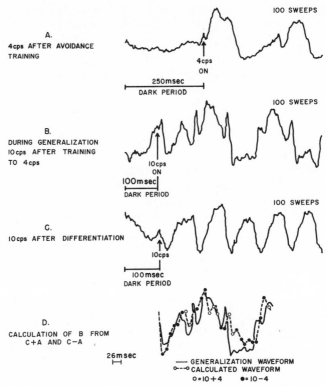

FIG. 10. Average response of reticular formation. Same conditions as Fig. 9, but data from mesencephalic reticular formation. (From M. Weiss, 1962.)

been found in records from the visual cortex and the reticular formation, but these "interference patterns" have not been observed elsewhere.

It is of further interest that quite the same conclusions had been reached on the basis of studies of differential approach-avoidance responses and the configurations of electrical activity during errors of commission and omission to the two conditioned stimuli involved, S^D and S^Δ. Previous work (John & Killam, 1960) led to the hypothesis that there was a comparator system such that a representation of past experience in nonspecific structures converged on the visual cortex, which acted as a coincidence detector by comparing the configuration for past experience with the configuration representing present events arriving along the classical neural pathways. The results of the computation just discussed are compatible with that hypothesis. This does not establish the hypothesis as true. However, the most probable interpretation of these data may be described rather simply: In some place in the animal's brain there existed a system which was established during prior learning experience; when the animal treated a new stimulus as if it were the CS to which that learned response had been established, those regions of the brain produced a readout from memory which reconstituted the electrical activity that had initially established the memory.

This interpretation would seem much more plausible were it not for the long and unsuccessful history of attempts to analyze the dynamics of memory. Previous failures have created an atmosphere in our field such that profuse qualifications and reservations are expected when one discusses mechanisms of memory. These attitudes generate a negativity, a reluctance to interpret data in a straightforward way. While the laboratory searches for other ways in which these results might be explained, a simultaneous attempt is made to further test the proposition that it is possible to code experience as a spatiotemporal sequence of potentials and that memory mechanisms somehow recreate the spatiotemporal configuration of potential which is characteristic of an event. To clarify this point further, the author is not concluding that information is coded as temporal sequence of potentials in a place, but he is suggesting that the temporal sequence of events which one records from a macroelectrode in a nucleus may very well reflect the spatial distribution of activity within that nucleus, propagating with characteristically different speeds across the region where the electrode is located so that one obtains in a macropotential recording of this sort what is in effect a spatiotemporal transform. The fact that there seems to be a correspondence between the configuration of this spatiotemporal transform and behavior suggests that an invariant *distribution of* activity may somehow be established in a population of cells by learning.

VII. DIFFERENTIATION

What has been already referred to a number of times—the changes in configuration of macropotentials in animals *differentially trained*—is illustrated by the following recordings. The recordings at the top of Fig. 11 are from a cat who was looking at a 10 per second flickering light. This cat had learned that whenever

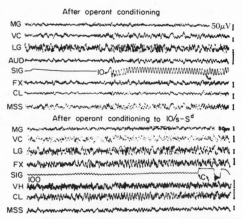

FIG. 11. Top: Effects of presentation of 10 cps flicker to cat which has been trained to obtain milk whenever it presses a lever. Arrow below SIG channel indicates occurrence of lever press. Bottom: Effects of same stimulus in same cat, but after the lever pressing response was brought under stimulus control, so that performance occurred only during 10 cps flicker. MG, medial geniculate; VC, visual cortex; LG, lateral geniculate; AUD, auditory cortex; SIG, flicker; FX, fornix; CL, nucleus centralis lateralis; MSS, medial suprasylvian cortex; VH, ventral hippocampus. (From John & Killam, 1960.)

he pressed a lever, he would obtain milk. He had no experience with 10 per second flickering light, which the experimenter was now presenting for the first time. The first deflection in the base line indicates a lever press and delivery of some milk. Ten per second flicker was presented following the first lever press and a second lever press happened to occur during the flicker. No striking frequency specific potentials were seen in the visual cortex, in the fornix at the intersection with the dorsal hippocampus, or in the centralis lateralis. Between the top and the bottom records, the lever-pressing for milk was brought under the control of the 10 per second flicker. Subsequently, presentation of 10 per second flicker elicited clear frequency specific potentials in the fornix, visual cortex, and centralis lateralis several seconds before the conditioned response, as can be seen in the bottom recordings.

Figure 12 represents a further stage. The response had now been differentiated so that lever pressing was still under the control of the 10 per second flicker, but a 6 per second flicker has been established as an S^Δ. It is of interest that in many structures frequency specificity is markedly enhanced by compelling differentiation with respect to frequency. For example, in the upper set of tracings for the visual cortex, fornix; and centralis lateralis there appears a more pronounced frequency specific response than was previously observed. Note also the change in waveform in visual cortex shortly before the conditioned response (CR), from a rounded to a more spikelike shape. This change in wave shape, in this animal and in a number of others in whom we have had comparable placements, was often observed when the centralis lateralis and visual cortex came into correspondence in their frequency pattern; it was almost invariably followed by performance of the conditioned response.

The lower set of tracings was obtained while this animal made a mistake, an error of omission. This failure to respond is interpreted as a mistake because he lived on dry dog biscuit in his home cage and received fluid only in the experimental situation: The animal is not indifferent, nor is he satiated; he is making a mistake. In response to the 10 per second flicker there was a large slow wave; interestingly, this was seen in the geniculate, in the fornix, and very regularly in centralis lateralis. The cat failed to press the lever; behaviorally, he was treating 10 per second stimulus as if it

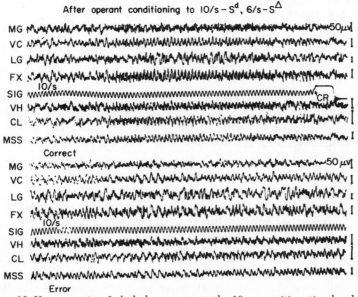

FIG. 12. Upper portion: Labeled responses to the 10 cps positive stimulus during correct performance. Lower portion: Labeled responses to the same stimulus during an error of omission.

172 E. ROY JOHN

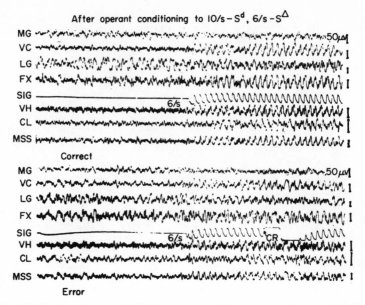

Fig. 13. Upper portion: Labeled responses to the 6 cps negative stimulus during correct inhibition of performance. Lower portion: Labeled responses to the same stimulus during an error of commission.

were 6. Slow waves in the visual cortex and geniculate now appear, not only in nonspecific structures.

The converse case is illustrated in Fig. 13. The upper tracings were obtained during correct performance to a 6 per second S^D— the cat did not press the lever. Massive 6 per second waves occur in the visual cortex, fornix, and centralis lateralis. The lower records illustrate an error of commission. The cat pressed the lever to a 6 per second flicker to S^Δ. Note that the potentials in the centralis lateralis after the stimulus onset are *not* at 6 per second. They are at approximately 10 per second, the frequency of the S^D.

This animal then received further training: He continued to get milk for pressing a lever during a 10 per second flicker, but had to jump a hurdle to avoid shock on the presentation of 6 per second flicker. Thus, the 6 per second flicker, which had been the signal to restrain the lever-pressing appetitive response, now became the discriminative stimulus for an avoidance response. As illustrated in Fig. 14, after the avoidance training the cat regularly displayed the same sequence of changes in recorded potentials in response to the 10 per second flicker. Presentation of this appetitive signal elicited a 10 per second potential in the visual cortex, in which occasional suggestions of a slow modulation could also be seen. In marked contrast, the potentials observed in the fornix and in the centralis lateralis upon presentation of the 10 per second flicker were initially massive slow waves at about 6 per second, the frequency of the aversive stimulus; superimposed on this slow wave, almost as a modulation, were spikes at 10 per second. The 10 per second potentials gradually emerged and became more dominant; there was a change from rounded wave shapes toward a more spike-like form; and the conditioned response was appropriately performed.

Research has shown that a cat placed into an approach-avoidance conflict will always resolve in favor of avoidance, which is prepotent in that species. The cat used to illustrate the phenomena under discussion first reacted to the presentation of the appetitive stimulus with a frequency like that of the aversive stimulus, but only in some nonspecific structures; the response from the suprasylvian cortex, as shown in Fig. 14, is frequency specific. The animal was then given a dose of reserpine, which blocked performance of the avoidance response to the 6 per second flicker. The 10 per second signal was then presented, and, as seen in Fig. 15, instead of the slow wave in the fornix and centralis lateralis, a regular 10 per second response appears. However, shown a 6 per second flicker, this animal would not perform the avoidance response. The reserpine action was then antagonized by methamphetamine, which in a matter of minutes restored performance of the avoidance response. As the avoidance response was restored to 6 per second,

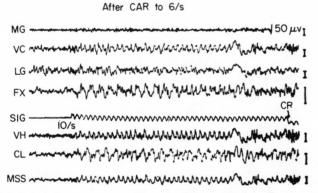

FIG. 14. Labeled responses to 10 cps positive stimulus after completion of avoidance training using the 6 cps flicker as the aversive stimulus.

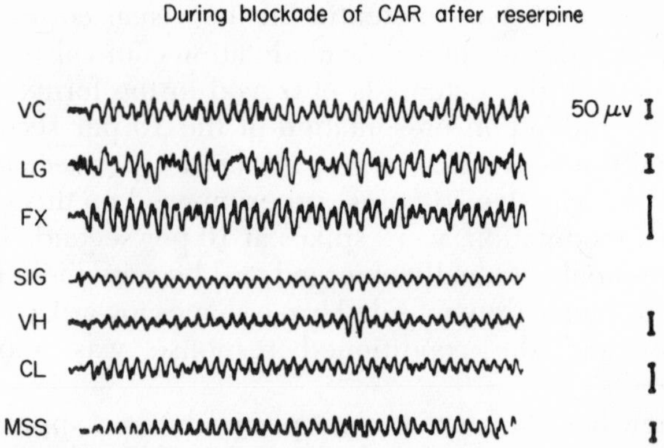

During blockade of CAR after reserpine

FIG. 15. Labeled responses to the 10 cps flicker during blockade of the avoidance response to 6 cps flicker by reserpine.

the slow wave in response to 10 per second reappeared in the fornix and centralis lateralis. These phenomena, then, suggest a concomitant variation between the appearance of potentials at a particular frequency in nonspecific structures and the appearance of different behaviors, as if a signal at that frequency had been presented to the animal peripherally.

VIII. Concurrent Central and Peripheral Stimulation

Next explored was the behavioral or functional significance of these macropotentials by using *concurrent central and peripheral stimulation*. We synthesized waveforms which were an approximation to the frequency specific events observed in certain structures during certain behaviors. Animals were implanted with all electrodes bilaterally symmetrical, so that it was possible to stimulate on both sides of the brain in the same anatomical structure. After such animals were taught to differentiate between two peripheral stimuli with frequencies F1 and F2, it was possible to investigate the behavioral consequences of central stimulation, concordant or discordant in frequency with the peripheral signal. The central stimuli were equated for total power so that electrical energy was not a discriminanda. The p values down the right column of Fig. 16 represent the probabilities of obtaining by chance the configurations of result which were recorded.

It became perfectly clear that one could control an animal's behavior by such central stimulation concurrent with peripheral stimulation. It was, unfortunately, not possible to control behavior in a fashion which depended upon the informational significance of the frequency. The animals were trained with counterbalanced frequency significance: Some animals were trained with F1 aversive and F2 appetitive and other animals were trained with the opposite configuration, but using the same F1 and F2. Apparently, in certain places slow frequencies, as central stimuli, were massively inhibitory. It was not known why this should be so. Those effects were so overriding that it was not possible to carry out the attempt to establish the functional significance of the observed macropotentials. Inadvertently, a low frequency had been selected as one of the stimuli, and the intrinsic inhibitory nature of this slow input was a confounding factor. This experiment, then, must be repeated using frequencies above this intrinsically inhibitory range.

However, with the research designed, it was decided to go

EFFECTS OF CONCURRENT STIMULATION

Structure	Cat	CS + central 4 cps		CS + central 10 cps		Current* (mAmp.)	Disruptive effects	P
		+	−	+	−			
BIL. VIS	4	12	3	11	3	3.4–4.0	=	—
	10	0	34	25	9	2.0–3.0	4 > 10	<0.001†
R. VIS	4	10	13	12	6	1.0–2.2	4 > 10	—
	10	5	26	27	4	2.1–2.5‡	4 > 10	<0.001§
L. VIS	4	20	69	62	25	1.0–1.7	4 > 10	<0.001†
	10	12	19	31	0	3.2–4.8	4 > 10	<0.001§
BIL. MSS	4	17	0	13	1	1.0–2.0‡	=	—
	10	17	4	16	5	1.35–3.0‡	=	—
BIL. AUD	4	3	9	7	5	1.0–1.9	4 > 10	—
	10	25	18	20	23	2.3–3.2	10 > 4	—
LG	4	39	61	26	43	0.2–1.0	=	—
	10	15	45	34	25	0.96–1.25	4 > 10	<0.001§
BIL. DORS H	4	9	1	3	10	0.13–0.36	10 > 4	<0.01¶
	10	3	8	0	11	1.1–2.1	10 > 4	—
BIL. VENT H	4	4	3	5	0	0.18–0.38	4 > 10	—¶
	10	17	7	9	15	1.0–1.15	10 > 4	<0.05§
BIL. RF	4	27	20	23	23	0.1–0.36	10 > 4	—
	10	30	23	18	35	0.28–0.36	10 > 4	<0.05§
BIL. CL	4	14	10	10	16	0.2–0.4	10 > 4	—
	10	16	25	13	28	0.45–1.0	10 > 4	—
CM	4	19	36	17	36	0.2–0.25	=	—
	10	42	64	38	69	0.70–0.85	10 > 4	—
MED. DORS	4	3	1	2	1	0.16–0.24	=	—
	10	21	16	7	30	0.48–0.68	10 > 4	<0.001¶

* The upper current value represents the occlusion threshold.
† Equally significant with power match.
‡ No occlusion threshold found.
§ No power match data.
¶ Not significant with power match.

FIG. 16. Effects of concurrent central and peripheral stimulation.

ahead and ask a number of other questions. In particular, we explored the possibility that this failure to demonstrate informational consequences to electrical stimulation of the nervous system in accordance with a temporal patterning stipulated by prior peripheral conditioning, might simply represent the fact that the nervous system speaks a different language to itself from the language being spoken to it. The central stimuli were composed of a high-frequency carrier wave amplitude modulated by a low-frequency square wave. It was obviously possible that the physiological consequences of these electrical inputs to the brain might be quite different from the physiological processes generating the macropotentials which were recorded, yet the observed macropotentials might reflect a function related to information processing. Therefore, it was decided to inquire as to whether or not one could establish such electrical inputs to the nervous system as differentially informational. We constructed two waveforms composed of trains of pulse pairs, such that, although the total electrical power and the shape and spacing of pulse pairs were identical, the temporal sequence of the trains was different. Precise stimulus parameters have been reported elsewhere (John, Leiman, & Sachs, 1961). We

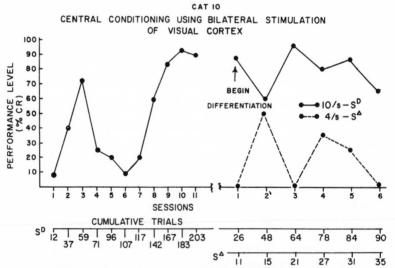

FIG. 17. Differential response to two different temporal patterns of electrical stimulation of visual cortex: 10/second positive stimulus 4/second negative stimulus—equated for total energy.

asked: If we deliver these two energy equated waveforms to the same electrode, can we teach animals to discriminate between two different *temporal sequences* at the same place?

The results in one animal are summarized in Fig. 17. The animal had previously been trained to press the lever for shock avoidance on presentation of 10 per second flicker, but not to press during 4 per second flicker. The lever-pressing response was then transferred to a central stimulation consisting of 10 per second trains of pulse pairs, delivered bilaterally to visual cortex. The rate at which this response was brought under control of the 10 per second central stimulus is shown by the early portion of the curve in Fig. 17. Differential training was then introduced to 10 per second central trains as S^D and 4 per second central stimulus trains as S^Δ. It is interesting that on the first presentation the animal's response to the 4 per second pulse trains on cortex was zero. Clearly, the 10 per second and 4 per second central inputs, equated for total electrical power, were processed differently from the very first differentiation session.

Figure 18 shows similar results for a second animal. This animal had previously been trained to differential avoidance using a 4 per second flicker as S^D and a 10 per second flicker as S^Δ, a meaning of

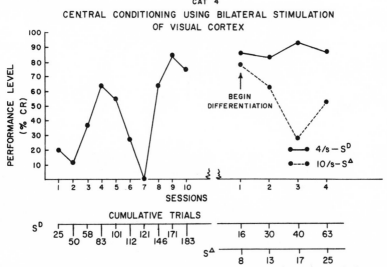

FIG. 18. Differential response to two different temporal patterns of electrical stimulation of visual cortex: 4/second positive stimulus, 10/second negative stimulus.

frequencies opposite to that employed with the previous animal. The first part of the curve describes the initial establishment of the avoidance response to bilateral central stimulation of the visual cortex with a 4 per second pulse train. The right side of the curve describes the course of differentiation to the two pulse trains. The same current intensity was used throughout this series, and the diminution in response seen for a period midway in training may represent a threshold increase. In contrast to the other animal, this animal did respond initially to the 10 per second input following 4 per second central training, but the response rapidly decreased. These data show that two temporal sequences of electrical stimuli, applied to the same place, equated for power and differing only in the time course of events, can be informationally distinguished by the nervous system. This does not prove that the time sequence of events propagating from one nucleus to another nucleus as a spatio-temporal transform of the distribution of activity within that nucleus constitutes information, but it does establish that the sequence of events at a particular place in the brain can be informational. It clearly does not exclude the possibility that identical events at different places could also be informational.

IX. Interaction between Specific and Nonspecific Systems

The last data to be presented are related to the question of the coincidence detector. We realized that it was possible to do an experiment which was really very simple, but could be quite informative. The evoked potential elicited by a flash in the visual cortex of a trained cat has two very distinct components, one early and one late. There is at first a primary response considered to represent the influence of the classical projection system on the visual cortex; there is then a much later, slower response which tends to be severely suppressed by nembutal and which is considered to arise from the arrival of slower influences from extra-lemniscal, multisynaptic pathways and in particular from the brain stem reticular and the diffuse projection systems. The data presented earlier on errors of commission and omission, the data on assimilation, and the computations obtained during generalization suggest that an interaction between the specific systems and the nonspecific systems is crucial in information processing. Recall that assimilated rhythms appear earliest, last longest, and are most marked in nonspecific structures. During generalization there appear, not in the geniculate but in the reticular formation and the visual cortex, waveforms which seem to include a component based upon prior experience as well as a component derived from the present event. Animals who correctly process information about a flicker frequency show a correspondence between frequency distribution in the specific structures of the visual system and in some nonspecific structures. Animals who behave inappropriately show a noncorrespondence, a tendency for the nonspecific structures to represent the frequency of a stimulus which would have been appropriate for the behavior that was omitted. These observations led to the belief that there was an essential step in discrimination behavior which required the interaction of these two neurophysiological systems, perhaps via a convergence on the visual cortex, which might serve as a coincidence detector. We devised a simple way to explore this hypothesis. A standard 4 per second central stimulus train was constructed consisting of bursts of differentiated pulse pairs, each burst lasting about 20 msec at specified current intensity. This standard electrical stimulus was delivered bilaterally to the visual cortex of an animal trained to perform a conditioned avoidance response to a 4 per second flicker. The central stimulus train was so timed as to reach the cortex simultaneously with the arrival of the early primary response to each light flash in the 4 per second flicker, *early*, or to arrive coincident with the later secondary cortical response to the flash, *late*. A counterbalanced stimulation sequence was utilized, consisting of:

4 per second flicker alone
4 per second flicker + *early* central stimulation
4 per second flicker + *late* central stimulation
4 per second flicker alone
4 per second flicker + *late* central stimulation
4 per second flicker + *early* central stimulation
4 per second flicker alone

Thus, effects of stimulus recency, activation due to peripheral stimulation, etc., were controlled. Only central stimulus trials bracketed by correct performance to the peripheral stimulus alone were considered in the data analysis. If *early and late* are identical central electrical stimuli, which differ only in the delay between

E. ROY JOHN

the flash of light and the application of the electrical perturbation to the visual cortex, will they have different behavioral effects?

Figure 19 shows that they clearly do. *Early* stimulation was always delivered 15 msec after each flash of the 4 per second flicker. In some experiments, *late* stimulation was delivered 80 msec after the flash; in other experiments a 110-msec delay was used. The chi square statistic has been calculated separately for these two *late* delays versus the *early* stimulation. Since these are independent measurements, they can also be combined. All differences were highly significant. Too low a stimulus failed to show any interference; too intense stimulation showed generalized interference with the response. However, the differential effects of *early* and *late* stimulation were really reliably elicited at the proper current values. Electrical stimuli arriving at cortex coincident with the *early* primary component of the evoked potential from flicker caused little or no interference with the behavioral response to the

EFFECT OF 4/SEC STIMULATION OF VISUAL CORTEX
AT VARIOUS DELAYS AFTER 4/SEC FLICKER-CAT 4

(2. 8 mA, 100/sec biphasic, 2 mS pulse width,
25 mS duration)

		CR	No CR	
DELAY	15 mS	34	22	$X^2 = 11.7$
	80 mS	15	39	

		CR	No CR	
DELAY	15 mS	16	12	$X^2 = 15.1$
	110 mS	2	26	

		TOTAL		
		CR	No CR	
DELAY	15 mS	50	34	$X^2 = 25.7$
	80 + 110 mS	17	65	

FIG. 19. Differential effects of electrical stimulation of the visual cortex during early and late components of the evoked response to a flickered conditioned stimulus.

GENERALIZATION OF DIFFERENTIATED RESPONSE
TO CENTRAL STIMULATION OF OTHER
ELECTRODE PLACEMENTS - CAT 10

	10/S		4/S	
	CR	NR	CR	NR
RIGHT VISUAL + other cortical sites	10	7	0	11
LEFT VISUAL + other cortical sites	1	18	2	4
SUB-CORTICAL SITES	0	15		

FIG. 20. Effects of stimulating single electrode used during training in combination with other sights.

peripheral conditioned stimulus, although the central stimulus parameters were identical with those which would cause severe disruption of conditioned response if delivered coincident with the *late* secondary component of the cortical response to the conditioned stimulus. This indicates that there is something crucial to the processing of information about peripheral stimuli by the visual system which takes place at the time of the arrival at visual cortex of the late influences of the nonspecific system. These findings are compatible with the suggestion that the visual cortex serves as a coincidence detector between the two converging systems, as previously proposed.

Figure 20 contains information which confirms something that Loucks (1961) reported in the Houston Symposium on Electrical Stimulation of the Brain, except that we extended those findings to differentiated responses. We established a conditioned response to electrical stimuli delivered to one electrode on the left visual cortex, the other electrode being on the right visual cortex. Stimuli were trains of biphasic pulses. The animal was trained to differentiate between two energy-equated temporal sequences, a 4 per second modulation and a 10 per second modulation of a carrier wave. We then tested for generalization of differentiation to stimulation of other places in the nervous system. We used one of the original input electrodes as one of the two electrodes across which stimulation was delivered and as the other we used any of the other cortical or subcortical electrodes available. With many combinations of this sort, we could get performance to the S^D frequency, but no performance to the S^Δ frequency. In contrast, no performance would be obtained if we shifted to the other electrode used for the initial conditioning, combining it with another site. We had used biphasic stimuli and varied cortex polarity in training. There is no reason to believe that during training the left visual cortex always received the first or the second pulse of a pulse pair; this possibility was eliminated by randomization. Yet it seems that only one of the two regions stimulated during training was effective in gaining access to the mechanism that was established by conditioning. The other site was not effective, even for performance, let alone for differentiation. Loucks (1961) reported a very similar finding, except that he did not include differentiation. He established a response between two electrodes A and B; when that response was elaborated, he paired A versus C, the third electrode of a triangle, and B versus C. He found that stimulation of A versus C always, and B versus C never, elicited the conditioned response. He reached the same conclusion we have: Only one of the two originally stimulated regions is an active site. Subcortically, we found that this input was unable to elicit generalized performance from any locus. However, it seems to be possible to establish performance very rapidly by reinforced subcortical stimulation, as if effective transfer were taking place. For example, one of the animals was trained to respond to reticular formation input, but we did not try to establish differentiated response. To establish differentiation between two temporal patterns of events delivered to the same electrode pair in the reticular formation, would suggest that the reticular formation can transmit specifically coded information. This would be a more discrete function than the tonic excitability regulation usually ascribed to this structure. Some of the data presented above suggest that its activities are not confined to this traditional function.

The results on the extent of generalization of central electrical stimulation between various sites indicate a spatial specificity of the response. Studies are in progress on the electrophysiological propagation of these differentiated central stimuli to find out whether such central inputs propage differentially, depending on whether they are S^D or S^Δ, or whether they are aversive or appetitive cues. We are also studying the interaction of appropriately coded, informationally adequate central conditioned stimuli with the propagation of previously established peripheral conditioned stimuli. Studies of this sort, particularly in situations where the central and peripheral signals are contradictory, should help clarify many of the problems raised by the findings to date.

X. CONCLUSION

In conclusion, it appears that, under the special circumstances described above, a marked correlation can be observed between the time course of potentials in certain brain structures and the behavior of a conditioned animal. It seems clear that the time course of events in a site in the brain can cause behavior, as evidenced by our ability to establish differential response to two central stimuli. It is not clear that the time course of events in a place in the brain is responsible for the behavior of an animal responding to a peripheral stimulus. It is by no means established that it is not responsible for the behavior; this is still an open question. The time course of events in a locus in the nervous system seems to be closely related to the spatial distribution of activity in the nucleus from which it is being recorded. It appears clear that something about the system which is elaborated in memory gives it the property to recreate a temporal sequence of potentials in certain places when memory is active. It also seems clear that memory is not maintained by a continuous, ongoing reverberation.

We have, then, posed a constraint, which, it seems, must be met by any proposed biochemical model of memory: There must somehow be a new property conveyed to an extensive population of neurons by some chemical alteration resulting from sustained neural activity produced by a stimulus; the property must be such that, when this system of neurons is appropriately stimulated at another time, the pattern of activity elicited reflects the spatio-temporal characteristics of the excitation which produced the chemical changes in the first instance, rather than reflecting only the characteristics of the present stimulation. In other words, there must be a readout from memory; and somehow the readout from memory must be in the same coin as the readin to memory. There must be a code for sensory events impinging upon the nervous system; there must be a code in which information is stored. Some place the code for what is stored and the code for what is happening at present must come into a common informational domain for the transactions which constitute remembering to take place.

REFERENCES

Chow, K. L., & John, E. R. (unpublished observations), 1956.

Glickman, S. E. Perseverative neural processes and consolidation of the memory trace. *Psychol. Bull.*, 1961, **58**, 218–233.

John, E. R., & Killam, K. F. Some electrical correlates of learned behavior (presented at the September, 1957, meetings of the American Pharmacological Society), *J. Pharm. exptl. Ther.*, 1958, **122**, 35A (Abstract).

John, E. R., & Killam, K. F. Electrophysiological correlates of differential approach-avoidance conditioning in cats. *J. nerv. ment. Dis.*, 1960, **131**, 183–201.

John, E. R., Leiman, A. L., & Sachs, E. An exploration of the functional relationship between electroencephalographic potentials and differential inhibition. *Ann. N.Y. Acad. Sci.* 1961, **92**, 1160–1182.

John, E. R., & Killam, K. F. Electrophysiological correlates of avoidance conditioning of the cat. *J. Pharmacol. exp. Ther.*, 1959, **125**, 252–274.

Livanov, M. M., & Polyakov, K. L. Electrical processes in the cerebral cortex of rabbits during the formation of the defensive conditioned reflex to rhythmic stimulation. *Bull. Acad. Sci. USSR*, 1945, **3**, 286–307. As reported in Rusinov, V. S., and Rabinovich, M. Y., Electroencephalographic researches in the laboratories and clinics of the Soviet Union. *Electroenceph. clin. Neurophysiol.*, 1958, Suppl. 8.

Loucks, R. B. Quoted in D. E. Sheer (Ed.), *Electrical stimulation of the brain.* Austin, Texas: Univer. of Texas Press, 1961.

Majkowski, J. EEG and EMG pictures of differentiation of conditional reflexes. *Acta Physiol. Polon.*, 1958, **9**, 565–581.

Stern, J. A., Ulett, G. A., & Sines, J. O. The electrocortical changes during conditioning. In J. Wartis (Ed.), *Recent advances in biological psychiatry.* New York: Grune & Stratton, 1960.

Weiss, Marc. Unpublished Master's Thesis, University of Rochester, 1962. Cited by John, E. R., Neural mechanisms of decision making in *Information storage and neural control.* Springfield, Ill.: Charles C Thomas, 1963.

Westbrook, W. H., & McGaugh, J. L. Drug facilitation of latent learning. *Psychopharmacologia*, 1964, **5**, 440–446.

CHAPTER 7

Biochemical Substrates of Behavior[*]

ROGER W. RUSSELL

Dean of Advanced Studies,
Indiana University,
Bloomington, Indiana

I. INTRODUCTION

William James (1899), in his notably forceful manner, early described the "essential problem" of psychology as the search for the nature and origin of the dynamics of behavior, which he de-

[*] Research from our laboratory reported in this chapter was supported by National Institute of Mental Health Research Grant MH 06997.

185

scribed as ". . . a stream, a succession of states, or waves, or fields (or of whatever you please to call them), of knowledge, of feeling, of desire, of deliberation. . . ." The search has taken the discipline far and in many directions since James defined the problem. Recently, with major cooperation from several of psychology's neighbors among the biological sciences, exciting and challenging progress has been made toward understanding relations which exist between behavior and biochemical events within the living organism, each of which is involved in the stream of changes which are the organism's adjustments to its internal and external environments.

Mention of the adjustment of organisms to their environments has the familiar ring of the Darwinian perspective about the evolutionary origin of life upon our planet. In Darwin's view the rise of new species as a result of natural selection taken together with gradually changing environmental conditions was accompanied by a similar continuity in the evolution of behavior (Darwin, 1872). More recently, the concept of evolutionary change has been extended to include the biochemical properties of living organisms (Bernal, 1962; Wald, 1952).

Wherever we turn in our study of living organisms we find chemical changes taking place, whether the organism is at rest or in action. Some of these biochemical events are involved in producing and storing sources of energy needed by the organism in its general bodily function; others are basic to the particular functions which define the organism's special capabilities. Research in comparative biochemistry (Baldwin, 1949) has lent strong support to the notion that living organisms closely resemble each other at the molecular level: that there is a fundamental ground plan which characterizes them all and upon which more complex biochemical superstructures have been built in the process of surviving in a variety of different chemical environments. This notion implies the occurrence, very early in the history of the earth, of a chemical evolution, which must have preceded the more familiar biological evolution that resulted in the various forms of plants and animals as we know them today. Recently, several experiments (S. L. Miller, 1953; S. L. Miller, 1955; S. L. Miller & Urey, 1959) have been designed to study the possible formation of biologically important substances under the influence of electric discharges through a mixture of gases approximating in composition the primitive atmosphere believed to have existed in those early times. Among the products of these experiments there have been isolated a variety of chemical substances of the kind which even today are the starting materials for the synthesis of many elaborate organic compounds. This view of how the fundamental ground plan was laid down gives an order of priority to the biochemical properties of living organisms. It suggests that other properties, including behavior, are, in a sense, "dependent upon" biochemical events. In the same sense, this priority evidences itself during the development of an individual organism, a process which is controlled at a molecular level, i.e., DNA, and proceeds by a wide variety of biochemical reactions.

With the development of knowledge about the biochemical substrate have come more specific hypotheses about interactions between biochemical events and behavior. Speculation and research have both directed attention upon biochemical events at two principal focal points: the molar dynamics of enzyme systems and the molecular events from which enzyme systems arise. To these should be added a third, which future research may prove to be of particular importance to such theoretical constructs in psychology as learning and memory: the actions of neural growth factors. What characteristics of these events have motivated such attention?

II: THE BIOCHEMICAL SUBSTRATE

New excitement in the search for relations between biochemical events and behavior has arisen from discoveries relating to the chemical coding of genetic information and the analogies with the process of memory at the behavioral level which they have suggested. Genetic information is conveyed from parental cells to their progeny by way of nucleic acids, which are constituents of the chromosomes in plants and animals. The information which determines the inherited characteristics of the offspring is encoded in the sequences of bases in one type of nucleic acid, deoxyribonucleic acid (DNA). A section of one of these large molecules is shown in Fig. 1, together with a sketch of its double helix or spiral shape. It has been estimated that there is sufficient DNA in a single cell of the human body to encode the information contained in about one thousand large textbooks. Important to its role in storing

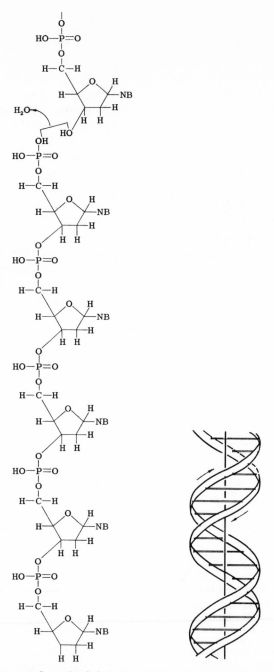

FIG. 1. Diagramed on the left is the chemical structure of a small section of deoxyribonucleic acid (DNA). Illustrated on the right is the double helix or spiral form of the nucleic acid molecule.

genetic information is the capability of these molecules to reproduce themselves at each cell division: Presumably the double helix uncoils and each strand forms its complementary partner by attracting appropriate units from the surrounding chemical environment. As would be expected if genetic information within a species is to be transmitted over countless generations, as it is, DNA molecules, once formed, must be very stable, resistant to changes in their physical and chemical environments (Alfert, 1957).

The second type of nucleic acid, ribonucleic acid (RNA), is involved in the synthesis of proteins. The mechanisms of this synthesis have been identified and may be outlined very sketchily as follows: DNA imposes some part of its pattern upon RNA molecules synthesized in the nucleus of the cell. Each of these messenger RNAs, then, is a copy of a DNA sequence, serving as a short-lived template in specifying the sequence of amino acids along the chain of the protein being synthesized. Transfer RNAs, each specific to one amino acid, localize activated amino acids from the surrounding chemical environment at their proper places on the chain, which is finally formed on the ribosomal particles in the cell. The order in which amino acids are lined up determines the special characteristics of the protein synthesized; even very slight differences in structure may result in very significant differences in their effects on the anatomical, physiological, and behavioral characteristics of the organism. Unlike DNA, RNA and the protein synthesis process may be widely influenced by the physicochemical conditions of the environment. Their production in nerve cells is at a rate which follows neuronal activity (Hydén, 1959); actively secreting cells contain nuclei which are larger in volume than those of nonsecreting cells, due primarily to differences in amounts of protein.

Among the proteins synthesized are enzymes which control the specialized as well as the nonspecific activities of each particular cell. The synthesis of these long-chain molecules is genetically determined in accordance with the "one gene–one enzyme" theory that each gene controls the structure of one enzyme and, conversely, that each enzyme is regulated by a single gene (Beadle & Tatum, 1941). Nearly all the chemical changes that go on in living tissues are changes which, *in vitro*, proceed too slowly to serve the functions they in fact serve *in vivo*. Living organisms possess numerous enzymes, serving as biocatalysts, which speed up the chemical reactions to the rates characteristic of biological systems. The roles of enzymes in a chain of biochemical events may be diagramed schematically as follows:

Substrate A
$\downarrow \leftarrow$ Enzyme 1
Substrate B
$\downarrow \leftarrow$ Enzyme 2
Substrate C

Enzyme 1 controls the velocity with which substrate A is converted to substrate B and enzyme 2, the velocity of the B to C step. Figure 2 illustrates the functions of enzymes using as an example the series of step reactions involved in the synthesis and later hydrolysis of the neurohumoral transmitter substance, acetylcholine (ACh), which is formed from acetyl-coenzyme-A + choline in the presence of the enzyme, choline acetylase; when released on stimulation of a nerve, ACh is hydrolyzed very rapidly to acetate and choline in the presence of another enzyme, acetylcholinesterase (AChE). The essential role of enzymes is shown clearly when the level of AChE activity is lowered and ACh accumulates—paralyzing nerve transmission, altering behavior, and, if too severe, leading to death. One characteristic of enzymes is their specificity in catalyzing only a comparatively small range of reactions; a second is the profound effects upon their functioning which are produced by changes in the physical and chemical nature of their environ-

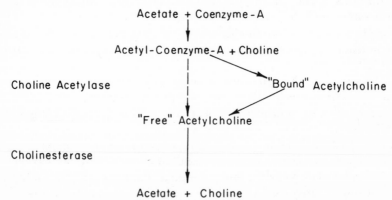

FIG. 2. Diagram of the step reactions involved in the synthesis and later hydrolysis of the neurohumoral transmitter substance, acetylcholine (ACh).

ments; and a third is their differential distribution in body tissues, being present in varying amounts in some tissues and not in others.

Among the many enzyme systems in the body, those involved in the activity of the nervous system have, understandably, held the center of attention in the search for interactions between biochemical events and behavior. During the years since the chemical hypothesis of nerve transmission was formally proposed, ample support has been obtained for the basic role of one of these, the ACh system, in neuromuscular transmission. Although not as fully documented, there is convincing evidence that ACh is released and acts as a chemical transmitter in the CNS (Crossland, 1960; Gaddum, 1962). Results of electron microscopy and cytochemical analyses support the view that ACh is stored in morphological units, synaptic vesicles, concentrated in close relationship to the synaptic membrane, and is released when an impulse reaches the nerve ending, an arrangement which indicates a fine compartmentalization of active substances and of enzymes within the nerve ending complex (De Robertis & Bennett, 1955; De Robertis, Salganicoff, Zieher, & Arnaiz, 1963; Whittaker, 1959). The action of the system as an intracellular or intramembranous process controlling sodium conductance associated with the generation of nerve action potentials has been defined in increasing detail (Nachmansohn, 1959; Nachmansohn, 1961). The evidence that other substances are also involved in nerve transmission is not as clear, although there is little doubt that others are involved. Among the catecholamines, it is now rather well established that norepinephrine (NE) is the principal neurohumor of adrenergic neurons (Florey, 1961). Although not yet adequately supported by sufficient specific data, the working hypothesis has been advanced that serotonin (5-HT) serves an important role in the central parasympathetic system (Crossland, 1960; Florey, 1961; Rothballer, 1959). Preliminary evidence has been obtained that the catecholamines are contained in the numerous granulated vesicles located in axons involved in autonomic neuromuscular contacts (Simpson & Devine, 1966).

Proteins are also involved in the growth, differentiation, and maintenance of nerve cells. Environmental changes which influenced protein synthesis might, therefore, be reflected in biochemical events whose final effect was to influence anatomical features within the organism. Recently, a series of experiments (Levi-Montalcini, 1964a; Levi-Montalcini, 1964b; Levi-Montalcini &

192   ROGER W. RUSSELL

Angeletti, 1961) has demonstrated the presence of growth-promoting substances, NGFs,* in a wide range of tissues and body
fluids, e.g., nerve cells, sarcomas, salivary gland extracts, and blood,
and in a variety of animal species, including man. These substances
are proteins in nature and are highly specific for nervous tissue.
The sympathetic nerve cells of birds and mammals are particularly
receptive to one of them; this same protein has been found to be a
normal constituent of the sympathetic cells, also being present in
blood and body fluids. One of the most interesting phases of the
research has been the preparation of an antiserum which selectively affects the sympathetic neurons of newborn animals without interfering with other nerve cells or other tissues, leaving experimental animals comparable in other ways to normal controls.
Differentiation and growth of other types of neurons may also depend upon other specific protein factors. This relatively new information suggests the interesting possibility that interactions may
occur between behavior and biochemical events involved in the
synthesis of NGFs, interactions which modify the structure of
nerve cells.

From its genetic control mechanisms to the final actions of its
enzyme systems, biochemical events truly constitute a dynamic
substrate of behavior, a substrate that would appear appropriate
for the continual stream of changes which characterizes the behavior of living organisms. It will take much more than such a
superficial analogy to convince us that lawful interactions do in
fact occur between the substrate and behavior, but analogies often
suggest hypotheses which can be put to empirical test.

III. INTERACTIONS BETWEEN BIOCHEMICAL EVENTS
AND BEHAVIOR

A number of such hypotheses have already been examined.
Taken together they conceive of biochemical events and behavior
as being reciprocally related:

$$\text{Biochemical Event} \underset{(2)}{\overset{(1)}{\rightleftarrows}} \text{Behavior}$$

Variables of either class may be antecedents or consequents:
Changes in biochemical events may produce concomitant changes
in behavior, as represented by arrow 1, or changes in behavior may
be reflected in persisting changes in biochemical events, the tem-

* NGFs, neural growth factors.

poral sequence represented by arrow 2. It will be worthwhile at this point to consider briefly some examples of the kinds of evidence which supports this conception, for it comes from a wide range of research carried on by investigators holding primary allegiance to several different disciplines. The basic experimental research approach used has involved the logic of scientific method to which John Stuart Mill gave the name, "method of concomitant variation": In some instances researchers have systematically varied biochemical events and measured consequent changes in behavior patterns; in others, they have varied behavior and sought concomitant changes in biochemical events. But advantage has also been taken of spontaneously occurring circumstances under which the two variables could be measured and the degree to which they were correlated determined.

A. Biochemical Events → Behavior

Let us first consider the hypothesis that biochemical events and behavior are related by asking what may appear at first glance to be a rather odd question: What would be the effect upon behavior of stopping *all* biochemical events? An obvious answer would seem to be that, when vital biochemical systems are inactive, an organism is no longer living and dead organisms do not respond to changes in their environments nor do they initiate responses. But, from a scientific point of view, this is only a partial answer. It is important to know not only what happens to behavior when all biochemical processes are stopped, but it is equally important to know what happens when these processes are started once again. A few years ago we (Andjus, Knöpfelmacher, Russell, & Smith, 1956) were able to study the full course of such drastic changes. In order to stop all biochemical events we took advantage of the fact that their velocities vary with the temperature of the environment in which they occur. Techniques had just been developed for reanimating rats whose deep body temperatures had been maintained below +15°C for as long as 70 minutes. In our studies we had groups of subjects whose deep body temperature was reduced to as low as 0°C. Such treatment results in complete arrest of heart beat, circulation, and respiration; it also suppresses electrical activity in the brain. In our animals, electrical brain activity may have been arrested for as long as one and a half to two hours. By the usual definitions, the animals were "dead" during this period. They were then reanimated and given a series of behavioral tests. The effects of arresting biochemical events in this way were striking, but perhaps different from what might be expected. Clearly no behavior could be elicited while the deep body temperatures were low. However, the aftermath of the treatment was much more interesting, we *failed* to find evidence that the arrest of vital biochemical processes produced any very serious effects on the behavioral patterns we were studying once an animal had been reanimated. There were no effects upon the memory of past training: Whatever the basis upon which prior learning had been stored, it was not disrupted by the temporary interruption of biochemical and electrophysiological processes. An impairment in learning new responses was noted, but it was very small and soon disappeared. The results indicated a relation between biochemical events and behavior such that, when the former were stopped, the latter disappeared; when the former were started once again, the latter reappeared.

These experiments demonstrated a very general interaction between biochemical events and behavior. Is there evidence for more specific relations? There is; and the evidence comes from several different sources. One of these involves research in human genetics. For many years it has been known that inherited metabolic faults observable in man are understandable if it is assumed that in each case the body fails to carry out one particular step in a normal series of biochemical events. This failure could be accounted for in terms of a congenital absence of the enzyme required for the biochemical step affected. It has been possible in a few instances to isolate the nature of the particular biochemical fault involved. Best known of these faults in man is a disorder known as phenylketonuria (PKU). For those interested in the chemical nature of the fault, it has been determined that a defect occurs in the breakdown of the amino acid, phenylalanine, characterized by failure of its normal conversion to tyrosine. For the development of our present theme, the important point is that this very specific, naturally occurring biochemical variation is reflected in marked abnormalities of behavior. Individuals diagnosed as phenylketonurics have been found to have some degree of intellectual impairment, being typically at the level of imbecility. One noticeable behavioral feature is an accentuation of reflexes; seizures and spasticity often appear. In contrast to the interaction between this biochemical fault and behavior are the effects of two other faults, alkaptonuria and tyrosinosis, which are chemically closely related to PKU, but which do not appear to be associated with significant behavioral effects of any kind. Here is an example of a relation between behavior and a very specific biochemical event. When such relations are known, the knowledge may be put to practical use, as in the case of PKU where early diagnosis and proper diet may lead to successful control of the abnormal condition and its behavioral effects.

The search for specific relations between biochemical events and behavior has also employed methods familiar in psychological studies of individual differences: Naturally occurring variables are measured and the magnitudes of relations between them determined by the statistical techniques of correlation; no experimental intervention is involved. The use of this approach is illustrated in an extensive series of investigations reviewed by Rosenzweig, Krech, and Bennett (1960). The research was designed to test certain specific hypotheses derived from the very general proposition ". . . that variation in brain chemistry is a major determinant of variation in adaptive behavior among normal individuals. . . ." The basic procedure involved the measurement of (a) "adaptive behavior" as evidenced in such standardized situations as the Krech hypothesis apparatus, the Lashley-III maze, Hebb-Williams maze, and the Dashiell maze; and (b) the activity level of the enzyme, cholinesterase, in various regions of the cerebral cortex and of the subcortex. Selective breeding techniques were also used to develop strains of subjects with relatively high or low brain ChE activity levels, i.e., to maximize the range of individual differences in the biochemical variable. The full story of the research series is is a long one with a number of complications, but it provided evidence that significant relationships did in fact exist at least at the level of the general proposition stated above.

Information from these approaches support the view that changes in biochemical events may be associated with changes in behavior and that such relations may be very specific. However, as Rosenzweig et al. (1960) have pointed out in regard to their own earlier studies: "Obviously it is hazardous to argue from correlations to existence of a causal relation . . . the traditional procedure in seeking . . . [such relations] . . . would be to manipulate experimentally the biochemical variable (the independent variable) and observe whether . . . performance (the dependent variable) changed . . ." in a manner appropriate for the hypothesis being tested. Because the discussion to follow draws almost exclusively upon the results of experimental manipulations of biochemical and behavioral variables, the author will not pause here to illustrate application of the experimental approach.

B. Behavior → Biochemical Events

Let us now turn to the other side of the coin, to some examples of evidence that changes in behavior may be reflected in persistent alterations of biochemical events. That such interactions can occur is a basic assumption underlying the diagnosis and treatment of the so-called psychosomatic illnesses in which behavioral stresses appear to precede signs of organic disorder. It is central in several recent lines of research which are seeking to understand how learning occurs and how experience is stored in memory.

Again, the evidence in support of this temporal order of interaction comes from several different research directions. One of the early approaches demonstrated that interactions between individuals in their social environments may produce lasting changes in important biochemical events (Chitty, 1955; Clarke, 1953). The investigators were interested in understanding the periodic fluctuations observed in animal populations living in their natural habitats. The fluctuations appeared to be related to the density of a population. Their hypothesis was that, as numbers and overcrowding increased, so did the frequency of interactions between individuals, interactions which often involved the stress of defending their home territories; these interactions produced persistent biochemical disturbances in parents which gave rise to abnormalities in their offspring, impairing their ability to survive and to adapt to their environment. The hypothesis was put to test in the laboratory, where the frequency and duration of interactions between experimental animals could be varied systematically. The results supported the hypothesis; significant weight changes occurred in the adrenal and thymus glands, the former increased while the latter decreased, suggesting that the effect of this kind of behavioral experience was to induce a disturbance in the adreno-pituitary system. The effect was as persistent as had been predicted, continuing to be evidenced long after the experimental treatment had ended.

Most prominent in the search for evidence that changes in behavior can be reflected in changes in biochemical events are two extensive series of experimental studies which are still under way and which will be referred to in detail at several points in the discussion to follow. One (Krech, Rosenzweig, & Bennett, 1964) has employed a standardized procedure by which different groups of subjects could be exposed to widely different environments for extended periods of time, the environments providing entirely different behavioral experiences. Analyses of brain tissue following the exposure have revealed certain significant differences in the acetylcholine system, which were related to the differences in experience. They have also shown certain variations in brain structure, again related to previous experience. The second major series of experiments has captured wide interest by suggesting that changes in behavior may produce concomitant changes in the rate of synthesis and/or the structure of RNA and proteins. Again the general experimental approach has been to vary behavior in one group of subjects and then to determine whether hypothesized changes have in fact occurred at the macromolecular level when comparisons are made with suitable control groups. Basic to the biochemical determinations have been the development of techniques for analysis of the macromolecules concerned in such tiny amounts as the 100 to 1000 $\mu\mu$g range (Edström, 1960; Edström, Grampp, & Schor, 1961) and for dissecting out, under the stereomicroscope, single nerve cells separated from their surrounding glia (Hydén, 1959).

Results from the use of all these approaches support the view with which this part of the present discussion began: There exist important reciprocal relations between behavior and its biochemical substrate. The evidence also indicates that such relations may be highly specific. Sufficient knowledge is already available to enable us to examine systematically the roles which biochemical events play in genetically precoded behavior, in the coding of new behavior patterns, and in the control of competing responses. It raises questions about the modes of action by which biochemical events influence behavior and about the control of behavior by the use of drugs to vary biochemical events.

IV. GENETICALLY PRECODED BEHAVIORAL PATTERNS

From its earliest scientific days the study of living organisms has suggested that the organization of the nervous system includes certain genetically determined patterns of behavior, which have traditionally been referred to as "instinctive" behavior. These are behavioral patterns which are *precoded* or programed in the genetic material from which the organism develops. Although they may be modified to limited extents by later interactions between the organism and its environment, i.e., the programs are "open" to various degrees, the basic behavioral patterns appear as soon as adequate sources of stimulation are present, apparently without opportunity for learning to take place. In these terms the behavior of some species of animals is more completely precoded than that of other species. It is, of course, clear that the programing of a wide variety of other behavioral patterns, though also limited by genetically determined potentialities, is acquired during an organism's lifetime.

Earlier, the author referred to the fact that the basic characteristics of living organisms—their anatomical, electrophysiological, and biochemical properties—are laid down in the genetic information encoded in DNA and read out, during development, by way of the RNA-protein synthesis process. Presumably any innate precoding of behavioral patterns must also be dependent upon information stored in DNA. Katz and Halstead (1950) anticipating more recent developments, suggested that: "In a very real sense, the genetic apparatus is a memory (recapitulation) device. It not only enables the organism to 'remember' its species identification characteristics, but is also involved in the transmission of certain behavior functions, namely, instinctual modes of behavior." If we accept the reasonable assumption that innately precoded behavior is transmitted in this way, we are immediately faced with questions about how the readout of the relevant genetic information is manifested in mechanisms mediating the behavioral patterns in question.

Efforts to understand the mechanisms have directed attention to the processes of biological communication (Rosenblith, 1961). Messages are conveyed not only between individuals and groups of individuals but are also involved in a multitude of events within individuals upon which the basic functions of metabolism and of reactions to changes in the internal and external environments depend. The study of biological communication processes has been oriented toward specifying the energy changes in the internal and external environments which constitute sources of information, the specialized neural receptors which encode the information, the neural circuitry over which it is conveyed, the central neural mechanisms in which it is processed and may be stored, the processes at the interfaces between this circuitry and effectors where messages are decoded, and the nature of muscular and glandular processes involved in the response outputs initiated by the information. Since biochemical events are involved in processes occurring at all these levels, it is not surprising that a concept of "neurochemical coding of behavior" has begun to be formulated (e.g., Fisher & Coury, 1962; Grossman, 1964a; N. E. Miller, 1965) as our knowledge about relations between biochemical events and behavior has grown.

A. Functional Neural Circuits

There is considerable evidence to show that precoded behavioral patterns are dependent upon activity in specific functional circuits within the nervous system, circuits that are selectively sensitive to the kinds of environmental change or stimulus input that elicit the responses. For example, an important part of the information regulating the consummatory response of drinking is carried by a functional neural circuit which involves several interrelated limbic and diencephalic structures (Fisher & Coury, 1962; Morgane, 1964). Studies of the circuit show its electrophysiological activity to be influenced by environmental changes which are capable of producing cellular dehydration, e.g., water deprivation (Steiner, 1962). Results of the traditional experimental approaches for identifying functionally related CNS structures show that: Creating lesions which interrupt the anatomical continuity results in cessation of drinking in water-deprived subjects; activation of the circuit by electrical stimulation causes satiated animals to drink; water deprivation is associated with significant changes in electrophysiological activity within the circuit.

Recently, it has become recognized that at least some of these functional circuits have another property which differentiates them from other circuits: They are *selectively sensitive* to direct chemical stimulation. In a sense this property is analogous to the color coding of subcircuits within a complex electronic system: It identifies certain structures as being functionally interrelated and qualitatively different in function from other structures that are not sensitive to the same chemical stimulation. This property will be referred to as *circuit coding.*

Attention was called to this coding of functional neural circuits mediating basic behavioral patterns by reports that differential chemical stimulation in the same circumscribed area of the hypothalamus elicits quite distinct and specific changes in "motivated behavior," adrenergic stimulation evoking food intake and cholinergic stimulation water intake, both in satiated subjects (Grossman, 1960; Grossman, 1962). Research which followed has shown that identical or similar chemical codings characterize other structures involved in the functional neural circuits underlying these behavioral patterns (Grossman, 1964a; Grossman, 1964b; Wagner & de Groot, 1963), and that the circuits themselves may be traced through their selective sensitivity to particular chemical stimuli (Fisher & Coury, 1962). The circumstances under which the specificity of circuit coding would appear to have maximum information value are when the structural elements of two or more different functional circuits are in close spatial proximity, as, for example, are the tightly packed pathways in the hypothalamus.

Research on functional circuits and on circuit coding suggests means by which information stored in DNA could be involved in the precoding of certain basic behavioral patterns: by assigning neural units to a functional circuit and coding the circuit neurochemically. Coding of this kind is qualitative in nature, serving, at the same time, to establish the integrity of units comprising a functional circuit and to discriminate one circuit from another.

B. Coding of Quantitative Information

These precoded behavioral patterns are very finely balanced. Within limits, their response outputs are related to the intensity of the environmental changes which evoke them; once activated, sensory and blood-borne feedback turns off the response. Presumably information relevant to both activation and satiation is encoded at the input end and transmitted in such a way as to be reflected *quantitatively* in the response output of the system.

The nature of this quantitative relation between input and output can be seen more clearly by examining the results of experiments in which the functional circuit mediating drinking behavior was activated by direct cholinergic stimulation through cannulae

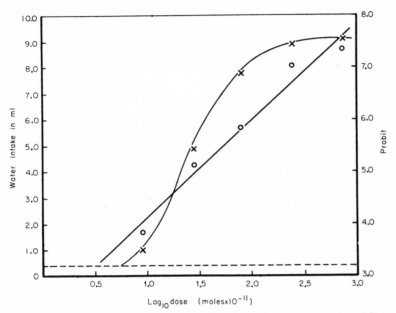

FIG. 3. The sigmoid-shaped curve shows the relation between intensity of direct cholinergic stimulation, i.e., varying concentrations of carbachol, in the lateral hypothalamus and water intake (data replotted from Miller *et al.*, 1964). The straight line is a log-probit plot of the same data.

implanted in the lateral hypothalamus (N. E. Miller, Gotterman, & Emery, 1964). Intensity of stimulation was varied systematically by the use of different concentrations of the cholinergic chemical agent, carbachol. Figure 3 shows the results replotted on a log base. As the sigmoidally shaped curve shows, within the central range of concentrations the response output, i.e., water intake, is approximately a linear function of the log intensity of the stimulus activating the system. This is a relation which characterizes the dynamic properties of a wide variety of neural circuits.

Above and below this central range the relation no longer holds: The response output levels off above the zero baseline and reaches its peak at a concentration of $24 \times 10^{-10}M$. Observation of the general behavior of the experimental subjects showed what was happening as these response asymptotes were approached. As stimulus intensity increased beyond $24 \times 10^{-10}M$ other competing responses were activated which interfered with drinking, responses characterized by "lethargy" and later, as dose level continued to increase, by "overt seizures." The state of affairs at low stimulus intensities was indicated in the Miller *et al.* (1964) experiments by the results of control trials involving mock injections and others in which isotonic saline solution was administered: Under both conditions some irregular drinking occurred. We have measured similar low levels of activity in unoperated subjects under two different control conditions: first, when they were on an ad libitum water schedule and, second, after they had been given a special 1-hour satiation period following 24 hours of deprivation. This activity is analogous to the "noise level" which characterizes communications systems generally; more pertinently, it is also analogous to the noise which occurs in sensory systems, e.g., to "retinal noise" which appears as an irregular succession of impulses in the optic nerve even after complete dark adaptation (Barlow, 1956; Barlow, FitzHugh, & Kuffler, 1954). Such noise limits the sensitivity of the system to changes of stimulus intensity at the low end of the scale.

The presence of these asymptotes defines the limits which restrict the linear relation between log stimulus intensity and magnitudes of response output of the system. Plotting such research results as those described above suggests that the transitions from the asymptotes to the linear function do not occur abruptly, that the over-all relation can be better described by a sigmoid curve. When the data are subjected to a log-probit analysis for sigmoid response curves (Finney, 1962) the points give a reasonable fit, as shown in the second curve of Fig. 3 where the line has been determined by the method of least squares. Such sigmoid response curves are familiar outcomes in a wide variety of biological assays involving quantal responses and also quantitative responses measured over an unrestricted range of stimulus intensities. Such a curve would occur if there were a population of units involved in determining the total response output and the thresholds of the units were normally and independently distributed.

In another series of experiments, Khavari and the author have obtained evidence that the inhibition or satiation of the drinking system follows a similar course. We have studied the response characteristics of the satiation process after the drinking system was activated by water deprivation and by both bilateral and unilateral stimulation of the lateral hypothalamus with carbachol. Some of our first studies (Khavari and Russell, 1966) showed that $23\frac{1}{2}$ hours of deprivation and 3 to 5 μg of carbachol in crystalline

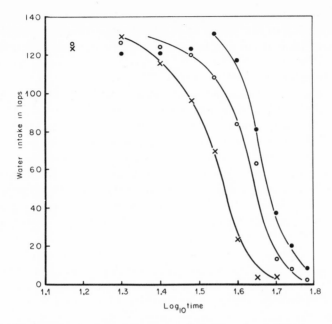

FIG. 4. The curves are plots of the course of satiation when ad libitum water was available after 23½ hours of water deprivation and after direct bilateral and unilateral cholinergic stimulation in the lateral hypothalamus.

form produced absolute levels of water intake which were closely similar in magnitude. Figure 4 shows the nature of the satiation process following activation of the system under these experimental conditions; the magnitude of the drinking response is plotted against log time after placing subjects in the test situation where water was available. Again it is possible to fit the empirical data with sigmoid response curves based upon the same reasoning about response asymptotes as that discussed above. Figure 5 shows that the results of a log-probit analysis of the data can, with reasonable accuracy, be fitted by linear regression lines of negative slopes.

Comparisons of response outputs under conditions of unilateral and bilateral stimulation provide additional information about the functioning of the system. For example, unilateral stimulation resulted in significantly fewer total responses than bilateral; this would be expected if response output were dependent upon the number of units activated within the system, unilateral stimulation involving $N/2$ of the total population of units available. Because

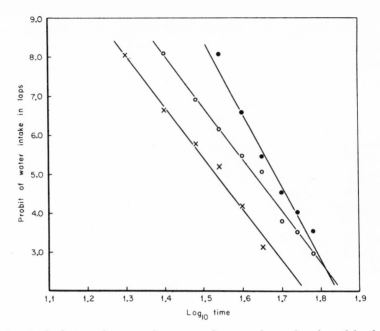

FIG. 5. The linear relations with negative slopes are log-probit plots of the data shown in Fig. 4.

of the difference in numbers of units involved, it might also be expected that the threshold for activating the response mechanism would be reached more rapidly with bilateral stimulation; the results support this prediction, there being no overlap in latencies of onset of responding between the two conditions. Although responses during the satiation period could, in both cases, be fitted by sigmoid curves, there was, over a major portion of the curves, a linear relation between log time and response output. The negative slope constants for the curves in Fig. 5, fitted by the least squares method to data obtained by the usual log-probit analysis, show that responding decreased more rapidly following unilateral than bilateral stimulation; the latter was almost identical with the corresponding slope constant for satiation following 23 hours of water deprivation.

These observed relations between stimulus intensity and response magnitudes could be accounted for in terms of information encoded and transmitted by a functional circuit with the following characteristics (Russell, 1966): (a) a circuit consisting of a finite number of units and, hence, limited in channel capacity; (b) the units having a variety of different thresholds, not necessarily normally distributed; (c) firing above threshold at frequencies which are a function of the stimulus intensity; and (d) a circuit with a noise level which limits its sensitivity at low stimulus intensities. Such a system would, of course, be laid down under the genetic control of DNA.

Since trains of nerve impulses within such a circuit are generated by changes in neurohumoral transmitter substances, it is reasonable to look among neurochemical events occurring within the circuit for the processes of encoding and transmission of information. The observed relation between stimulus input and response output would obtain if two contingencies were met: (a) if the rate of production or liberation of a transmitter chemical at the input end were proportional to the log of the stimulus intensity, and (b) if there were linear relations between the concentrations of transmitter chemicals secreted by units along the circuit to the response output end. Transmitter chemicals associated with cellular dehydration would excite units within the circuit and those associated with sensory and blood-borne feedback from water intake could inhibit them; the output of the system as a whole might be thought of as some function, perhaps algebraic, of the two. Rushton (1961) has presented arguments for a model of this kind in connection with peripheral coding in the nervous system, suggesting that ". . . the sole function of nerve is to secrete rapidly at a distant spot a hormone whose concentration is a linear replica of the mean input concentration."

C. "Motivational" Properties

In the normal course of events the precoded behavioral patterns under discussion do not occur as isolated responses to environmental changes. The "pure" consummatory response, with its resulting inhibitory feedback, is usually the final behavioral unit in a series which includes a variety of instrumental responses. Even in the simple test situations involved in the studies of drinking behavior which the author has been using as an example of precoded systems, instrumental components were involved: Each subject went through a preliminary training period during which he learned, under conditions of water deficit, to approach the drinking tube where water was available. The sequence of events was one

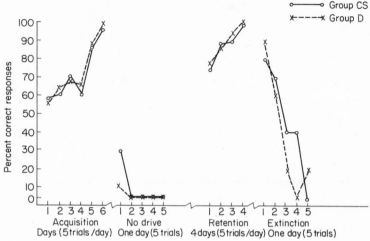

FIG. 6. The various curves show the comparability of acquisition, relearning, and extinction of a T-maze response under conditions of 23½ hours water deprivation and of direct cholinergic stimulation in the lateral hypothalamus.

in which instrumental responses were interposed in a position before the final ingestion of water. The variety of responses which initially compete for positions in the sequence is, of course, limited by environmental circumstances, but we have been observing a surprising array of individual differences among subjects even in what would appear to be the very restricted response of licking the drinking tube. We have watched this response undergoing modification in individual subjects during the course of a series of test trials when the total water intake per trial remained relatively constant. What the author has been discussing as the consummatory response is certainly not a precoded push-button, slot machine unit of behavior. Stimulation of the neurochemically coded drinking system does have two general features in common for all subjects: It initiates an increase of general activity and it is associated with the selection from among available competing responses of sequences terminating in water intake, sequences which, however, may differ from subject to subject. These are properties which are encompassed by the theoretical construct, "motivation" or, in the specific example the author has been using, "primary drive."

Normally, the drinking system is activated by stimulation arising from cellular dehydration induced by a water deficit within the

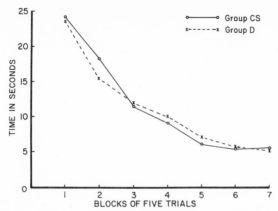

FIG. 7. The acquisition of a simple straightway approach response is shown in these curves to be as effective with central stimulation as with water deprivation.

body; conditions are involved which are peripheral to the functional circuit mediating the behavior. In order to determine whether these conditions play any special roles in the motivational properties of the system, we (Khavari and Russell, 1966) have conducted two series of experiments designed to compare the effects of central cholinergic stimulation and of deprivation on the learning and performance of instrumental responses leading to water intake. Pilot studies demonstrated that stimulation in the lateral hypothalamus with 3 to 5 μg of carbachol induced magnitudes of consummatory responding very similar to those produced by $23\frac{1}{2}$ hours of water deprivation; therefore, these were selected as our stimulus conditions. Results of one of the experiments on learning are summarized in Fig. 6. They show that the two kinds of stimulation were equally effective in supporting the acquisition and relearning of a T-maze response and that they also were related to similar effects during the extinction of the behavior when water reinforcement was not available. The acquisition of a simple straightway approach response, shown graphically in Fig. 7, was likewise as effective with central stimulation as with water deprivation.

Our second series of experiments provided an additional kind of information. As Fig. 8 shows, test trials under carbachol were not introduced until after both groups of subjects had learned the straightway approach response under conditions of $23\frac{1}{2}$ hours of water deprivation. The two sets of curves on the left present the mean times for the response during 14 preoperative and 9 post-

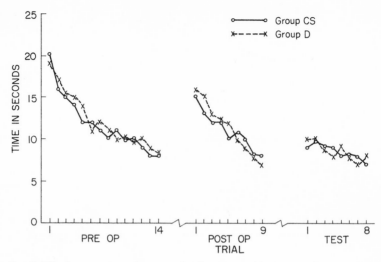

FIG. 8. The first two sets of curves plot the course of learning and relearning with
$23\frac{1}{2}$ hours water deprivation. The third set shows that the capability of eliciting the
learned response readily transferred to activation of the drinking circuit by direct
cholinergic stimulation.

operative daily trials; there were no significant differences between
the groups and the asymptotic levels of performance with practice
were similar to those achieved in the previous experimental series
when the response was acquired under conditions of central cholinergic stimulation as well as of water deprivation. The third set of
curves in this figure summarizes performance of the learned response during critical trials when group CS, then on ad libitum
water, was centrally stimulated and group D remained on $23\frac{1}{2}$ hours
of water deprivation. There were no significant differences between
levels of performance: From the first critical trial, direct cholinergic
stimulation of the drinking circuit was as effective as deprivation
in eliciting the response, which we may consider in this instance
as having been "precoded by learning." Figure 9 shows that the
consummatory responses of the two groups, as measured during
2-minute test periods immediately following the straightway approach response, were also similar in magnitudes. Perhaps the most
interesting observation in this series of experiments was the fact
that the instrumental response could be so readily evoked by a
mode of activating the central functional circuit, i.e., direct chemical stimulation, which was so different from that involved during

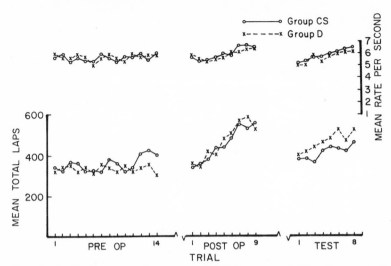

FIG. 9. The first two sets of curves establish the comparability of two groups of Ss in their consummatory responses under conditions of water deprivation before and after implantation of cannulae into the lateral hypothalamus. The third set shows that the responses were also similar in magnitudes when the CS group, with ad libitum water available, received direct cholinergic stimulation.

the learning process, i.e., water deprivation. Whereas in the first experiments we showed that either mode of activating the circuit would support the learning of new instrumental responses, results of the second series demonstrated that the capability of eliciting performance of a learned response could readily transfer from one mode to the other.

Results of this line of research have indicated that direct chemical stimulation of the functional circuit mediating drinking has motivational properties analogous to those of water deprivation. It has capabilities of doing more than merely initiating precoded consummatory responses in a reflex manner. Programing of the circuit is "open" in the sense that other responses may be added to the sequence of behavioral events which is initiated by stimulation of the circuit and ends with water intake.

Sperry (1962), in discussing problems of molecular coding, expressed the opinion that: "When one turns to the neural basis of behavior patterns that are inherited rather than acquired, problems of chemical coding can be more clearly outlined. . . ." Even in genetically precoded systems, the neurochemical coding of behavior is complex. Clearly it extends considerably beyond the selective sensitivity of functional neural circuits to particular chemical stimuli, i.e., beyond circuit coding. Although the drinking system has been used as an example, it is a reasonable hypothesis that, when studied in as much detail, other systems will be found to have similar properties.

V. CODING OF NEW BEHAVIORAL PATTERNS

Although the study of genetically precoded systems can provide important basic information about interactions between biochemical events and behavior, the still more complex processes involved in the learning of new behavioral patterns has attracted the imagination and effort of many investigators from a number of different disciplines. The attempt has been to devise and to test hypotheses about ways in which biochemical events may mediate the effects of experience in modifying behavior and the persistence of new behavioral patterns once established. Criteria which candidates for roles in these biochemical events must satisfy have been set in terms of the basic behavioral characteristics of learning and memory.

Certain of these basic characteristics are illustrated in the acquisition of the instrumental responses just discussed. Faced with a new environmental situation our subjects modified their behavior in ways which led to water, the sequence of responses terminating in the precoded consummatory response of drinking. In Fig. 6, the curve representing the behavioral properties of the process by which the modification took place shows an increase in numbers of correct responses with repeated practice in the new situation. In order for this to occur, there must have been a carry over of effects from one practice trial to another and there must have been a cumulation of such effects as practice progressed since performance continued to improve until errorless trials predominated. This carry-over effect, one of the most pervasive phenomena in the behavior of living organisms, has long held a central role in psychological research and theory. The behavioral changes involved have been called "memory" or "retention." To account for the carry over of practice effects, psychologists have traditionally introduced the theoretical construct of "memory trace," which assumes that practice produces an alteration in the basic properties of living organisms other than the behavioral, i.e., in the anatomical, biochemical, or electrophysiological property, or in some combination of these.

From psychological research has come evidence that, during the acquisition of new behavioral patterns, processes do in fact occur upon which such alterations depend. As long ago as 1900, Muller and Pilzecker (1900) in order to account for their research results, described a perseveration-consolidation principle according to which the degree of fixation of the memory trace depends upon the extent of perseveration of neural activity initiated by a practice trial. Since then the importance to fixation of a consolidation period has been demonstrated in numerous studies in which memory has been found to be altered by a variety of posttrial treatments (Deutsch, 1962): Electroconvulsive shock, hypoxia, and depressant drugs impair memory, while other treatments, e.g., injection of strychnine sulfate, have the opposite effect of facilitating memory. The magnitude of effect produced has been shown to decrease with time after input of the information to be stored. Clearly, dynamic events are initiated by the input, processes which can be manipulated both chemically and electrically.

An understanding of how new behavioral patterns are coded depends upon more precise knowledge of these processes. New developments in biochemistry and microbiology have directed the search for the basic "engram" for memory (Lashley, 1950) toward events occurring within the CNS at a molecular level and at the level of enzyme systems involved in the transmission of nerve impulses. In order to account for the behavioral facts a candidate at either level must satisfy certain requirements:

(1) It must be capable of undergoing change as a function of interactions between the organism and its environment: memory *fixation*. Since such interactions involve sensory input to the CNS, the question most frequently put to experimental test has been: Does the proposed engram change as sensory input is systematically altered?

(2) Clearly the fixation process involves more than merely any change in the proposed engram. The change must be specific in the sense that it reflects the unique characteristics of the information input, both qualitatively and quantitatively. It is important to demonstrate that particular molecules or enzyme systems are sensitive to sensory input, but, as Dingman and Sporn (1964) have recently emphasized, this could mean only that the molecules or

enzymes participate in CNS activity. To establish that particular molecules or enzymes are in fact involved in memory storage requires evidence that changes in them are related more uniquely to the parameters of the specific sensory input inducing the change.

(3) Any candidate for the role of memory engram must be able to persist in its altered form in the absence of the sensory input which induced it: memory *storage*. From the experimental point of view this means that evidence for the continued existence of memory at the behavioral level must be accompanied by evidence for the continued existence of the engram and that, if the engram disappears or is specifically destroyed, the memory no longer exists. The well-known problems of measuring memory under the influence of competing responses which suppress it often make clearly definitive tests of this requirement very difficult.

(4) Associated with the engram there must exist a means by which information, once stored, can be *retrieved* or *read out*. Generally speaking, the processes by which a particular engram is selected from among all others and its information transduced into effector changes comprising a response pattern are still the least explored of the problems we are discussing.

None of the candidates proposed as biochemical engrams for memory has yet been shown to satisfy these requirements fully. However, a growing body of research results is focusing attention upon certain possibilities, which, because of the importance of understanding how behavioral patterns are coded, are exciting and challenging. Characteristically, science proceeds by a series of approximations and it is still too early to expect an *experimentum crucis*, if, indeed, any single such experiment is possible.

A. *"Biological Memory"*

Research on what has come to be called "biological memory" (Schmitt, 1962) has led to certain analogies which suggest worthy candidates that may meet these requirements. The question of how information is stored is one of as basic importance to other biological sciences as it is to psychology. "Where or how," wrote Boring (1950), "does the brain store its memories? That is the greatest mystery. How can learning persist unreproduced, being effected by other learning while it waits?" Similar questions were being asked at that time by scientists in the fields of genetics and microbiology. To maintain the species differences arrived at through biochemical and organic evolution requires some means for storing information which can enable a newly developing organism to "remember" its species identification. When this mystery was solved a few years later, genetic "memory traces" were found to be coded molecularly, as sequences of units in DNA molecules.

More recently the construct of memory trace has also been introduced into immunology in connection with certain characteristics of antibody formation. The empirical observation is that a second dose of antigen provokes antibody production which greatly exceeds the response to the original dose, even though the concentration of the antibody in the host's blood may have fallen to a low level between doses, i.e., there remains some "memory trace" of past chemical "experience." Since antibodies are proteins with very narrow specificities for action, this carry-over effect is associated with the intervention of antigens in protein synthesis.

There are obvious analogies between biological memory of these kinds and memory at a behavioral level. Indeed, the relation seems to be more than an analogy in the case of what the author has called genetically precoded behavioral patterns, where information controlling the behavior appears to have been encoded and stored as a result of long-term evolutionary processes. In contrast, the analogy with immunological memory is more similar to the coding of new behavioral patterns arising from interactions between an organism and its environment which occur during the organism's lifetime. The analogies have led to hypotheses that the behavioral memory trace is stored in the CNS by the formation or alteration of a particular molecule or group of related molecules involved in the protein synthesis process.

B. Macromolecular Coding

Four types of macromolecules have been suggested as possible engrams for memory storage: DNA, RNA, proteins, and lipids. Because of its known capacity to encode genetic information, DNA is an obvious candidate. But problems arise when the requirements of the fixation process are applied to a molecule as stable as DNA. Its configuration can be altered by the use of certain chemical agents and, obviously, during mutation. However, there is no indication that DNA can be modified by such stimulation as sensory input; and the amount of DNA per cell nucleus remains relatively constant, even under conditions when RNA and protein content are changing drastically (Alfert, 1957; Davison, 1962). The stability of DNA under conditions in which a memory engram would be expected to change has, understandably, raised general skepticism about its role in this capacity. However, Gaito and Zavola (1964) have pointed out that most investigations of the characteristics of DNA have been on DNA from nonneural tissue; DNA from neural tissue may possess different properties. And, therefore, fully adequate evidence for eliminating DNA as a candidate is not yet available.

In contrast there have been a number of experiments to demonstrate that RNA does indeed vary with sensory input. For example, deprivation of visual stimulation produces retinas highly deficient in RNA (Brattgård, 1952; Riesen, 1958). Hydén (1961) has reported that, although the structures of neurons in sensory systems following stimulus deprivation appear normal, the cells are in fact impoverished in RNA and proteins; increased sensory input, on the other hand, is associated with increases in RNA and proteins. He has pointed out that they are produced in nerve cells at rates which follow neuronal activity (Hydén, 1959). With his co-worker, Egyházi (Egyházi & Hydén, 1961), he has experimentally induced changes in the base composition of the RNAs of isolated nerve cells and their related glial cells. Here then is a type of molecule in individual neurons which is capable of wide alteration depending upon physiochemical conditions of the environment.

The question arises next as to whether RNA changes in some systematic manner as behavior is altered during learning. Two experiments are fast becoming classics as initial attempts to answer the question. Both employed analytical methods (Edström, 1960; Edström *et al.*, 1961) which make it possible to determine the nucleic acid content of single nerve cells and to analyze the nucleic acid for its composition or base ratios. The elegance of the methods is apparent when we consider that the biochemical analyses were conducted on intracellular material in micromicrogram quantities. In the first experiment (Hydén & Egyházi, 1962; Hydén & Egyházi, 1963) rats were required to learn a sensorimotor task having a strong vestibular component, i.e., to traverse a tight-wire pathway in order to reach food. Allowed a 45-minute practice period daily, experimental animals increased their proficiency from three to five successful runs on day 1 to about 20 on day 4. During similar four-day periods, one litter-mate control group remained in single cages and another was subjected, for 25 minutes daily, to "rotation" which induced "passive" vestibular stimulation. Following these treatments the subjects were sacrificed and analyses made of the RNA content of Deiter's cells from the vestibular nucleus of the medulla. Comparisons between the experimental and control groups showed greater amounts of RNA per nerve cell and a significant increase in the adenine to uracil ratio in the former. The investigators interpreted their controls as excluding". . . the possibility that the chemical changes observed in the nuclear RNA of the nerve cell were due to demands on the neural function per se," i.e., that the molecular effects were indeed related to the learning process. In a later report (Hydén & Egyházi, 1963) they pointed out that RNA analyses of neurons from parts of the brain other than the vestibular nucleus showed no production of nuclear fractions with changed base ratios, although increases in amounts of RNA per cell were found. It was also observed that the adenine to uracil ratio of glial RNA increased significantly in the experimental animals.

The second of the two experiments (Hydén & Egyházi, 1964) presented a quite different learning task to the rats: the change in handedness from the preferred to the nonpreferred side. Following learning the animals were sacrificed and analyses made of RNA in a small section of the anterior dorsal cortex, which is involved in mediating this characteristic of behavior. Significant increases in amounts of RNA were found to have occurred in cells of the cortex contralateral to the newly dominant side; significant changes were also observed in base ratios: adenine, guanine, and uracil increased, while cytosine decreased. No significant changes appeared in cells of the ipsilateral side.

Results of these kinds suggest that RNA is not only sensitive to information input, but that it is also capable of responding differentially depending upon the nature of the information involved. From the behavioral point of view the information stored during learning of such response patterns as those described above would be expected to vary as practice continued, the typical learning curve showing a progressive change in responding. Recently, Hydén and Lange (1965) have reexamined the data from the experiments on sensorimotor learning and change in handedness in order to discover whether differential changes occurred in neuronal RNA early as compared with late during the learning period. In the case of the phylogenetically older vestibular neurons they have reported that ". . . . a highly asymmetric, adenine-rich nuclear RNA was formed in the rats which increased their performance curve . . ." and that ". . . the nuclear RNA formed in the neurons of these rats had a ribosomal type of base composition." In the transfer of handedness experiment, cortical neurons produced small amounts of RNA with high adenine and uracil values early during practice, with notable changes later when performance was still improving: The level of RNA production increased, and the RNA changed in base composition to that of a ribosomal type.

Evidence that changes induced in RNA during learning persist after practice is over has been sought using an approach which has recently attracted much attention. The general reasoning has been that, if such changes are persistent, the effects of information storage should be apparent when RNA from trained subjects is transferred to naive animals, e.g., a significant savings should occur in the latter's learning of the task concerned. Reports of research based upon this reasoning appear to present confirmatory results, although they must still be interpreted with considerable caution. Babich, Jacobson, Bubash, and Jacobson (1965b) have described transfer effects in an operant conditioning situation when the response observed was approach to the food cup upon presentation of an auditory stimulus. Rats were trained for six days and then sacrificed, RNA being extracted from brain tissue. Similar extractions were made from the same brain areas of untrained subjects to serve as a control. Eight hours later intraperitoneal injections were administered to naive animals and tests for performance of the approach response were given at 4, 6, 8, 22, and 24 hours. The investigators report that: "The untrained rats then manifested a significant tendency (as compared with controls) to approach the food cup when the click, unaccompanied by food, was presented." These findings have been supported by a second report (Jacobson, Babich, Bubash, & Jacobson, 1965) describing results of new experiments involving additional controls and experimental treatments. Among the latter was the introduction of a second discriminative stimulus, a blinking light, thus enabling comparisons to be made between effects of approach responses learned in association with stimuli in two different sense modalities. Ribonucleic acid extracted from animals trained to respond to auditory clicks and to the visual stimulus was injected intraperitoneally into naive subjects. Tests were made of approach responses to both stimuli, with results which suggest that the RNA effect ". . . is to a substantial extent specific rather than general." In a third experiment (Babich, Jacobson, & Bubash, 1965a) these investigators undertook to test the hypotheses that the RNA effect would be evidenced in transfer of learning *between* as well as within species. The same basic research design and procedure was used, with the introduction of an additional control. Hamsters were trained in a Skinner box to approach the food cup on presentation of the auditory click. A "yoked" control group was run simultaneously, each animal receiving the discriminative stimulus whenever it was presented to the paired experimental animal; however, the control subjects were never fed in the box. Ribonucleic acid was extracted from both groups and administered intraperitoneally to untrained rats. The results during five test sessions following injection at 6, 8, 10, 22, and 24 hours showed a highly significant difference between the behavior of animals treated with RNA extract from the experimental as compared with the control hamster subjects, performance of the former being superior.

Among the questions which arise from the techniques used in these experiments are two which are answered in part by experiments described in the third report (Fjerdingstad, Nissen, & Røigaard-Petersen, 1965). The first concerns the rather unusual choice of "magazine training" as the learning task: Would similar results be obtained with other learned responses? The second involves the matter of biotransformation (Brodie, 1962). Ribonucleic acid administered intraperitoneally would have to pass through many cellular barriers, e.g., "blood-brain barrier," and many different chemical environments to reach its site of action in the CNS: Can it do so without being broken down in the process? In the experiments reported by Fjerdingstad et al. (1965), training of the donor rats took place in a two-alley runway, one alley being illuminated and the other darkened. Daily sessions were terminated after a subject, on a water-deprivation schedule, made 60 reinforced responses to the lighted alley, regardless of the number of entries into the nonreinforced dark alley. Training continued to a criterion of less than five errors per 100 reinforcements during three consecutive sessions. Ribonucleic acid was then extracted from the brain tissue of subjects meeting the criterion and from a comparable group of untrained animals. The extracts were injected *intracis-ternally* into naive subjects in amounts "equal to the content of one brain [of the donor animals] minus the loss occurring during preparation and purification" of the RNA. The effects of these treatments were evidenced in the superior performance in the original learning situation of animals receiving extract from trained as compared with untrained donors; the superiority appeared consistently up to the seventh day of training, when both groups approached an asymptote in learning. There were no apparent differences in performance between animals injected with extract from untrained donors and a control group of uninjected subjects. The authors note that repetition of the experiment "in an improved test situation" has confirmed these results. In a personal communication they have reported, from results of further experiments not yet published, that: ". . . the RNA effect is dependent on the *type* of training used before RNA extraction. This would seem to exclude most unspecific explanations of the effect, e.g., that the RNA formed in the animal under training might, in some way or another, act equally stimulating to any other type of training regardless of the special conditions involved."

Evidence supporting the specificity of the RNA effect is particularly important in testing the hypothesis that the effects of learning are *uniquely* coded in RNA. Since RNA molecules are important constituents of neural tissue, it could well be that RNA metabolism is affected by neuronal function activated during learning without the molecules themselves serving as the memory engram. That effects of nonspecific RNA supplements may affect learning has been reported by Cook, Davidson, Davis, Green, and Fellows (1963) in describing experiments involving the acquisition and extinction of a conditioned avoidance response. Rats in experimental groups received intraperitoneal injections of *yeast* RNA at doses of 160 mg/kg, control animals receiving comparable amounts of normal saline solution. Rates of acquisition were significantly faster for the experimental than for the control subjects; after the level of errorless performance had been reached, latency of responding among the former was approximately half that of the latter; and, the former were significantly more resistant to extinction. Clearly, it is essential to demonstrate that RNA functions in a more specific manner if its claim to the role of the primary memory engram is to be substantiated.

Adding further to the circumstantial evidence suggesting an important role for RNA in memory storage are the results of studies in which the administration of RNA supplements to elderly patients suffering from impaired memory has been reported (Cameron, 1963a; Cameron, 1963b; Cameron & Solyom, 1961) to affect significant improvement. Reports by Hydén (1961) indicate that RNA, at least in motor neurons of the brain stem, varies during different periods of the human life span: increasing significantly during the ages of 3 to 40, remaining relatively constant until 60, and then declining rapidly. In their 1961 study, Cameron and Solyom administered, orally and intravenously, doses of both DNA and yeast RNA to elderly patients, finding improvement on tests for immediate memory with RNA treatment but not with DNA. In some cases almost complete recovery occurred. Clinical observations indicated increases in "alertness, interest, initiative, and confidence" following administration of RNA. As with the results reported by Cook *et al.* (1963), the effects obtained under these conditions cannot be used to differentiate between the possible role of RNA as the primary memory engram and its involvement in the over-all processes of neuronal function.

Another experimental approach to testing the general hypothesis that RNA is involved in memory storage is to interfere biochemically with the synthesis of RNA or to alter its composition through the use of chemical compounds which act as analogs of bases normally involved in the molecular structure. Several experiments applying this approach have been reported, providing evidence favorable to the hypothesis. First among these was an experiment by Dingman and Sporn (1961) in which labeled 8-azaguanine-2-^{14}C was injected intracisternally into rats as the experimental subjects. Incorporation, which occurred maximally during the 30 minutes following injection, resulted in an unnatural or "fraudulant" RNA. Tests for recall of a previously learned response made 15 minutes after injection showed no significant differences between experimental and control groups. In contrast, during learning of the same response experimental animals made significantly more errors, the greatest differences between performances of the two groups occurring during the period of maximum incorporation of the 8-azaguanine. There were no differences in other characteristics of responding such as locomotion. These results suggest that changes in the normal composition of RNA differentially affect the fixation of new memory engrams without altering those already established. More recent experiments have used other chemical agents which block the synthesis of RNA, e.g., actinomycin-D (Appel, 1964; Barondes & Jarvik, 1964), and which suppress protein synthesis, e.g., puromycin (Agranoff, Davis, & Brink, 1965; Flexner, Flexner, & Stellar, 1963). The results show that the different treatments have differential effects upon the fixation and storage of information; for example, Agranoff *et al.* (1965) have proposed ". . . that puromycin specifically disrupts the formation but not the maintenance of long-term memory, and that temporary, or short-term, memory is insusceptible to puromycin." Further research using this approach by chemical "dissection" will add greatly to our understanding of how the various phases of the proteins synthesis processes are related to the coding of new behavioral patterns.

Throughout much of the discussion of the hypothesis that RNA may serve as the engram for memory, emphasis has been placed upon RNA in nerve cells. Yet research has shown that, during the course of new learning, concomitant changes occur in glial as well as in neuronal RNA. Hydén and Egyházi (1963) have interpreted the changes in RNA base composition in both the neuron and its glia as demonstrating ". . . that the glia share with their neurons the capacity to house at least part of the chemical substrate utilized in learning." Galambos (1961) proposed a theoretical model of how the functions of the brain may be divided between these two different structural units:

Glia is here conceived as genetically charged to organize and program neuron activity so that the best interests of the organism will be served; the essential product of glia action is visualized to be what we call innate and acquired behavioral responses. In this scheme, neurons in large part merely execute the instructions glia give them.

This possibility is important to the understanding of how new behavioral patterns are coded, just as the notion of functional circuits was important in the earlier discussion of genetically precoded responses. If behavior is chemically coded, the events involved must take place within some structural site. Until there is evidence to the contrary, Hydén's results require that attention be paid to the role(s) which the functions of glia may play among the biochemical substrates of behavior (Landauer, 1964).

C. Changes in Enzyme Activity

Having raised the matter of possible functional interactions between different structural units in the CNS provides a suitable opportunity to reexamine the relations between events involved in cellular metabolism. The brief description of the biochemical substrate with which the author began may have left the incorrect impression that cellular metabolism is a stereotyped order of events. In fact, the cell has a flexibility arising from a number of different regulatory mechanisms affecting the synthesis of RNA by DNA and feedback systems by which the functional activities of enzymes are regulated. The processes of fixation, storage, and retrieval of information must involve the functioning of these mechanisms both within the cell and between cells. These interactions will continue to be important to any comprehensive theory of the coding of new behavioral patterns, even if it is fully established that the primary engram for memory is at a macromolecular level. Evidence already exists that changes in behavior may be reflected in persisting changes of enzyme activity and that experimental variation of such activity may induce significant changes in behavior. On the basis of this evidence and of certain related theoretical considerations it has been argued that the coding of new behavioral patterns is more likely to occur at an enzyme level rather than in the rearrangement of molecular structures (Briggs & Kitto, 1962; Smith, 1962).

In the search for interactions between enzyme activity and behavior, major attention has been focused upon the alleged neurohumoral transmitter systems and in particular upon the acetylcholine (ACh), norepinephrine (NE), and serotonin (5-HT) systems. These systems are differentially distributed in the brain areas which ablation and stimulation studies suggest have special relations to behavior; they are significantly affected by drugs which are known to produce changes in behavior.

To be considered as involved in the coding of new behavioral patterns an enzyme must satisfy the same general requirements as were prescribed for the testing of candidates at the molecular level. The first among these calls for evidence that the enzyme is capable of changing in response to sensory input. Changes in the physical and chemical nature of their immediate environments produce very marked effects upon the functioning of enzymes. Can similar effects be induced by changes arising from sensory stimulation? Brattgård (1952) demonstrated the importance to the chemical composition of retinal ganglion cells during early postnatal development of adequate sensory input. X-ray microradiographs of individual cells in the rabbit retina showed a drastic reduction in one protein fraction, pentose nucleoprotein, as a result of total light deprivation; concomitant changes occurred with variations in stimulation and in dark adaptation over relatively short periods of time, e.g., 10 minutes to 6 hours. Research reported by Liberman (1962) illustrates a similar approach to answering the question. One of two groups of age-matched rats was reared for 17 weeks, with the mothers, in total darkness; the other, under normal light-dark conditions. Assay of the retinas at the end of the period showed the total acetylcholinesterase (AChE) activity of the former to be very significantly lower than that of the latter. Presumably the lower level of stimulation under the dark conditions resulted in less transmitter chemical, ACh, being released in the retina: "If the synthesis and maintenance of acetylcholinesterase are dependent upon the level of acetylcholine then the lower acetylcholinesterase activity found in the retina of dark-raised rats would be explained (Liberman, 1962)." The specificity of the effects observed by Liberman is indicated by the fact that the activities of other cholinesterases, which are closely related chemically to AChE, were not affected. Studies of retinal rods and cones (De Robertis & Franchi, 1956) using electron microscopy have revealed a sharp decrease in the size of synaptic vesicles after nine days in complete darkness. This relation between functional load and enzyme activity has been confirmed by Glow and Rose (1964) employing the technique of occluding one eye of the rat with an opaque contact lens and using the retina of the other eye as the light-dark control. They have also demonstrated ACh-induced AChE synthesis by arterial infusion of exogenous ACh into the retina in which the rate of synthesis of AChE was reduced in the manner just described and by intravitreous injection of drugs (Glow & Rose, 1966a; Rose & Glow, 1965). The retina, an embriological outgrowth from the diencephalon and capable of neural integrating functions, may be viewed as part of the CNS. Results of the kind just described would then suggest at least the possibility that enzyme activity centrally as well as peripherally, can be affected by sensory stimulation. Further support for this conclusion has come from experiments by Krech, Rosenzweig, and Bennett (1963; 1964) whose results ". . . suggest that modifying the amount of experience in one sensory modality can affect rather significantly the brain regions serving that modality."

Given that enzyme activity can be affected in this way, the question next arises as to whether it can be found to vary concomitantly with changes in behavior. Evidence that it can comes from the extensive series of studies by Krech, Rosensweig, Bennett, and Diamond (e.g., Krech *et al.*, 1964; Rosenzweig, 1966; Rosensweig, Bennett, & Krech, 1964) briefly referred to earlier in discussing the reciprocal nature of interactions between biochemical events and behavior.

Searching for specific changes within the CNS, they have used neurochemical and neurohistological methods of analysis in demonstrating significant alterations both in enzyme activity and in modifications of brain structure in rats exposed to very different behavioral experiences (Bennett, Krech, & Rosenzweig, 1964; Diamond, Krech, & Rosenzweig, 1964; Krech, Rosenzweig, & Bennett, 1960). The standard procedure was to assign litter-mate animals to two groups, which, from the time of weaning, lived in markedly different environments. Subjects in an "enriched environment" group, ECT, were housed in groups of 10 to 12 in large cages, which provided a variety of experiences; they were also given training in a series of maze problems. Members of the "impoverished" group, IC, lived in individual cages with restricted stimulus conditions and no contact with other animals. These different treatments continued for 80 days, after which the animals were sacrificed and the brain tissues analyzed. Because of their special interest in the neurohumoral transmitter system involving acetylcholine and its inactivating enzyme, acetylcholinesterase, the analyses were first directed toward the discovery of differences in AChE activity which might have resulted from the different treatments of the two groups. The results showed that differences did indeed exist: The *total activity* of AChE was significantly greater in the ECT than in the IC subjects both in the cortex and in the rest of the brain. More detailed analyses, which provided measures of both AChE and the less specific cholinesterases (ChE) present in the brain tissue, showed that cortical ChE activity *per unit weight* increased as a function of experience, while AChE activity per unit weight decreased. In other brain structures, there were no changes in ChE activity, while AChE activity increased. Since neurons are richer than glia in AChE and glia richer in ChE, these differential effects suggested that glial cells might proliferate in the cortex as a result of the enriched experience, an hypothesis which was supported by histological analysis. There is preliminary evidence that neuronal changes may also occur, which would account, at least in part, for the effects of enriched experience on AChE activity.

Whenever, during the discussion so far, reference has been made to the possibility that neurohumoral transmitter systems may be involved in the coding of new behavioral patterns, the ACh system has interjected itself into the scene, particularly the inactivating enzyme AChE. The reasons for this favored position center around the fact mentioned earlier that the evidence supporting the claim of this system to involvement in neurohumoral transmission is stronger than that for other neurochemicals. A dilemma is that the analysis for the transmitter itself is, at present, dependent upon bio-assay methods, which do not provide the precision nor consistency of measurement obtainable by chemical assay procedures of, for example, AChE. Earlier, in discussing the biochemical substrate, the point was made that NE has strong support as the principal neurohumor of adrenergic neurons (Florey, 1961); there also continues to be considerable interest in the role(s) which serotonin (5-HT) may play in central parasynpathetic activity. Recently (Rosenzweig, 1966) the results have been reported of experiments designed to determine the effects on these substances, if any, of exposure to the ECT and IC environments. Comparisons between animals following these different treatments replicated results described in the preceding paragraph insofar as effects upon brain weight and total AChE are concerned. There were no consistent effects upon serotonin; however, NE was significantly higher under IC than ECT treatments. The increases in NE concentration differed from one brain area to another: about 30% greater in the cortex of IC animals, a twofold increase in the colliculus, and some fivefold increase in the caudate nucleus. Dopamine, a precursor of NE, also showed large increases in the cortex and particularly in the caudate nucleus. Although considerably more information is needed in order to interpret these results clearly, they do indicate that biochemical systems other than the ACh are affected by differential experience and they encourage further study of these systems using other experimental approaches.

It has been suggested that the effects observed may involve a process of enzyme induction (Krech et al., 1960) or that the ". . .

change in activity could occur because of alteration in concentration of a co-factor or because the enzyme itself is allosteric and is changed from a form with one level of activity, to a form with another (Rosenzweig, 1966)." The first of these suggestions emphasizes changes in amounts of existing enzymes and the second, alteration of activity without changes in amount. The mere production of enzymes does not mean that they are active; the synthesis of inactive enzymes in animals is well known. The level of enzyme activity may be regulated by processes of *activation* and *inactivation* or by processes of *stimulation* and *inhibition*. All these processes ". . . appear to depend on the presence of specific regulatory sites (allosteric sites) on the enzyme. When small molecules combine with or dissociate from these sites, the stability and the activity of the enzyme can be modified (Pardee & Wilson, 1963)." The regulatory sites on a particular enzyme may be modified by other specific enzymes and by other compounds which are metabolically, but not necessarily structurally, related to that enzyme, e.g., metabolic end-products, metabolites from other biochemical systems, hormones, and analogs of metabolites. The biochemical correlates of behavior may involve the level of activity of a key enzyme through any of these control mechanisms as well as the amount of the enzyme through control over the rate of its synthesis. Despite extensive modifications of behavior, the relatively small changes in amounts of AChE which Krech *et al.* (1960) report may reflect only one aspect of the biochemical modifications produced by the behavior; other modifications may have taken place through the other mechanisms referred to above, which control the activity of the enzyme.

The research just described was concerned with situations in which modification of behavior produced persisting changes in the amount or activity of particular enzymes. An alternative approach to studying relations between these two classes of variables is to alter experimentally the activity of an enzyme system and to observe concomitant changes in behavior, if any. A number of such studies have been conducted, with understandable emphasis upon neurohumoral transmitter systems.

Earlier the author referred to the kinds of evidence which suggest that occurrence of a "consolidation" period during the fixation process, which, when interferred with by such treatments as electroconvulsive shock or hypoxia, may lead to significant decrements in memory. It would seem likely that biochemical events are involved in this process and that, by altering enzymes controlling their activity or by changing the concentrations of the substrates themselves, the fixation process could be impaired or enhanced. The variety of experiments incorporating procedures for interfering chemically with these events have been reviewed on several occasions (e.g., Deutsch, 1962). Their design has been based upon the administration of chemical agents at various intervals before and after training and noting the proactive or retroactive effects on performance of the responses involved. Despite methodological difficulties in obtaining unequivocable results, it appears clear that chemical intervention with anesthetics, e.g., ether, pentobarbital, and convulsive agents such as metrazol, can produce serious impairments of memory (Leukel, 1957; Pearlman, Sharpless, & Jarvick, 1961). The research literature supports the conclusion that behavior may also be enhanced by drugs (Plotnikoff, Birzis, Mitoma, Otis, Weiss, & Laties, 1960). Contributing to this conclusion have been studies on the facilitating effects of strychnine sulfate and of d-amphetamine on behavior in a variety of discrimination and maze-learning situations (Hearst & Whalen, 1963; McGaugh, 1961; McGaugh & Thompson, 1962; Petrinovich, 1963). It has been suggested that ". . . the heightened neural excitability produced by strychnine produces greater perseverative activity in the association cells of the central nervous system (Petrinovich, 1963)." Lack of information about the specific changes in biochemical events induced by the drugs limits the interpretation of these results for our present purposes.

Illustrative of research designed to provide both biochemical and behavioral data under the same experimental conditions are reports by Glow and Rose (1965; 1966b) and Richardson (1966) of effects of reduction in ChE activity induced by administration of the organophosphorus compound, diisopropylfluorophosphate (DFP), upon visual discrimination learning. Chronically reduced ChE, maintained at approximately 30% of normal, produced significant impairment in the learning of complex pattern discrimination, but had little, if any, effect upon simple brightness discrimination. The effect was obtained under conditions of food reinforcement of correct responses but disappeared with the addition of shock for errors. Glow and Rose (1966b) interpret these results as indicating ". . . that reduced ChE does not directly interfere with stimulus analysis . . . ," but that the principal effect ". . . is to reduce stability of performance." Earlier we (Russell, 1954; Russell, 1958; Russell, Watson, & Frankenhaeuser, 1961) reported studies in our laboratory using the same general design, but reducing ChE activity by administration of a different organophosphorus agent (OO-diethyl-S-ethylmercaptoethanol thiophosphate) and different behavioral situations. Our results indicated that the speed of acquisition of new responses in these situations was not altered significantly even by reductions in ChE activity by as much as 76.5% of normal. On the other hand, speed of extinction of responses, once established, tended to be inversely related to ChE activity.

The process of extinction is intimately related to the coding of new behavioral patterns; indeed, resistance to extinction is often used as a measure of learning. Extinction refers to the weakening and eventual disappearance of a learned response when it is repeatedly elicited without reinforcement. The evidence is that such changes cannot be understood in terms of the mere passage of time but must be viewed in terms of active processes related to the condition of nonreinforcement (Kimble, 1961). Just as enzyme systems may be involved in the consolidation processes associated with the coding of new responses, so may they participate in extinction processes. Evidence that they do is already accumulating from experiments in which the ACh system is varied systematically during a period when a previously acquired response is elicited without reinforcement.

In a series of studies designed to obtain empirical evidence about effects upon a wide range of behavioral patterns of experimentally induced changes in the level of ChE activity, Russell (1954; 1958) reported that *chronic* reduction to about 40% normal activity was associated with differential effects upon behavior: Certain aspects of behavior were affected and not others. One of the central features of the results was that, although the acquisition of new response patterns appeared not to be affected by the reduction, extinction was slower for experimental than for control animals. Further investigation (Russell *et al.*, 1961) confirmed the differentiation between conditioning and extinction when the same operant response was involved and showed further that the relation between ChE activity and extinction is not a linear one. There was a "critical level" between 40 and 50% of normal ChE activity below which significant decrements in behavior occurred. In all our experiments we have found a consistent tendency for the efficiency of responding to increase at levels of ChE activity between this critical level and normal, but the effect has never been sufficiently great to be statistically significant. The over-all biphasic relation is reminiscent of that reported by Metz (1958) between brain acetyl-cholinesterase activity and a respiratory reflex: Plots of the Metz data show a crossover from potentiation to decline at about 40% of normal AChE activity. This critical level is in the range where the enzyme loses control of its substrate, ACh content in nervous tissue analyzed increasing rapidly below this level (Aprison, 1962). It is also at about this level that a sharp drop in nerve conductance begins to occur (Wilson & Cohen, 1953). Crossland (1960) has pointed out that ". . . an excessive accumulation of acetylcholine at a neurone which it has excited will prevent the cell from firing again because it holds the neurone in a depolarized state. A relatively small increase will convert a stimulating dose into a paralyzing one." Such similarities suggest the possibility that behavioral changes during extinction are related to changes in the ACh system.

The general nature of these results has been confirmed and considerably extended in a series of studies by Glow and Rose (1965; 1966b), which have included observations of the extinction of several different behavioral patterns after varying periods of time on a chronic ChE reduction schedule. They have reported that: "The longer the ChE had been reduced the more days on which the resistance [to extinction] became manifest and the nearer to the start [of the extinction trials] did it occur." Their experiments also provided evidence that the resistance ". . . could not be attributed to motivational or performance factors as these become rapidly attenuated as the animals' tissues adjust to the low ChE activity." Acute, compared to chronic, reduction in ChE activity was also found to be related to slower extinction of responding under non-reinforcement conditions. As in our experiments, the effect occurred when ChE activity was reduced to below 40 to 45% of normal activity. Glow and Rose confirmed by bio-assay of brain tissue under their conditions for varying ChE activity, that there occur ". . . runaway, or out of control, increases in ACh after acute ChE reduction to below 40% . . ." of normal.

Warburton (1965), working in our laboratory, has designed experiments to study in greater detail the nature of the behavioral mode of action by which these effects upon extinction are produced. The general context within which the author has been discussing the coding of new behavior suggests two preliminary hypotheses: The effect of altering the ACh system may be to interfere with or to retard the encoding of information relevant to the change in conditions of reinforcement; or, the information, once encoded, may not be put to use. To test these hypotheses, Warburton has used a single alternation, go–no go, lever-pressing situation in which rats are reinforced with sucrose solution for making 10 lever presses whenever the discriminative stimulus, a light, is presented. Presses during the intertrial interval postpone the onset of the next trial for 10 seconds. Under these conditions an FR 10 response is established to a criterion of 90% on five successive sessions. In one type of experiment the ACh system has been altered at this point by injection of an anticholinesterase, eserine, or an anticholinergic, atropine, and the reinforcement schedule changed so that only alternate trials are reinforced. The effect of both drugs has been to delay the onset of extinction of the non-reinforced alternate responses but not to affect the extinction process itself once it was under way, the learning parameter derived using the single operator learning model of Bush and Sternberg being the same for both drugs. This effect has also been found in experiments using the more conventional procedure of withholding reinforcements on all trials. A second type of experiment has studied the effects of the drugs on the maintenance of the alternation behavior after it was established. According to the first of the above hypotheses, it would be predicted that at this point, when alternation responding was stable and its coding completed, altering the ACh system would have no effect upon its maintenance. On the other hand, the second hypotheses would lead to the prediction that the extinguished response would reappear following changes in the ACh system. Warburton's experiments show that injections of eserine just prior to tests on the maintenance of alternation behavior produced no change in responding; however, administration of atropine was followed by an increase in appearance of the previously extinguished response. Eserine also had no effect upon intertrial responding, while atropine increased it. Looking at the results of both types of experiments suggests that the anticholinesterase delays the onset of extinction by interfering with the encoding of information relevant to the change in conditions of reinforcement which are introduced by the extinction procedure. Atropine, on the other hand, appears to interfere with the use of the information once it is encoded.

Arising from these studies of possible relations between events in the ACh system and the behavioral process of extinction is the obviously important question of the relative importance of involvement of the system at central and peripheral sites. Early studies (Russell, 1958; Russell *et al.*, 1961) had turned up no measurable signs of peripheral sensory effects nor of effects on locomotion or consummatory responses on the peripheral motor side. Clearly, these sources of evidence were not sufficient to eliminate the possibility that more subtle peripheral effects may have been involved, particularly since reductions in body weight, eating, and drinking have been observed by workers (Glow and Rose, 1966b; Richardson, 1966) using another organophosphorus compound to alter AChE activity. Experiments designed specifically to answer this question have been conducted by Glow and Rose (1965; 1966b) and in our laboratory using several different approaches. Glow and Rose have studied effects of selective reduction of ChE activity by comparing the behavior of animals in which whole-body reduction had been induced by intramuscular injection of the organophosphate DFP with the behavior of others receiving concurrent administration of DFP plus a potent reactivator of phosphorylated ChE (1,3 bis, 4-hydroxyiminomethylpyridinium) which does not readily pass through the blood-brain barrier. The combined treatment thus provided some protection to peripheral ChE. Glow, Rose & Richardson (1966) report that ChE activity measured in the gastrocnemius muscle dropped to less than 60% normal within the first 24 hours after administration of the two drugs; without protection the activity level decreased to about 30% during this period. The two treatments caused no significant differences in level of brain ChE activity, in each instance the level after 24 hours being approximately 30% normal increasing to 70% of control values within 25 days. Their several experimental analyses of behavior under conditions of extinction following these comparative treatments led Glow and Rose (1965) to conclude that a peripheral component was significantly implicated and to suggest that ". . . resistance to extinction was due to feedback irregularities . . ." to the CNS.

In our experiments eserine and atropine have been injected centrally via cannulae implanted in the lateral ventricle and comparisons made with the effects of peripheral administration of quaternary compounds which pass through the blood-brain barrier with difficulty. The results so far support the conclusion ". . . that extinction is a central process with very little peripheral component, if any (Warburton, 1965)." Earlier, Carlton (1963) reached a similar conclusion by comparing the effects of atropine and methylatropine, which mimics the peripheral effects of atropine but has difficulty in passing into the central circulation. In the case of the anticholinesterases, differences in the agents used could account for the differences in effects: DFP produces an irreversible inhibition of ChE activity, recovery from which is presumably dependent upon *de novo* synthesis of ChE; eserine is a reversible ChE inhibitor.

D. Structural Changes

The emphasis the author has given to the involvement of molecular structure and of enzyme activity in the coding of new behavioral patterns should not lead us to ignore the fact that changes in neural structure have long been given prominence in theories of learning and memory. On the basis of evidence available in 1949, D. O. Hebb felt justified to state: "The assumption we must accept is that the memory trace, the basis of learning, is in some way structural and static. . . ." Reverberating circuits might account for transient retention of sensory input, as long as ". . . some more permanent structural change reinforces it." Developments in knowledge since 1949 have suggested the kinds of "dynamic" alternatives discussed in the preceding sections, but we are still far from certain about their validity. Caution in treating the structural change hypothesis too lightly is also reinforced by recent evidence that differences in behavior do indeed lead to structural differences in the CNS.

This evidence comes from research by the team, whose contributions to knowledge about relations between behavior and enzyme activity the author discussed earlier (Bennett et al., 1964; Diamond et al., 1964; Krech et al., 1964; Rosensweig, 1966; Rosenzweig et al., 1964). They have described highly consistent differences in the weight of the cerebral cortex between litter-mate rats exposed to their standard conditions of enriched, ECT, as compared to restricted, IC, experience. While brain tissue outside the cortex actually showed a small, but significant decrease in the ECT animals, clearly differentiated regional increases occurred within the cortex, being greatest, 6.2%, in the visual areas and least, 2.7%, in the somesthetic with corresponding increases in thickness of 6.2 and 3.8%, respectively. Adult animals showed changes which were comparable to those observed in young animals; thus the effects cannot be attributed to changes normally associated with early growth and development. Control studies indicated that the structural differences cannot be accounted for in terms of differences in handling nor general locomotion and, indeed, are due to enriching rather than restricting experience. While these results indicate that the CNS is responsive to differences in the environment, they do not establish that the coding of new behavioral patterns is mediated by changes in brain structure. Krech *et al.* (1964) have stated: "We wish to make clear that finding these changes in the brain consequent upon experience does not prove that they have anything to do with storage of memory." However, the possibility that they are in fact involved continues to be a challenge for further research.

The major question raised by these results, a question which has always been a stumbling block to supporters of the structural change hypothesis, concerns the mechanism by which such changes may be induced. A new step toward a possible answer has been recent discoveries of the role of proteins in the differentiation and growth of nerve cells described earlier in discussing the biochemical substrate. The series of experiments by Levi-Montalcini and her colleagues (Levi-Montalcini, 1964; Levi-Montalcini, 1964b; Levi-Montalcini & Angeletti, 1961) demonstrated the presence of growth-promoting substances, neural growth factors, highly specific for nervous tissue. It seems a reasonable hypothesis that there may exist a mechanism by which, during the coding of new behavioral patterns, the effects of information input on protein synthesis increase the production of protein molecules capable of modifying the structure of nerve or glial cells. The structural modifications would then serve as engrams for long-term memory storage.

E. Summary

Consideration of the coding of new behavioral patterns immediately raises questions about the fixation, storage, and retrieval of information in biological systems. Biochemical events are involved in these processes from the encoding of sensory input to the muscular and glandular activities of the final motor output. Stimulated by analogies, theoretical models, and empirical discoveries, attention has come to be focused upon the step reactions of protein synthesis and its products for the secrets of fixation and storage. All three types of hypotheses discussed have this in common: The macromolecules whose composition is alleged to change are involved in protein synthesis; enzymes are products of protein synthesis, as are neural growth factors. To look at one of these hypotheses, excluding the others, may prove to be an exercise similar to that of the fabled blind men describing the elephant by each examining a different part of its anatomy. Whatever the view, the evidence supporting any of the three types of hypotheses is still indirect, although each new discovery is a step in the series of successive approximations which lead to modifications of the current ideas while approaching closer to definitive answers to the basic questions. Among these questions, those concerning the means by which information, once stored, is selectively retrieved are in greatest need of attention, although there is still wide scope for imaginative effort in formulating and testing hypotheses about all aspects of the processes by which new behavioral patterns are coded.

VI. COMPETING RESPONSES

In the preceding pages attention was directed to biochemical events as they may be related to the coding of individual behavioral patterns. But each such pattern does not normally function on its own without reference to other responses within the organism's behavioral repertoire. Observation of behavior under even the most restricted environmental circumstances shows that an array of different responses are initially available to the organism, the majority of which soon cease to appear as exposure to the situation continues. Some of these are genetically precoded; others have become coded through the processes of learning. That those responses which cease to appear have not been "destroyed" can be demonstrated by altering some major feature of the situation; the effect is to reinstate some or perhaps all of the original array, indicating that, during exposure to the situation, competing responses had merely been suppressed. The suppression of competing responses has long been a basic concept in the "interference theory" of the behavioral extinction process (Kimble, 1961). The phenomenon drew Pavlov's (1927) particular attention when he observed that the presentation of additional external stimuli produced investigatory and other responses which led to decrements in ongoing behavior, his concept of "external inhibition." Competing responses appeared prominently in reflex physiology when it was observed that the activation of one reflex reduced the magnitude of another. They were implicated in studies of retroactive inhibition, where periods of decreased activity following practice were found to be associated with better retention than were periods of normal or heightened activity. These, and other lines of evidence, involve competing responses in the answers to two general questions: How may competing responses affect the coding of new behavioral patterns? How, in any particular situation, do certain responses in the already coded array available to the organism persist while others are suppressed?

During recent years the possibility that biochemical events may enter into the "control" of competing responses has begun to attract attention. Reasoning on the basis of the interference theory of behavioral extinction it could be hypothesized that the relations between extinction and the level of ChE activity discussed earlier are dependent upon the effects of the enzyme system on competing responses. If reduction in ChE activity were to enhance their suppression, competing responses would not be as readily available to interfere with the dominant, reinforced behavior and, hence, the latter would be more resistant to extinction. Such an interpretation would be consistent with Carlton's (1963) imaginative analysis entitled "Cholinergic Mechanisms in the Control of Behavior by the Brain." Carlton stated that ". . . there are inferential grounds for supposing that a cholinergic system selectively antagonizes the effect of activation on certain behavior and that the basis of this selectivity is the extent to which that behavior is unrewarded." In the majority of experiments cited by Carlton in support of this hypothesis, administration of anticholinergics, e.g., atropine and scopolamine, was interpreted as attenuating the usual effects of nonreinforcement. Presumably anticholinesterases could have the opposite influence of enhancing the effects of nonreinforcement, increasing suppression of competing or interfering responses and thereby retarding the extinction process.

The results of Warburton's (1965) experiments referred to earlier illustrate how this "control system" would be expected to function. Stable single alternation behavior was established by reinforcing

FR 10 responding to a light stimulus only on every nth trial; responses on $n + 1$ trials were nonreinforced and were extinguished. Intraventricular administration of the anticholinergic, atropine, was followed by an increase in the occurrence of the extinguished responses and also by an increase of responding during intertrial intervals, behavior which had been extinguished much earlier during the initial FR 10 training. In contrast, administration of the anticholinesterase, eserine, had no such effects. Atropine "released" responses which under normal control conditions would have been suppressed; eserine did not and, had the necessary tests been possible under the experimental conditions, may have been found to enhance normal suppression.

Another study in our laboratory (Banks & Russell, 1966) was designed to determine the effects of chronic reduction in ChE activity on behavior in a more complicated, serial problem-solving situation. This situation may be viewed as one in which the availability of competing responses played a particularly important role. Preliminary training left the animals, rats, with an initial array of responses from which those required to solve each of the problems could be drawn. During trials on the first problem certain of these responses were reinforced and others not, reinforcement increasing the strength of the responses concerned and increasing their likelihood of occurrence on subsequent trials. Introduction of the second problem made at least some of these responses irrelevant and began the reinforcement of certain competing responses elicited from the initial array; the more readily the latter were available, the sooner would errors have been eliminated and the adequate behavioral pattern established. The same would hold for shifts to subsequent problems. In terms of this view, anything that affected the availability of competing responses would be reflected in the error score. Five groups of animals participated in the experiments; conditions were the same for all except for their levels of ChE activity, which were: 100, 59, 41, 30, and 25% of normal. The results, summarized in Fig. 10, showed a highly significant trend toward increasing total error scores with decreasing ChE activity below a critical level between 40 and 50%. This critical level corresponds with those observed in studies of extinction (Glow & Rose, 1965; Russell *et al.*, 1961), of the control of ACh by ChE (Aprison, 1962), and of relations between ChE activity and nerve conduction (Wilson & Cohen, 1953). The effects could not be accounted for in terms of

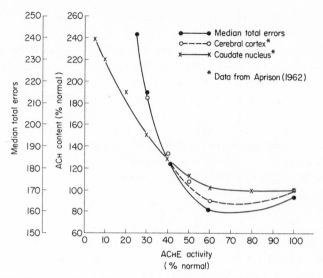

FIG. 10. The curve for median total errors in a serial problem solving situation shows a highly significant trend toward increasing error scores with decreasing ChE activity below a critical level between 40% and 50% of normal. The other curves show that at this level ChE loses control of its substrate, ACh.

differences in weight, food intake, locomotion, nor speed of approach to a food incentive. Figure 11 shows the analysis of cumulative error scores. There were no significant differences among the groups in performance on the first problem in the series; thereafter, the cumulative error scores could be fitted as linear functions, with different slope constants for each group, which increased in magnitude as ChE activity decreased. The fact that there were no significant initial differences among the groups indicates that the effects of reducing activity must have been associated with processes going on during the problem-solving period. These results are consistent with predictions from Carlton's hypothesis: as ChE activity decreased, progressively greater suppression would be exerted upon the nonreinforced responses; these responses would, therefore, be less readily available when needed for the solution of a new problem.

Other experiments providing results which can be interpreted in similar terms have been reviewed by Carlton (1963). Assuming the validity of the general hypothesis that some cholinergic system in the brain is involved in the suppression which normally occurs

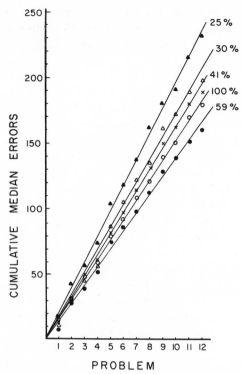

FIG. 11. Cumulative error curves for performance in the serial problem solving situation begin with no significant differences among groups. Thereafter, the error scores can be fitted as linear functions, with different slope constants, which increase as ChE activity level decreases.

when the behavior is unrewarded, there still remains the more specific question of how the system produces its effects. What is its behavioral mode of action? The terms in which the results of the experiment described in the preceding paragraph were discussed could be interpreted as emphasizing involvement of the efferent or response output side of the behavioral patterns studied. But clearly, the experiment was not designed to specify where in the chain of events between stimulus input and response output the cholinergic system might have its operative effects; the final motor response measured was the outcome of all these events. Experiments recently reported by Carlton (1964) have been designed to examine one of the possible modes of action more precisely: ". . . that brain acetylcholine is involved in the functional elimination of stimuli from the world with which the animal must cope." The experiments took advantage of the fact that the introduction of a stimulus for the first time disrupts ongoing behavior. A brief description of one of the experiments will illustrate the general procedure used. In phase 1, one group of animals was given a series of exposures to a flashing light following injection of the anticholinergic drug, scopolamine; a comparable group received the same treatment after administration of saline. In phase 2 animals in both groups were placed on a water-deprivation schedule and given two weeks of trials in an experimental chamber where water was available. In phase 3 the flashing light was introduced during the drinking trial. None of the animals received injections during phase 2 or 3 and none was exposed to the light stimulus during phase 2. The results showed that drinking behavior during phase 3 was disrupted to a significantly greater extent in animals who had been exposed, in phase 1, to the light stimulus while under the effects of scopolamine than it was in animals who had received the same stimulus exposure but no injection of the drug. The effect of the anticholinergic drug was to disrupt the reduction in stimulus effectiveness which normally accompanies repeated exposure. Other experiments in the series employed different behavioral patterns in phases 2 and 3, checked upon the specificity of the effect produced by cholinergic drugs, and tested the possibility that the effects could be accounted for in terms of stimulus change arising from the fact that the experimental subjects were exposed to the light stimulus in phase 1 while under drug and tested in phase 3 without the drug. The results of the series as a whole have been interpreted by Carlton as suggesting that the cholinergic system which he had hypothesized in his earlier analysis may play its role through the process of stimulus selection.

In our experiment (Banks and Russell, 1966) the effect of reducing ChE activity below the critical level of 40 to 50% was to increase errors in serial problem solving, presumably by suppressing competing responses when they were needed for the solution of new problems. The operation of such a mechanism could be conceived as resulting, under extreme circumstances, in the appearance of stereotyped behavioral patterns despite wide variations in the organism's environment. Stereotyped responding has been described by Feldberg and Sherwood (1954) following intraventricular injections of eserine, DFP, and ACh into cat brain. They have also reported that with large doses: "Stupor and 'catatonia' appear to be characteristic features of the presence of acetylcholine or anticholinesterases in the ventricular system." Such a state could be thought of as representing the most extreme suppression of competing responses or "functional elimination of stimuli" to use Carlton's expression. The possibility that this extreme behavioral condition in human patients suffering from catatonic schizophrenia might be altered by intraventricular administration of ChE was studied by Sherwood (1952), who reported marked but temporary relief of the major symptoms. Callaway and Stone (1960) have described the effects of anticholinergic substances, i.e., atropine, on the behavior of human subjects, who, following injection, ". . . are more than ordinarily susceptible to interference from peripheral stimuli, yet they perform more efficiently than do control subjects when apparently irrelevant stimuli actually serve a useful function." Observations of these kinds are consistent with the results of research on infrahuman animal subjects. They also suggest hypotheses of how biochemical factors may function in human behavioral disorders (Russell, 1965).

VII. PROSPECTS

"We may say that physiological psychology tries to devise physiological hypotheses about the nature of some of psychology's 'intervening variables' with the hope of sharpening the ideas in question, but not superseding them (Hebb, 1958)." The search for relations between biochemical events and behavior has begun to make important advances in this direction. With the development of knowledge and techniques in biochemistry and related disciplines has come tests of hypotheses about the neurochemical substrates of genetically coded behavioral patterns, about how new behavior may be coded biochemically, and about how competing responses may be mediated through biochemical control. It seems entirely clear from present evidence that the interaction between behavior and biochemical events is reciprocal in the sense that changes in either may be reflected in concomitant variations in the other. Results from a number of different research approaches have implicated biochemical events at three different but related levels: the macromolecules involved in protein synthesis, enzyme systems underlying neurohumoral transmission within the CNS, and neural growth factors controlling structural changes in the CNS. The direction of research is toward the more precise description of the natures of specific interactions and toward the statement of such relations in quantitative terms. The rapidly increasing attention which this general area of research is receiving from psychologists and from members of a number of other disciplines attests to the belief that its problems are important and that the prospects of solving them are good. For some, the understanding of relations between biochemical events and behavior is a prerequisite to the rational development of psychopharmacology and more adequate methods for the pharmacotherapy of behavioral disorders. Its promise and its current limited knowledge place the study of the biochemical substrates of behavior at one of the frontiers in physiological psychology.

REFERENCES

Agranoff, B. W., Davis, R. E., & Brink, J. J. Memory fixation in the goldfish. *Proc. nat. Acad. Sci. U. S.*, 1965, **54**, 788–793.

Alfert, M. Some cytochemical contributions to genetic chemistry. *In* W. P. McElroy & B. Glass (Eds.), *The chemical basis of heredity*. Baltimore: Johns Hopkins Press, 1957.

Andjus, R. K., Knöpfelmacher, F., Russell, R. W., & Smith, A. U. Some effects of severe hypothermia on learning and retention. *Quart. J. exp. Psychol.*, 1956, **8**, 15–23.

Appel, S. *Symposium on the role of macromolecules in complex behavior*. Manhatten, Kansas: Kansas State Univer., 1964.

Aprison, M. H. On a proposed theory of the mechanism of action of serotonin in brain. *Recent Advanc. biol. Psychiat.*, 1962, **4**, 133–146.

Babich, F. R., Jacobson, A. L., & Bubash, S. Cross-species transfer of learning: effect of ribonucleic acid from hamsters on rat behavior. *Proc. nat. Acad. Sci. U. S.*, 1965, **54**, 1299–1302.(a)

Babich, F. R., Jacobson, A. L., Bubash, S., & Jacobson, A. Transfer of a response to naive rats by injection of ribonucleic acid extracted from trained rats. *Science*, 1965, **149**, 656–657.(b)

Baldwin, E. *An introduction to comparative biochemistry*. London and New York: Cambridge Univer. Press, 1949.

Banks, A., & Russell, R. W. Effects of chronic reductions in acetylcholinesterase activity on serial problem solving behavior. Submitted for publication.

Barlow, H. B. Retinal noise and absolute threshold. *J. opt. Soc. Amer.*, 1956, **46**, 634–639.

Barlow, H. B., FitzHugh, R., & Kuffler, S. W. Resting discharge and dark adaptation in the cat. *J. Physiol. (London)*, 1954, **125**, 28–29P.

Barondes, S. H., & Jarvik, M. E. The influences of actinomycin-D on brain RNA synthesis and on memory. *J. Neurochem.*, 1964, **11**, 187–195.

Beadle, G. W., & Tatum, E. L. Genetic control of biochemical reactions in Neurospora. *Proc. nat. Acad. Sci. U. S.*, 1941, **27**, 499–506.

Bennett, E. L., Krech, D., & Rosenzweig, M. R. Reliability and regional specificity of cerebral effects of environmental complexity and training. *J. comp. physiol. Psychol.*, 1964, **57**, 440–441.

Bernal, J. D. Biochemical evolution. In M. Kasha & B. Pullman (Eds.), *Horizons in biochemistry*. New York: Academic Press, 1962.

Boring, E. G. *A history of experimental psychology*. New York: Appleton-Century-Crofts, 1950.

Brattgård, S. O. The importance of adequate stimulation for the chemical composition of retinal ganglion cells during early post-natal development. *Acta radiol., Stockh.*, 1952, Suppl. 96.

Briggs, M. H., & Kitto, G. B. The molecular basis of memory and learning. *Psychol. Rev.*, 1962, **69**, 537–541.

Brodie, B. B. Difficulties in extrapolating data on metabolism of drugs from animal to man. *Clin. Pharmacol. Ther.*, 1962, **3**, 374–380.

Callaway, E., & Stone, G. Re-evaluating focus of attention. In L. Uhr & J. G. Miller (Eds.), *Drugs and behavior*. New York: Wiley, 1960.

Cameron, D. E. Effects of ribonucleic acid on memory defect in the aged. *Amer. J. Psychiat.*, 1963, **120**, 320–325.(a)

Cameron, D. E. The processes of remembering. *Brit. J. Psychiat.*, 1963, **109**, 325–340.(b)

Cameron, D. E., & Solyom, L. Effects of ribonucleic acid on memory. *Geriatrics*, 1961, **16**, 74–81.

Carlton, P. L. Cholinergic mechanisms in the control of behavior by the brain. *Psychol. Rev.*, 1963, **70**, 19–39.

Carlton, P. L. Brain-acetylcholine and stimulus selection. Symposium on Central Cholinergic Mechanisms and Behavior. Paper read at Annu. Meeting of the Amer. Psychol. Ass., 1964.

Chitty, D. Adverse effects of population density upon the viability of later generations. In J. B. Cragg & N. W. Pirie (Eds.), *The numbers of man and animals*. London: Oliver & Boyd, 1955.

Clarke, J. R. The effect of fighting on the adrenals, thymus and spleen of the vole (Microtus agrestis). *J. Endocrinol.*, 1953, **9**, 114–126.

Cook, L., Davidson, A. B., Davis, D. J., Green, H., & Fellows, E. J. Ribonucleic acid: effect on conditioned behavior in rats. *Science*, 1963, **141**, 268–269.

Crossland, J. Chemical transmission in the central nervous system. *J. Pharm. Pharmacol.*, 1960, **12**, 1–36.

Darwin, C. *Expression of the emotions in man and animals*. London: John Murray, 1872.

Davison, P. F. Biological coding: A summary. In F. O. Schmitt (Ed.), *Macromolecular specificity and biological memory*. Cambridge, Mass.: M.I.T. Press, 1962.

De Robertis, E., & Bennett, H. S. Some features of the submicroscopic morphology of synapses in frog and earthworm. *J. biophys. biochem. Cytol.*, 1955, **1**, 47–58.

De Robertis, E., & Franchi, C. M. Electron microscope observations on synaptic vesicles in synapses of the retinal rods and cones. *J. biophys. biochem. Cytol.*, 1956, **2**, 307–318.

De Robertis, E., Salganicoff, L., Zieher, L. M., & Arnaiz, G. R. deL. Acetylcholine and cholinacetylase content of synaptic vesicles. *Science*, 1963, **140**, 300–301.

Deutsch, J. A. Higher nervous function: the physiological bases of memory. *Ann. Rev. Physiol.*, 1962, **24**, 259–286.

Diamond, M. C., Krech, D., & Rosenzweig, M. R. The effects of an enriched environment on the histology of the rat cerebral cortex. *J. comp. Neurol.*, 1964, **123**, 111–119.

Dingman, W., & Sporn, M. B. The incorporation of 8-azaguanine into rat brain RNA and its effect on maze-learning by the rat: an inquiry into the biochemical basis of memory. *J. psychiat. Res.*, 1961, **1**, 1–11.

Dingman, W., & Sporn, M. B. Molecular theories of memory. *Science*, 1964, **144**, 26–29.

Edström. J. E. Extraction, hydrolysis, and electrophoretic analysis of ribonucleic acid from microscopic tissue units (Microphoresis). *J. biophys. biochem. Cytol.*, 1960, **8**, 39–43.

Edström, J. E., Grampp, W., & Schor, N. The intracellular distribution and heterogeneity of ribonucleic acid in starfish oocytes. *J. biophys. biochem. Cytol.*, 1961, **11**, 549–557.

Egyházi, E., & Hydén, H. Experimentally induced changes in the base composition of the ribonucleic acids of isolated nerve cells and their oligodemoglial cells. *J. biophys. biochem. Cytol.*, 1961, **10**, 403–410.

Feldberg, W., & Sherwood, S. L. Behavior of cats after intraventricular injections of eserine and DFP. *J. Physiol. (London)*, 1954, **125**, 488–500.

Finney, D. J. *Probit analysis*. London and New York: Cambridge Univer. Press, 1962.

Fisher, A. E., & Coury, J. N. Cholinergic tracing of a central neural circuit underlying the thirst drive. *Science*, 1962, **138**, 691–693.

Fjerdingstad, E. J., Nissen, T., & Røigaard-Petersen, H. H. Effect of ribonucleic acid (RNA) extracted from the brain of trained animals on learning in rats. *Scand. J. Psychol.*, 1965, **6**, 1–6.

Flexner, J. B., Flexner, L. B., and Stellar, E. Memory in mice as affected by intracerebral puromycin. *Science*, 1963, **141**, 57–59.

Florey, E. Comparative physiology: transmitter substances. *Annu. Rev. Physiol.*, 1961, **23**, 451–484.

Gaddum, J. H. Chemical transmission in the central nervous system. In J. D. French (Ed.), *Frontiers in brain research*. New York: Columbia Univer. Press, 1962.

Gaito, J., & Zavola, A. Neurochemistry and learning. *Psychol. Bull.*, 1964, **61**, 45–62.

Galambos, R. A glia-neural theory of brain function. *Proc. nat. Acad. Sci. U. S.*, 1961, **47**, 129–136.

Glow, P. H., & Rose, S. Effects of light and dark on the acetylcholinesterase activity of the retina. *Nature*, 1964, **202**, 422–423.

Glow, P. H., & Rose, S. Effects of reduced acetylcholinesterase levels on extinction of a conditioned response. *Nature*, 1965, **206**, 475–477.

Glow, P. H., & Rose, S. Activity of cholinesterase in the retina with different levels of physiological stimulation. *Aust. J. exp. Biol. med. Sci.*, 1966, **44**, 65–72.(a)

Glow, P. H., & Rose, S. Some relationships between enzyme activity levels and behavior. *Proceedings of the XVIII international congress of psychology*, 1966, to be published.(b)

Glow, P. H., Rose, S., & Richardson, A. The effect of acute and chronic treatment with diisopropyl fluorophosphate on cholinesterase activities of some tissues of the rat. *Aust. J. exp. Biol. med. Sci.*, 1966, **44**, 73–86.

Grossman, S. P. Eating or drinking elicited by direct adrenergic or cholinergic stimulation of hypothalamus. *Science*, 1960, **132**, 301–302.

Grossman, S. P. Direct adrenergic and cholinergic stimulation of hypothalamic mechanisms. *Amer. J. Physiol.*, 1962, **202**, 872–882.

Grossman, S. P. Behavioral effects of chemical stimulation of the ventral amygdala. *J. comp. physiol. Psychol.*, 1964, **57**, 29–36.(a)

Grossman, S. P. Effect of chemical stimulation of the septal area on motivation. *J. comp. physiol. Psychol.*, 1964, **58**, 194–200.(b)

Hearst, E., & Whalen, R. E. Facilitating effects of *d*-amphetamine on discrimination-avoidance performance. *J. comp. physiol. Psychol.*, 1963, **56**, 124–128.

Hebb, D. O. *The organization of behavior.* New York: Wiley, 1949.

Hebb, D. O. Alice in wonderland, or psychology among the biological sciences. In H. F. Harlow & C. N. Woolsey (Eds.), *Biological and biochemical bases of behavior.* Madison: Univer. Wisconsin Press, 1958.

Hydén, H. Biochemical changes in glial cells and nerve cells at varying activity. In F. Brücke (Ed.), *Biochemistry of the central nervous system.* New York: Macmillan (Pergamon), 1959.

Hydén, H. Biochemical aspects of brain activity. In S. M. Farber & R. H. L. Wilson (Eds.), *Control of the mind.* New York: McGraw-Hill, 1961.

Hydén, H., & Egyházi, E. Nuclear RNA changes of nerve cells during a learning experiment in rats. *Proc. nat. Acad. Sci. U. S.*, 1962, **48**, 1366–1373.

Hydén, H., & Egyházi, E. Glial RNA changes during a learning experiment with rats. *Proc. nat. Acad. Sci. U. S.*, 1963, **49**, 618–624.

Hydén, H., & Egyházi, E. Changes in RNA content and base composition in cortical neurons of rats in a learning experiment involving transfer of handedness. *Proc. nat. Acad. Sci. U. S.*, 1964, **52**, 1030–1035.

Hydén, H., & Lange, P. A differentiation in RNA response in neurons early and late during learning. *Proc. nat. Acad. Sci. U. S.*, 1965, **53**, 946–952.

Jacobson, A. L., Babich, F. R., Bubash, S., & Jacobson, A. Differential-approach tendencies produced by injection of RNA from trained rats. *Science*, 1965, **150**, 636–637.

James, W. *Talks to teachers on psychology.* London: Longmans, Green, 1899.

Katz, J. J., & Halstead, W. C. Protein organization and mental function. *Comp. Psychol. Monogr.*, 1950, **20**, No. 103.

Khavari, K. A., & Russell, R. W. Acquisition, retention, and extinction under conditions of water deprivation and of central cholinergic stimulation. *J. comp. physiol. Psychol.*, 1966, **61**, 339–345.

Kimble, G. A. *Conditioning and learning.* New York: Appleton-Century-Crofts, 1961.

Krech, D., Rosenzweig, M. R., & Bennett, E. L. Effects of environmental complexity and training on brain chemistry. *J. comp. physiol. Psychol.*, 1960, **53**, 509–519.

Krech, D., Rosenzweig, M. R., & Bennett, E. L. Effects of complex environment and blindness on rat brain. *Arch. Neurol.*, 1963, **8**, 403–412.

Krech, D., Rosenzweig, M. R., & Bennett, E. L. Chemical and anatomical plasticity of brain. *Science*, 1964, **146**, 610–619.

Landauer, T. K. Two hypotheses concerning the biochemical basis of memory. *Psychol. Rev.*, 1964, **71**, 167–179.

Lashley, K. S. In search of the engram. *Sympos. Soc. exp. Biol.*, 1950, **4**, 454–482.

Leukel, F. A. A comparison of the effects of ECS and anesthesia on acquisition of the maze habit. *J. comp. physiol. Psychol.*, 1957, **50**, 300–306.

Levi-Montalcini, R. Events in the developing nervous system. In D. P. Purpura and J. P. Schadé (Eds.), *Progress in brain research*. Vol. 4. *Growth and maturation of the brain*. Amsterdam: Elsevier, 1964.(a)

Levi-Montalcini, R. Growth control of nerve cells by a protein factor and its antiserum. *Science*, 1964, **143**, 105-110.(b)

Levi-Montalcini, R., & Angeletti, P. U. Growth control of the sympathetic system by a specific protein factor. *Quart. Rev. Biol.*, 1961, **36**, 99-108.

Liberman, R. Retinal cholinesterase and glycolysis in rats raised in darkness. *Science*, 1962, **135**, 372-373.

McGaugh, J. L. Facilitative and disruptive effects of strychnine sulphate on maze learning. *Psychol. Rep.*, 1961, **8**, 99-104.

McGaugh, J. L., & Thompson, C. W. Facilitation of simultaneous discrimination learning with strychnine sulphate. *Psychopharmocologia*, 1962, **3**, 166-172.

Metz, B. Brain acetylcholinesterase and a respiratory reflex. *Amer. J. Physiol.*, 1958, **192**, 101-105.

Miller, N. E. Chemical coding of behavior in the brain. *Science*, 1965, **148**, 328-338.

Miller, N. E., Gotterman, K. S., & Emery, N. Dose response to carbachol and norepinephrine in rat hypothalamus. *Amer. J. Physiol.*, 1964, **206**, 1384-1388.

Miller, S. L. A production of amino acids under possible primitive earth conditions. *Science*, 1953, **117**, 528-529.

Miller, S. L. Production of some organic compounds under possible primitive earth conditions. *J. Amer. Chem. Soc.*, 1955, **77**, 2351-2361.

Miller, S. L., & Urey, H. C. Organic compound synthesis on the primitive earth. *Science*, 1959, **130**, 245-251.

Morgane, P. J. Limbic-hypothalamic-midbrain interaction in thirst and thirst motivated behavior. *Thirst*. Proceedings First International Symposium on Thirst in the Regulation of Body Waters. New York: Macmillan (Pergamon), 1964.

Müller, G. E., & Pilzecker, A. Experimentelle beiträge zur lehre vom gedächtnis. *Z. Psychol., Ergänzungsband*, 1900, **1**, 1-288.

Nachmansohn, D. *Chemical and molecular basis of nerve activity*. New York: Academic Press, 1959.

Nachmansohn, D. Chemical factors controlling nerve activity, *Science*, 1961, **134**, 1962-1968.

Pardee, A. B., & Wilson, A. C. Control of enzyme activity in higher animals. *Cancer Res.*, 1963, **23**, 1483-1490.

Pavlov, I. P. *Conditioned reflexes* (Translated by G. V. Anrep) London and New York: Oxford Univer. Press, 1927.

Pearlman, C. A., Sharpless, S. K., & Jarvik, M. E. Retrograde amnesia produced by anesthetic and convulsant agents. *J. comp. physiol. Psychol.*, 1961, **54**, 109-112.

Petrinovich, L. Facilitation of successive discrimination learning by strychnine sulphate. *Psychopharmacologia*, 1963, **4**, 103-113.

Plotnikoff, N., Birzis, L., Mitoma, C., Otis, L., Weiss, B., & Laties, V. *Drug enhancement of performance*. Baltimore: Johns Hopkins Univer. Med. Sch., Contract Nonr-2993(00), 1960.

Riesen, A. H. Plasticity of behavior: psychological aspects. In H. F. Harlow and C. N. Woolsay (Eds.), *Biological and biochemical bases of behavior*. Madison: Univer. Wisconsin Press, 1958.

Richardson, A. Effects of reduced cholinesterase activity on discriminative behavior in rats. Ph.D. thesis, Univer. of Adelaide, Adelaide, Australia, 1966.

Rose, S., & Glow, P. H. Effects of intravitreous injection of drugs on the cholinesterase of the retina. *Aust. J. exp. Biol. med. Sci.*, 1965, **43**, 737–742.

Rosenblith, W. A. (Ed.) *Sensory communication*. New York: Wiley, 1961.

Rosenzweig, M. R. Changes in brain chemistry as consequences of differential experience. *Proceedings of the XVIII international congress of psychology, 1966*, to be published.

Rosenzweig, M. R., Krech, D., & Bennett, E. L. A search for relations between brain chemistry and behavior. *Psychol. Bull.*, 1960, **57**, 476–492.

Rosenzweig, M. R., Bennett, E. L., & Krech, W. Cerebral effects of environmental complexity and training among adult rats. *J. comp. physiol. Psychol.*, 1964, **57**, 438–439.

Rothballer, A. B. The effects of catecholamines on the central nervous system. *Pharmacol. Rev.*, 1959, **11**, 494–547.

Rushton, W. A. H. Peripheral coding in the nervous system. In W. A. Rosenblith (Ed.), *Sensory communication*. New York: Wiley, 1961.

Russell, R. W. Effects of reduced brain cholinesterase on behavior. *Bull. Brit. psychol. Soc.*, 1954, No. 23, 6.

Russell, R. W. Effects of "biochemical lesions" on behavior. *Acta psychol. (Amsterdam)*, 1958, **14**, 281–294.

Russell, R. W. Biochemical factors in mental disorders. In B. B. Wolman (Ed.), *Handbook of clinical psychology*. New York: McGraw-Hill, 1965.

Russell, R. W. Neurochemical coding of behavior. *Proceedings of the XVIII international congress of psychology, 1966*, to be published.

Russell, R. W., Watson, R. H. J., & Frankenhaeuser, M. Effects of chronic reductions in brain cholinesterase activity on acquisition and extinction of a conditional avoidance response. *Scand. J. Psychol.*, 1961, **2**, 21–29.

Schmitt, F. O. (Ed.), *Macromolecular specificity and biological memory*. Cambridge, Mass.: M.I.T. Press, 1962.

Sherwood, S. L. Intraventricular medication in catatonic stupor. *Brain*, 1952, **75**, 68–75.

Simpson, F. O., & Devine, C. E. The fine structure of autonomic neuromuscular contacts in arterioles of sheep renal cortex. *J. Anat.*, 1966, **100**, 127–137.

Smith, C. E. Is memory a matter of enzyme induction? *Science*, 1962, **138**, 889–890.

Sperry, R. W. Problems of molecular coding. In F. O. Schmitt (Ed.), *Macromolecular specificity and biological memory*. Cambridge, Mass.: M.I.T. Press, 1962.

Steiner, W. G. Electrical activity of rat brain as a correlate of primary drive. *Electroenceph. clin. Neurophysiol.*, 1962, **14**, 233–243.

Wagner, J. W., & de Groot, J. Changes in feeding behavior after intracerebral injections in the rat. *Amer. J. Physiol.*, 1963, **204**, 483–487.

Wald, G. Biochemical evolution. In E. S. G. Barrow (Ed.), *Modern trends in physiology and biochemistry*. New York: Academic Press, 1952.

Warburton, D. M. The effect of the reduction of acetylcholine activity on acquisition, maintenance and extinction of single alternation behavior. Paper presented to the Indiana Psychol. Ass., 1965, Indianapolis, Indiana.

Whittaker, V. P. The isolation and characterization of acetylcholine-containing particles from brain. *Biochem. J.*, 1959, **72**, 694–706.

Wilson, I. B., & Cohen, M. The essentiality of acetylcholinesterase in conduction. *Biochim. Biophys. Acta*, 1953, **11**, 147–156.

AUTHOR INDEX

Numbers in italics refer to pages on which the complete references are listed.

247

SUBJECT INDEX

The Subject Index is subdivided into four major sections corresponding to the four properties of living organisms, i.e., anatomical or structural, behavioral, biochemical, and electrophysiological. Listings are arranged alphabetically within each section. Cross references are often made between sections; even when such referencing is not specific, the reader can expect to find that the item he seeks is, in fact, treated as an integral part of the somatic substrates of behavior.

SECTION I:

ANATOMICAL OR STRUCTURAL PROPERTY

A

Antagonistic hypnogenic structures, in caudal portion of brain stem, 134

B

Betz cells, facilitating effect of cortical stimulation on, 34–35

C

Cerebral cortex
  changes following exposure to
    different environments
  in thickness, 232
  in weight, 231–232
  neuronal mechanisms of, 21–50
Concentric-receptive-field cells, vision, 79, 81
Cortical cells, vision, 79–82
Cortico-cortical link, in lateral transmission of cortical responses, 29–32
Crossed-lesion experiment, on visual function of inferotemporal area, 99–105

D

Decerebrate preparation, 139
Desensitizing adaptation circuit, in vision, 69

F

Functional neural circuits, 199–200
  hypothalamic pathways, 200–201
  limbic and diencephalic structures in drinking behavior, 199

G

Glial cells
  involvement in learning, 220, 224
  RNA in, 214

I

Inferotemporal area, interaction with visual system
  callosal transection, 103–105, 108–109
  cortical pathway, 98–99
  crossed-lesion experiment, 99–105
  subcortical pathway, 97–98

L

Localization studies, visual mechanisms, 94–95

M

Movement-sensitive cells, vision, 84–87

SECTION II:

BEHAVIORAL PROPERTY

SECTION III:

BIOCHEMICAL PROPERTY

SECTION IV:

ELECTROPHYSIOLOGICAL PROPERTY